NEW ELEMENTARY MATHEMATICS

SYLLABUS D

1

Sin Kwai Meng
MSc, Cert Ed

General Editor
Dr Wong Khoon Yoong
PhD, BSc (Hons), Dip Ed

EPB PAN PACIFIC

Published by EPB Pan Pacific

An imprint of Panpac Education Private Limited
Times Centre
1 New Industrial Road
Singapore 536196

Panpac Education

Email: panpmktg@panpaceducation.com
Website: http://www.panpaceducation.com

EPB Pan Pacific is a trademark of Times Publishing Limited

ISBN 978-981-271-411-4

First published 1991
Reprinted 1991
Reprinted 1992
Reprinted 1993
Reprinted 1994
New Edition 1996
Reprinted 1997
Reprinted 1998 (twice)
Reprinted 1999
Reprinted 2001 (twice)
Reprinted 2003
Reprinted 2004 (twice)
Reprinted 2005 (twice)
Reprinted 2006 (twice)
Reprinted 2007

Printed by Utopia Press Pte Ltd

Printed in Singapore

PREFACE

THE SERIES

NEW ELEMENTARY MATHEMATICS is a series of six course books. The first two books follow closely the latest Mathematics Syllabus for Lower Secondary Schools issued by the Ministry of Education, Singapore, for use from 1992. Books 3A, 3B, 4A and 4B cover the Singapore-Cambridge G.C.E. 'O' Level Mathematics Syllabus D.

THE APPROACH

Throughout the series, emphasis is placed on the development of better understanding of mathematical concepts and their applications, as well as on proficiency in problem solving, mathematical reasoning and higher order thinking.

To facilitate this, we have included the following:

- **investigative work**
- **communication skills in mathematics**
- **appropriate computational and estimation skills**
- **mental calculation and**
- **problem-solving heuristics**

THE FEATURES

EXERCISES

Numerous exercises are provided for pupils of varied abilities and the problems are **graded**. The more difficult questions are marked with asterisks (*).

CHAPTER REVIEW

At the end of every chapter, there is a *Chapter Review* which **recapitulates concepts** learnt.

CHALLENGER

This section just after the *Chapter Review* is specially designed to provide **interesting and challenging problems** on that particular chapter topic for the abler and more adventurous students.

PROBLEM SOLVING

Problem Solving exercises are given to enable students to practise their problem-solving skills.

REVISION EXERCISES

Sets of **revision exercises** are also included at appropriate intervals to provide students with the necessary **practice and reinforcement**.

MISCELLANEOUS EXERCISES

These exercises are given at chapter intervals. They provide pupils with many questions in which to apply various concepts learnt.

INVESTIGATION

Problems in the *Investigation* section provide opportunities for students to **explore**, **experiment with and discuss mathematical ideas**.

MATHSTORY

A story or history on mathematics is given at the side margin where appropriate. This section is meant to enrich students with the knowledge of how mathematics develops over the years.

It is hoped that this series will help students gain confidence in and better insights into the subject, and above all, that students will look upon Mathematics as something both exciting and rewarding.

I am grateful to all those who have, in one way or another, rendered assistance and offered invaluable suggestions.

I am also grateful to the University of Cambridge Local Examinations Syndicate and EPB Publications Pte Ltd for permission to reproduce some of the examination questions.

Sin K. M.

CONTENTS

CHAPTER 1   WHOLE NUMBERS   1

1.1   System of Numeration   2
    Class Activity 1   3
1.2   The Four Operation   4
    Class Activity 2   5
    Combined Operations   5
1.3   Factors and Multiples   7
    Natural Numbers   7
    Factors   7
    Multiples   8
    Relationship Between Factors and Multiples   8
    Class Activity 3   9
1.4   Prime Numbers and Prime Factorisation   10
    Prime Numbers   10
    Class Activity 4   11
    Prime Factorisation   12
    Index Notation   12
1.5   Highest Common Factor   13
1.6   Least Common Factor   15
1.7   Number Patterns   17
    Class Activity 5   19
1.8   Variables   21
    Class Activity 6   23
1.9   Basic Number Laws   25
    Class Activity 7   26
Chapter Review   28
Challenger 1   29
Problem Solving 1   30

Sept.

**CHAPTER 2   FRACTIONS, DECIMALS AND
APPROXIMATION**   32

2.1   Fractions   33
    Equivalent Fractions   33
    Reduction to Lowest Terms   34
    Comparison of Fractions   34
    Improper Fractions and Mixed Numbers   35
    Relationship Between Fractions and Division   35
2.2   Addition and Subtraction of Fractions   39
2.3   Multiplication and Division of Fractions   41
    Multiplication   41

	Division	42
2.4	**Decimals**	**45**
	Shifting of Decimal Point	46
	Addition	46
	Subtraction	47
	Multiplication	47
	Division	47
2.5	**Approximation**	**49**
	Rounding Off	49
	Significant Figures	53
2.6	**Conversions Between Fractions and Decimals**	**57**
2.7	**Estimation**	**62**
	Chapter Review	**65**
	Challenger 2	**67**
	Problem Solving 2	**68**

Oct

CHAPTER 3	**ARITHMETIC PROBLEMS**	**70**
3.1	**Units of Measure**	**71**
	Class Activity 1	72
	Conversion of Units	75
3.2	**Simple Word Problems**	**77**
3.3	**Multi-Step Word Problems**	**81**
3.4	**Estimation in Daily Life Situations**	**85**
	Class Activity 2	86
	Chapter Review	87
	Challenger 3	**88**
	Problem Solving 3	**88**

CHAPTER 4	**REAL NUMBERS**	**92**
4.1	**Negative Numbers**	**93**
	Class Activity 1	93
	Integers	94
	Order of Integers	95
	Numerical Value	95
4.2	**Addition and Subtraction of Integers**	**96**
	Class Activity 2	97
4.3	**Multiplication of Integers**	**103**
	Squares and Square Roots	104
	Cubes and Cube Roots	104
	Class Activity 3	105
4.4	**Division of Integers**	**108**
4.5	**Real Numbers**	**110**
	Rational Numbers	110
	Irrational Numbers	111
4.6	**Order of Calculation**	**114**

Contents

Nov.

4.7	**Mental Calculations**	**116**
	Recalling Facts	116
	Grouping	117
	Decomposing	118
Chapter Review		**120**
Challenger 4		**121**
Problem Solving 4		**122**

REVISION EXERCISE 1	**124**
MISCELLANEOUS EXERCISE 1	**130**
INVESTIGATION 1	**133**

CHAPTER 5 SIMPLE ALGEBRAIC EXPRESSIONS	**136**

5.1	**Algebraic Expressions**	**137**
	Algebraic Notation	137
	Writing Algebraic Expressions	137
	Class Activity 1	138
5.2	**Evaluation of Algebraic Expressions**	**140**
5.3	**Algebraic Terms**	**142**
5.4	**Use of Brackets**	**144**
5.5	**Collecting Like Terms**	**146**
Chapter Review		**148**
Challenger 5		**148**
Problem Solving 5		**149**

Dec.

CHAPTER 6 OPEN SENTENCES AND EQUATIONS	**152**

6.1	**Open Sentences**	**153**
6.2	**Equations**	**154**
	Class Activity 1	154
	Equivalent Equations	155
	Solving Equations	156
6.3	**Equations with Fractional and Decimals Coefficents**	**159**
6.4	**Evaluation of Formulae**	**162**
6.5	**Algebraic Problems**	**164**
Chapter Review		**167**
Challenger 6		**168**
Problem Solving 6		**169**

Jan.

CHAPTER 7 RATE, RATIO AND PERCENTAGE	**171**

7.1	**Rate and Speed**	**172**
	Rate	172
	Speed	172
7.2	**Ratio**	**175**
7.3	**Direct and Inverse Proportions**	**182**

Direct Proportion   182
Inverse Proportion   182
7.4   Percentage   **187**
7.5   Applications of Percentages   **190**
Chapter Review   **195**
Challenger 7   **196**
Problem Solving 7   **197**

REVISION EXERCISE 2   **200**
MISCELLANEOUS EXERCISE 2   **205**
INVESTIGATION 2   **208**

**CHAPTER 8   SOLVING PROBLEMS INVOLVING
                     FINANCIAL TRANSACTIONS**   **210**
**8.1   Earnings, Profit and Loss, Commissions and
          Discounts**   **211**
Earnings   211
Profit and Loss   211
Commissions   212
Discounts   212
8.2   Interest and Hire Purchase   **217**
Simple Interest   217
Compound Interest   218
Hire Purchase   219
8.3   Taxation and Money Exchange   **222**
Taxation   222
Money Exchange   222
Chapter Review   **226**
Challenger 8   **227**
Problem Solving 8   **227**

CHAPTER 9   INTRODUCING GEOMETRY   **230**

9.1   Line Segment, Line and Angles   **231**
Line Segment   231
Line   231
Angles   232
Class Activity 1   236
9.2   Angle Properties Related to Straight Lines **238**
Class Activity 2   238
9.3   Perpendicular and Parallel Lines   **242**
Class Activity 3   243
9.4   Angle Properties Related to Parallel Lines **245**
Class Activity 4   245
Chapter Review   **252**
Challenger 9   **254**
Problem Solving 9   **255**

Feb.

Contents

CHAPTER 10   POLYGONS   **258**

10.1 Triangles   **259**
10.2 Angle Properties of A Triangle   262
      Class Activity 1   262
10.3 Isosceles and Equilateral Triangles   **266**
      Class Activity 2   266
10.4 Angle Properties of A Polygon   **270**
      Class Activity 3   272
10.5 Quadrilaterals   **276**
10.6 Properties of Quadrilaterals   **279**
      Class Activity 4   279
Chapter Review   **284**
Challenger 10   **286**
Problem Solving 10   **287**

**CHAPTER 11   SYMMETRIES AND NETS OF SOLID
               FIGURES**   **289**

11.1 Line Symmetry   **290**
      Class Activity 1   290
11.2 Rotational Symmetry   **294**
11.3 Patterns   **298**
11.4 Symmetries of Solid Figures   **302**
      Class Activity 2   303
      Symmetries in Space   305
11.5 Nets of Solid Figures   **310**
Chapter Review   **314**
Challenger 11   **315**
Problem Solving 11   **316**

REVISION EXERCISE 3   **318**
MISCELLANEOUS EXERCISE 3   **326**
INVESTIGATION 3   **328**

CHAPTER 12   AREA AND PERIMETER   **330**

12.1 Perimeter and Area of Polygon   **331**
      Perimeter   331
      Area   331
      Class Activity   333
12.2 Circumference and Area of Circle   **339**
12.3 More Problems on Area and Perimeter   **342**
Chapter Review   **347**
Challenger 12   **348**
Problem Solving 12   **349**

Mar.

Apr.

Contents

May

CHAPTER 13 VOLUME, SURFACE AREA AND DENSITY   351

13.1 Volume and Surface Area of Prism and Cylinder   **352**
Prism   352
Cylinder   354
13.2 Density   **359**
13.3 More Problems on Volume and Surface Area   **361**
Chapter Review   **366**
Challenger 13   **367**
Problem Solving 13   **368**

CHAPTER 14 SIMILARITY AND CONGRUENCE   370

14.1 Similar and Congruent Figures   **371**
Class Activity 1   372
14.2 Designs and Tessellations   **381**
Designs   381
Class Activity 2   382
Tessellations   382
Class Activity 3   383
14.3 Scale Drawing   **386**
Class Activity 4   388
Chapter Review   **389**
Challenger 14   **394**
Problem Solving 14   **395**

June

REVISION EXERCISE 4   **398**
MISCELLANEOUS EXERCISE 4   **402**
INVESTIGATION 4   **405**

ASSESSMENT 1   **407**
ASSESSMENT 2   **412**
ANSWERS   **417**

PROBLEM SOLVING TIPS FOR THE STUDENT

In this book, you will have an opportunity to apply several strategies to solve interesting problems. These problems are given at the end of each chapter.

Checklist for Solving Problems

1. **Accept the problem**
   - Accept the challenge to solve unfamiliar or difficult problems.

2. **Understand the problem**
   - Read the question carefully several times and understand the key words.
   - Ascertain what is given, what is the unknown and what are the conditions.
   - Draw a diagram, make a model or act it out.
   - Describe the problem in your own words.

3. **Devise a plan**
   - Search for information to relate relevant data to the unknown.
   - Use strategies such as:
     (i) Guess and check with logical thinking.
     (ii) Simplify the problem, use tabulation or look for a pattern.
     (iii) Think of a related problem.
     (iv) Use a diagram or a model.

4. **Carry out the plan**
   - Apply the strategies and monitor your progress.
   - Check each step carefully.
   - Read the question again to make sure that you are on the right track.
   - Avoid getting stuck in one method for too long. Try another method.
   - If you are still stuck, take a break. Do something different and come back to the problem later.

5. **Look back**
   - Reflect, extend and seek improvement.
   - Check the result. (Is it reasonable? Does it satisfy the given conditions?)
   - Check the solution. (Can I do it a different way?)
   - Improve on the method used.
   - Extend the method. (How do I solve the problem if some of the conditions are changed?)

The checklist has been prepared to help you improve your problem-solving skills. This is what you should do:

- Copy the checklist onto a card.
- Keep it in your exercise book.
- Refer to it frequently when you solve problems.
- Add your own notes to the card when you learn or discover new strategies.

In learning to solve problems, it is important to take time to think about what you have done. At the end of each practice session, ask yourself some of the following questions.

1. What do I like most about the problem?
2. What strategies did I use? Why?
3. What did I do when I got stuck? Which strategy helped me to get started?
4. Did I check my work carefully.
5. What kind of mistakes did I make?
6. What were the easiest and hardest problems I solved? Why were they easy or hard?
7. Did I feel frustrated, scared or bored concerning these problems? What did I do to overcome these bad feelings?
8. Did I feel satisfied, happy and excited after doing these problems?

You may write down your thoughts in a notebook. At the end of the term, see how much you have improved in your problem-solving skills.

ENJOY SOLVING THE PROBLEMS!

Chapter 1

Whole Numbers

Chapter Highlights

- The idea of place value.
- Use of the four operations for calculations with whole numbers.
- Finding the highest common factor and lowest common multiple of two to four given numbers.
- Continuing a given number sequence and describing simple number patterns.
- Representing the general term of a sequence by algebraic expressions.
- The commutative, associative and distributive laws.

Chapter 1

1.1 SYSTEM OF NUMERATION

The numbers zero, one, two, three, four and so on are referred to as **whole numbers**.

In symbols we write

$$0, 1, 2, 3, 4, \ldots$$

Number symbols are called **numerals**. Our numerals are built on ten basic symbols called **digits.** They are

$$0, 1, 2, 3, 4, 5, 6, 7, 8 \text{ and } 9.$$

With these ten digits, we can write any number using the idea of **place value**.

Let us take, for example, a 3-digit numeral 168. What number does this numeral represent? Let us enter the digits in a place value table as follows:

Hundred thousands	Ten thousands	Thousands	Hundreds	Tens	Ones
			1	6	8

Table 1.1

Note that the digit 1 at the 'hundreds' place represents 1 hundred, the digit 6 at the 'tens' place represents 6 tens, and the digit 8 at the 'ones' place represents 8 ones. So, the numeral 168 represents the number 'one hundred sixty-eight'.

Notice also that as we move to the left of Table 1.1, the place value for each position is ten times the place value of the previous position.

Our system of numeration is a base ten system. It is referred to as the **decimal system** or **denary system**.

In the decimal system, we can carry out calculations such as additions, subtractions, multiplications and divisions in a vertical manner.

For example,

```
    3   5   2
+   2   7   6
───────────────
            8
```

MATHSTORY

People from different cultures have invented different ways of writing numbers.

Egyptian |∩⌒⫰
Babylonian ▸⟨
Chinese 五百
Roman I V X M

Today, we use the Hindu-Arabic numeration system which was created before 200 BC and has used in arithmetic textbooks written by Arab mathematicians around 700 AD.

Thinking process
1. Add the ones
   - $2 + 6 = 8$ (ones)
   - Enter '8' under the 'ones' column

```
  1
  3  5  2        2.   Add the tens
+ 2  7  6             •   5 + 7 = 12 (tens)
        2  8          •   Rename 12 tens as 1 hundred 2 tens
                      •   Enter '2' under the 'tens' column
                      •   Enter '1' above the 'hundreds' column
```

```
  1
  3  5  2        3.   Add the hundreds
+ 2  7  6             •   1 + 3 + 2 = 6 (hundreds)
  6  2  8             •   Enter '6' under the 'hundreds' column
```

Class Activity 1

1. Explain the thinking processes involved in the following calculations.

(a)
```
   1  1
   3  2  9
+  2  7  6
   6  0  5
```

(b)
```
        3  12
   3    4  2
-  2    1  7
   1    2  5
```

(c)
```
      3
      7  4
×        8
   5  9  2
```

(d)
```
          5  9
  7 ) 4   1  3
      3   5
          6  3
          6  3
```

2. Using three different digits, form three-digit numerals which represent
   (a) the greatest number,   (b) the smallest number.
   Explain your methods.

3. Form three-digit numerals which represent
   (a) the greatest number,   (b) the smallest number.
   Explain the difference between this question and Question 2.

Exercise 1.1

answers on p. 417

1. Copy and complete the following by finding a digit for each *.

(a)
```
    5 * 7
+   * 3 8
    8 0 5
```

(b)
```
    1 * * *
-     3 * 9
      7 3 4
```

(c)
```
    7 * * 8 9
+     9 9 * *
    * 0 0 3 6
```

(d)
```
    2 3 * *
-   * * 6 9
      1 3 3
```

(e)
```
    * * * 4 6
-     2 8 9 7 *
      2 1 4 2
```

(f)
```
      7 * 4
+     * 8 *
    * 0 3
```

3

2. Copy and complete the following by finding a digit for each *.

(a)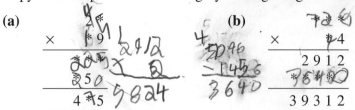

(b)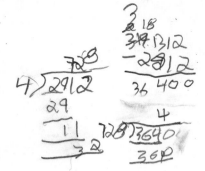

(c)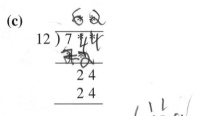

(d)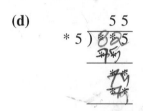

(e)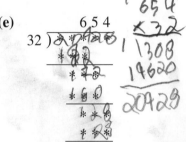

(f)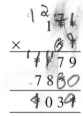

3. Using all the digits 0, 1, 2, 3, 4, 5, 6, 7, 8 and 9, form two 5-digit numbers so that their sum is
(a) the greatest, **(b)** the smallest.
Write down the sum in each case.

*4. Using all the digits 0, 1, 2, 3, 4, 5, 6, 7, 8, 9, form two 5-digit numbers so that their difference is
(a) the greatest, **(b)** the smallest.
Write down the difference in each case.

1.2 THE FOUR OPERATIONS

We refer to addition, subtraction, multiplication and division as the **four operations**.

An operation may be described in various ways. For example,

'Calculate 12 + 34' may be expressed verbally as

'Add 12 and 34',
'Find the sum of 12 and 34',
'What is 12 plus 34?', etc.

Class Activity 2

Without using the calculator, write down the answers for the following questions. Working may be omitted. Record the time you take to answer all the questions.

1. Add 24 and 432.
2. Find the difference between 432 and 24.
3. Find the product of 24 and 432.
4. Find the sum of 432 and 24.
5. Divide 432 by 24.
6. Take away 24 from 432.
7. Find the total value of 432 and 24.
8. Find the quotient when 432 is divided by 24.
9. Multiply 432 by 24.
10. Subtract 24 from 432.
11. Divide 24 into 432.
12. Reduce 432 by 24.
13. What is 432 plus 24?
14. By how much does 432 exceed 24?
15. What number is equal to 432 times 24?
16. What number is 432 more than 24?
17. What number is 24 less than 432?
18. What number is 24 times as large as 432?
19. What is the value when 432 is increased 24 folds?
20. Decreasing 432 by 24 gives what number?
21. Increasing 432 by 24 gives what number?
22. What is 432 minus 24?

Combined Operations

When doing combined operations, we use the following order of calculation.

> **Expressions without brackets**
> * **Working from left to right, do multiplication or division before addition or subtraction.**
>
> **Expressions with brackets**
> * **Simplify the expression within the brackets first.**
> * **If there is more than one pair of brackets, simplify the expression within the innermost pair of brackets first.**

Worked Example 1

Evaluate the following expressions, showing the order of calculation.

(a) $527 + [(324 - 235) \times (14 - 3)]$
(b) $\{[6 + 3 \times (4 + 5)] \times 7\} + (8 \times 5)$

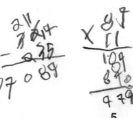

Solution:

(a) $527 + (324 - 235) \times (14 - 3)$
$= 527 + 89 \times 11$
$= 527 + 979$
$= 1\ 506$

(b) $[6 + 3 \times (4 + 5)] \times 7 + 8 \times 5$
$= (6 + 3 \times 9) \times 7 + 8 \times 5$
$= (6 + 27) \times 7 + 8 \times 5$
$= 33 \times 7 + 8 \times 5$
$= 231 + 40$
$= 271$

Most scientific calculators use the order of calculation mentioned above. To evaluate the above expressions using a calculator, we proceed as follows:

(a) 527 ⬚+ ⬚(324 ⬚− 235 ⬚) ⬚× ⬚(14 ⬚− 3 ⬚) ⬚EXE

(b) ⬚(6 ⬚+ 3 ⬚× ⬚(4 ⬚+ 5 ⬚) ⬚) ⬚× 7 ⬚+ 8 ⬚× 5 EXE

Exercise 1.2

answers on p. 417

No calculators may be used for questions 1 to 8.

Evaluate the following expressions, showing the order of calculation.

1. (a) $4 \times (6 \div 8) + (32 - 12)$
   (b) $(42 \div 7 \times 3 - 11) + 9$
   (c) $(16 - 7 + 9 \times 5 \div 45)$
   (d) $23 + 80 - (105 \div 7 \times 3)$
   (e) $(54 - (32 \times 8 \div 16) + 73)$
   (f) $76 + (24 \div 12 \times 7 - 26)$

2. (a) $(72 \div (5 + 4) \times 6)$
   (b) $15 \times (34 - 29) \div 25$
   (c) $56 \div 8 \times (24 + 11)$
   (d) $25 \times 9 \div (31 - 16)$

3. (a) $36 \div (28 - (2 \times 8) \div 3)$
   (b) $13 \times (5 - 45 \div 9) + 18$
   (c) $6 + (7 \times 7 - 7) \div 6$
   (d) $27 - (405 \div 45 \div 9) \times 4$

4. (a) $(323 - 213) \times (161 - 153)$
   (b) $(126 + 30) \div (96 - 83)$
   (c) $(264 \div 12 - 3) \times (330 \div 15)$
   (d) $(13 + 26 \times 5) \div (15 \times 6 - 79)$

5. (a) $4 \times [(12 + 8) \times 2 + 3] + 4$
   (b) $15 + [568 - (283 - 265) \times 12] \times 3$
   (c) $300 - [(345 - 264) \times 3] \div 9$
   (d) $264 \div [(127 - 124) \times 4] - 22$

6. (a) $\{[(174 - 120) \times 9 + 14] \times 5] - 24\} \times 7$
   (b) $\{[(211 - 102) \times 7 + 26] \times 3 - 312\} \div 15$
   (c) $\{[(185 + 19) \div 12 + 13] \div 2 + 66\} \div 9$
   (d) $3 \times \{81 + [13 - (7 + 5) \div 3]\}$

7. Fill in the correct operations to make the following mathematical sentences true.
   (a) $24 \times 3 + 6 \boxed{} 2 = 75$ **(b)** $54 + 7 \square 3 - 20 \div 4 = 70$
   (c) $21 \div 3 \square 7 - 6 \square 4 = 47$ **(d)** $16 \square 8 - 9 \square 9 \times 2 = 0$

8. Insert brackets to make the following mathematical sentences true.
   (a) $10 + 15 \times 5 + 15 \div 5 = 70$ **(b)** $38 + 21 - 7 \times 15 = 248$
   (c) $32 - 13 \times 16 - 5 = 209$ **(d)** $18 \div 12 - 9 \times 2 = 3$

9. Check your answers for questions 1 to 6 using a calculator. Show the 'keying order' for question 6.

1.3 FACTORS AND MULTIPLES

Natural Numbers

In section 1.1, we have learnt about whole numbers. The non-zero whole numbers, i.e. 1, 2, 3, 4, 5, . . ., are called **natural numbers**. These are the numbers we use for counting.

Factors

Let us take 28 as a given number and express it as a product of two natural numbers as follows:

$$28 = 4 \times 7$$

The numbers 4 and 7 are called **factors** of the given number 28.

Clearly, 28 can be divided exactly by 4 and by 7, i.e. 28 is **divisible** by 4 and by 7.

In general, factors of a number divide that number exactly without leaving any remainder.

A perfect number is one whose factor add up to the number itself.

Listing of factors:
We can find all the factors of 28 by expressing 28 as a product of two natural numbers in as many ways as possible:

$$28 = 1 \times 28$$
$$28 = 2 \times 14$$
$$28 = 4 \times 7$$

So, the factors of 28 are

$$1, 2, 4, 7, 14 \text{ and } 28.$$

Note: We can simply list the factors in pairs as indicated:

$$1 \quad 2 \quad 4 \quad 7 \quad 14 \quad 28$$

Divisibility Tests
1. A number is divisible by 2 if its ones digit is 0, 2, 4, 6 or 8.
2. A number is divisible by 3 if the sum of its digits is divisible by 3.
3. A number is divisible by 5 if its ones digit is 0 or 5.
4. A number is divisible by 10 if its ones digit is 0.

Multiples

Let us take 4 as a given number and multiply it by another natural number as follows:

$$4 \times 7 = 28$$

The product 28 is called a **multiple** of the given number 4. Similarly, 28 is also a multiple of 7.

A multiple of a whole number is the product of the number and some other whole number.

Listing of multiples:

We can obtain as many multiples of 4 as we please by multiplying the number 4 by 1 and then by 2 and then by 3 and so on as follows.

$$4 \times 1 = 4$$
$$4 \times 2 = 8$$
$$4 \times 3 = 12$$
$$\vdots$$

So, the multiples of 4 are

$$4, 8, 12, 16, 20, \ldots$$

Note: We can simply begin with 4 and count in steps of 4 to obtain the list.

Similarly, the multiples of 7 are

$$7, 14, 21, 28, 35, \ldots$$

Relationship between Factors and Multiples

Let us look at the number sentence

$$28 = 4 \times 7.$$

We have
  - 4 is a factor of 28.
  - 28 is a multiple of 4.

We also have
  - 7 is a factor of 28.
  - 28 is a multiple of 7.

Let us take the special case

$$\mathbf{28} = 1 \times 28.$$

We have
  - 1 is a factor of **28**.
  - **28** is a multiple of 1.

We also have
  - 28 is a factor of **28**.
  - **28** is a multiple of 28.

Class Activity 3

No calculators may be used except for question 10.

1. When 124 is divided by 31, the exact answer is 4. Refer to 124 as the **dividend**, 31 as the **divisor** and 4 as the **quotient** and state whether each of the following statements is true or false.
   (a) The divisor is a factor of the dividend. T
   (b) The quotient is a factor of the dividend. T
   (c) The divisor is a factor of the quotient. F
   (d) The quotient is a factor of the divisor. F
   (e) The dividend is a multiple of the divisor. T
   (f) The quotient is a multiple of the dividend. F
   (g) The divisor is a multiple of the quotient. F
   (h) The quotient is a multiple of the divisor. F

2. State whether each of the following statements is true or false.
   (a) The number 12 is greater than each of its factors. F
   (b) All multiples of 12 are greater than 12. F
   (c) 1 is a factor of all natural numbers. T
   (d) Any natural number is a factor of itself. T
   (e) Any natural number is a multiple of 1. F
   (f) Any natural number is a multiple of itself. T
   (g) Zero is divisible by any natural number. ✓ ✗
   (h) If one natural number is divisible by another natural number, the first number is a multiple of the second number. T

3. Which of the following numbers have 14 as a factor?
   42, 126, 168, 180, 210

4. Which of the following numbers are factors of 96?
   1, 2, 3, 8, 9, 12, 15, 16, 24, 48, 52, 96

5. Which of the following are multiples of 7?
   12, 36, 35, 40, 42, 20, 28, 45, 49, 55, 48, 60, 63, 70, 92

6. Which of the following have 196 as a multiple?
   3, 4, 6, 18, 28

7. Without using the term 'factor', reword the 'instruction' for question 3.
   number have in them *Which of the following*

8. Without using the term 'multiple', reword the 'instruction' for question 6.
   Which of the following are in 196

9. Which of the following numbers have exactly two factors each?
   11, 12, 13, 14, 15, 16, 17, 18, 19, 20

*10. Express 323 as a product of two factors so that the factors are each greater than 10.

Exercise 1.3 ✎

answers on p. 417

No calculators may be used.

1. List all the factors of each of the following.
    (a) 15 (b) 28 (c) 42
    (d) 78 (e) 63 (f) 120

2. List the first ten multiples of each of the following.
    (a) 3 (b) 5 (c) 6
    (d) 9 (e) 15 (f) 19

3. List all the factors of (a) 60, and (b) 96.
    Then list all the common factors found in your lists for (a) and (b).

4. List the first twelve multiples of (a) 12, and (b) 18.
    Then list all the common multiples found in your lists for (a) and (b).

*5. Find the largest multiple of 7 less than (a) 100, (b) 200, (c) 500, and (d) 1000.

1.4 PRIME NUMBERS AND PRIME FACTORISATION

Prime Numbers

Look at the following table.

List *A*	List *B*
2 has factors 1 and 2.	4 has factors 1, 2 and 4.
3 has factors 1 and 3.	6 has factors 1, 2, 3 and 6.
5 has factors 1 and 5.	8 has factors 1, 2, 4 and 8.
7 has factors 1 and 7.	9 has factors 1, 3 and 9.
11 has factors 1 and 11.	10 has factors 1, 2, 5 and 10.

Table 1.2

A natural number which has exactly two factors, 1 and itself, is called a **prime number**. In list *A*, the numbers 2, 3, 5, 7 and 11 are prime numbers.

MATHSTORY

More than 2 000 years ago, the Greek mathematician Euclid proved that there is no largest prime number. However, mathematicians continue searching for larger prime numbers. Why they bother? For the thrill perhaps.

A natural number which has more than two factors is called a **composite number**. In list B, the numbers 4, 6, 8, 9 and 10 are composite numbers.

Is the number 1 a prime or a composite number? Explain.

Eratosthenes, a Greek mathematician, suggested a method for finding all the prime numbers less than a given number. It is called the **sieve of Eratosthenes**. One way of describing the sieve is as follows:

1. List all the natural numbers from 2 to the given number.
2. Cross out all the numbers that have 2 as a factor, except 2 itself.
3. Cross out all the remaining numbers that have 3 as a factor, except 3 itself.
4. The next number which is not crossed out is 5. Now, cross out all the remaining numbers that have 5 as a factor, except 5 itself, and so on.

After this process is completed, the numbers remaining in the list are prime numbers.

In finding the prime numbers less than 26, the working would look like this:

2   3   ̶4̶   5   ̶6̶   7   ̶8̶   ̶9̶   ̶1̶0̶   11   ̶1̶2̶   13
̶1̶4̶   ̶1̶5̶   ̶1̶6̶   17   ̶1̶8̶   19   ̶2̶0̶   ̶2̶1̶   ̶2̶2̶   23   ̶2̶4̶   ̶2̶5̶

The numbers which are not crossed out are the prime numbers less than 26. This set consists of 2, 3, 5, 7, 11, 13, 17, 19 and 23.

Class Activity 4

No calculators may be used.

1. State whether each of the following statements is true or false. If it is false, give a counter example.

   E.g. The statement "All odd numbers are prime numbers" is false. A counter example is "The odd number 9 is not a prime number".

   (a) If a natural number can be expressed as a product of two factors, then the natural number is a prime number. *True*

   (b) A prime number is not divisible by any natural number other than 1 and itself. *true*

   (c) If a natural number is divisible by 1 and itself, then the natural number is a prime number. *true*

   (d) All composite numbers can be expressed as a product of prime numbers. *n.k.*

   (e) If a natural number is not a composite number, then it is a prime number. *False because 2 can't be a composite number*

   (f) If a composite number is divisible by a second composite number, then the first composite number is divisible by each of the prime factors of the second composite number. *true*

2. Find the largest prime number less than
    (a) 30,   **(b)** 40,   **(c)** 50,   **(d)** 60.

3. Use the sieve of Erathosthenes to find all the prime numbers less than 50. *2, 3, 5, 7, 11, 13, 17, 19, 2*
29, 31, 37, 41, 43, 47,

4. Find two prime numbers whose product is divisible by 2. Must one of these be 2?

5. Find two prime numbers whose product is not divisible by 2. Can any prime number other than 2 be used?

Prime Factorisation

60 is a composite number. It can be written as the product $2 \times 2 \times 3 \times 5$. Notice that these factors are all prime numbers. We call them **prime factors**.

When we express a number as a product of prime factors, we have actually factorised it completely. We refer to this process as **prime factorisation**.

Index Notation

The product of repeated factors can be written in a shorter way. For example,

$$2 \times 2 = 2^2, \qquad\qquad 3 \times 3 = 3^2,$$
$$2 \times 2 \times 2 = 2^3, \qquad\qquad 3 \times 3 \times 3 = 3^3,$$
$$2 \times 2 \times 2 \times 2 = 2^4, \qquad\qquad 3 \times 3 \times 3 \times 3 = 3^4.$$

The raised number 3 in 2^3 is referred to as an **index**; the index of 3^4 is 4. The index is also known as the **exponent**.

Worked Example 2

Factorise 504 completely and give your answers in index notation.

Solution:

$$504 = 2 \times 2 \times 2 \times 3 \times 3 \times 7$$
$$= 2^3 \times 3^2 \times 7$$

Note: To express 504 as a product of prime factors, we can use the following methods.

    (a) Repeated division method   (b) Factor tree method

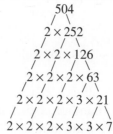

```
2 | 504
2 | 252
2 | 126
3 |  63
3 |  21
7 |   7
  |   1
```

MATHSTORY

Sometimes, we deal with very small or very large numbers. For example, the diameter of the Sun is 1 392 000 km and that of a hydrogen atom is 0.000 000 000 1 m. To make it easier to work with such numbers, scientists have developed the index notation.

Exercise 1.4 ✎ *answers on p. 417*

No calculators may be used except for question 4.

1. Rewrite the following in index notation.
   (a) $5 \times 5 = 5^2$
   (b) $3 \times 3 \times 3 = 3^3$
   (c) $17 \times 17 \times 17 = 17^3$
   (d) $2 \times 2 \times 7 \times 7 \times 7 = 2^2 \times 7^3$
   (e) $3 \times 3 \times 3 \times 5 \times 5 \times 11 \times 11 = 3^3 \times 5^2 \times 11^2 =$
   (f) $7 \times 7 \times 13 \times 17 \times 17 \times 71 = 7^2 \times 13 \times 17^2 \times 71 =$

2. Express each of the following as a product of prime factors and give your answer in index notation.
   (a) 10
   (b) 15
   (c) 16
   (d) 18
   (e) 20
   (f) 36
   (g) 48
   (h) 72
   (i) 144
   (j) 256

3. Factorise each of the following completely.
   (a) 9
   (b) 12
   (c) 21
   (d) 24
   (e) 30
   (f) 42
   (g) 108
   (h) 125
   (i) 216
   (j) 648

4. Find the largest prime number less than
   (a) 100,
   (b) 120,
   (c) 150,
   (d) 200.

1.5 HIGHEST COMMON FACTOR

Consider the numbers 60 and 96.
The list of all factors of 60 is **1**, **2**, **3**, **4**, 5, **6**, 10, **12**, 15, 20, 30 and 60.
The list of all factors of 96 is **1**, **2**, **3**, **4**, **6**, 8, **12**, 16, 24, 32, 48 and 96.
The list of all the common factors of 60 and 96 is 1, 2, 3, 4, 6 and 12.

The largest of these common factors is 12, and thus we call 12 the **highest common factor** (HCF) of 60 and 96.

The above method of finding HCF can be quite tedious. Simpler methods such as the following can be used.

Method 1
Using prime factorisation, we have

$$60 = 2 \times 2 \times 3 \times 5,$$
$$96 = 2 \times 2 \times 2 \times 2 \times 2 \times 3.$$

Rearranging the prime factors gives

$$60 = 2 \times 2 \times 3 \times 5, \qquad \qquad \dots\dots\dots\dots\dots\dots\dots(1)$$

$$96 = 2 \times 2 \times 3 \times 2 \times 2 \times 2. \quad \dots\dots\dots\dots\dots\dots(2)$$

The largest product found in both (1) and (2) is $2 \times 2 \times 3$ which is 12. Thus, the HCF of 60 and 96 is 12.

Note: We may also write the prime factors using indices as follows:

$$60 = 2^2 \times 3 \times 5$$
$$96 = 2^5 \times 3$$

We rewrite the above as

$$60 = 2^2 \times 3 \times 5,$$

$$96 = 2^2 \times 3 \times 2^3.$$

Thus, the HCF of 60 and 96 is $2^2 \times 3$, i.e. 12.

Method 2

Extract the common prime factors of 60 and 96 and form a product to give the HCF.

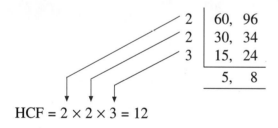

```
    2 | 60,  96
    2 | 30,  34
    3 | 15,  24
      _____
        5,   8
```

HCF = $2 \times 2 \times 3 = 12$

Therefore, the HCF of 60 and 96 is 12.

Worked Example 3

Find the HCF of 36, 24, 144 and 96.

Solution:

```
2 | 36,  24,  144,  96
2 | 18,  12,   72,  48
3 |  9,   6,   36,  24
  _____
     3,   2,   12,   8
```

Therefore, the HCF is $2^2 \times 3$, i.e. 12.

Exercise 1.5 ✍

answers on p. 418

No calculators may be used.

1. Find the HCF of each of the following pairs of numbers.

(a) 8, 9	**(b)** 11, 13	**(c)** 12, 42
(d) 15, 16	**(e)** 15, 27	**(f)** 15, 42
(g) 15, 60	**(h)** 15, 63	**(i)** 16, 56
(j) 18, 45	**(k)** 20, 21	**(l)** 24, 19
(m) 24, 48	**(n)** 24, 108	**(o)** 28, 54
(p) 36, 162	**(q)** 36, 243	**(r)** 42, 36
(s) 42, 63	**(t)** 45, 42	**(u)** 60, 84
(v) 96, 36	**(w)** 108, 48	**(x)** 165, 99
(y) 425, 200	**(z)** 546, 1 521	

2. Find the HCF of each of the following sets of numbers.

(a) 4, 5, 9	**(b)** 12, 42, 72	**(c)** 16, 72, 104
(d) 35, 420, 245	**(e)** 47, 9, 25	**(f)** 4, 5, 7, 9
(g) 24, 156, 180, 204	**(h)** 30, 126, 105, 255	**(i)** 96, 144, 136, 344

*3. The HCF of two numbers is 12. If the sum of the two numbers is 72, find the numbers.

*4. The HCF of two numbers is 8. If the sum of the two numbers is 72, find the numbers. (Give all the possible pairs of numbers.)

1.6 LEAST COMMON MULTIPLE

Consider the numbers 12 and 18.
The list of all the multiples of 12 is 12, 24, **36**, 48, 60, **72**, . . .
The list of all the multiples of 18 is 18, **36**, 54, **72**, 90, 108, . . .
The list of all the common multiples of 12 and 18 is 36, 72, . . .

The smallest of these common multiples is 36, and thus 36 is the **least common multiple** (LCM) of 12 and 18.

There are other simpler methods of finding the LCM such as the ones shown below.

Method 1
The prime factorisations of 12 and 18 are

$$12 = 2 \times 2 \times 3,$$
$$18 = 2 \times 3 \times 3.$$

The product of all the prime factors, i.e. $2 \times 2 \times 3 \times 2 \times 3 \times 3$, is clearly a common multiple of 12 and 18.

But can we find another common multiple smaller than this product?

Let us arrange the prime factorisations and extract the prime factors from either one or both of 12 and 18 as follows:

$$12 = 2 \times 2 \times 3$$
$$18 = \quad 2 \times 3 \times 3$$
$$2 \times 2 \times 3 \times 3$$

Notice that $2 \times 2 \times 3 \times 3$ is the smallest product which contains $2 \times 2 \times 3$ as well as $2 \times 3 \times 3$.

Thus, the LCM of 12 and 18 is $2 \times 2 \times 3 \times 3$, i.e. 36.

Note: Using indices, we have

$$12 = 2^2 \times 3,$$
$$18 = 2 \times 3^2.$$

The smallest product which contains $2^2 \times 3$ and 2×3^2 is $2^2 \times 3^2$.
Thus, the LCM is $2^2 \times 3^2$.

Method 2

Extract the prime factors from either one or both of 12 and 18 as shown below. Then, form the product to give the LCM.

```
2 | 12,  18
2 |  6,   9
3 |  3,   9
3 |  1,   3
  |  1,   1
```

$$\text{LCM} = 2 \times 2 \times 3 \times 3 = 36$$

Note: In the second line, $6 \div 2 = 3$, so we enter the quotient 3 in the third line of the working. 9 is not divisible by 2, so we write down 9 itself in the third line of the working, and so on.

Worked Example 4

Find the LCM of 35, 420 and 245.

Solution:

$$
\begin{array}{r|ccc}
5 & 35, & 420, & 245 \\
7 & 7, & 84, & 49 \\
7 & 1, & 12, & 7 \\
12 & 1, & 12, & 1 \\
\hline
& 1, & 1, & 1
\end{array}
$$

Therefore, the LCM is $5 \times 7^2 \times 12$, i.e. 2 940.

Exercise 1.6

answers on p. 418

1. Find the LCM of each of the following pairs of numbers.
   - **(a)** 2, 17
   - **(b)** 3, 5
   - **(c)** 4, 9
   - **(d)** 5, 12
   - **(e)** 6, 9
   - **(f)** 6, 12
   - **(g)** 6, 15
   - **(h)** 12, 8
   - **(i)** 12, 9
   - **(j)** 12, 20
   - **(k)** 14, 6
   - **(l)** 15, 9
   - **(m)** 15, 20
   - **(n)** 16, 10
   - **(o)** 16, 36
   - **(p)** 18, 9
   - **(q)** 18, 24
   - **(r)** 20, 25
   - **(s)** 78, 56
   - **(t)** 81, 225
   - **(u)** 108, 132
   - **(v)** 110, 231
   - **(w)** 126, 195
   - **(x)** 135, 120
   - **(y)** 168, 248
   - **(z)** 700, 82

2. Find the LCM of each of the following sets of numbers.
   - **(a)** 8, 12, 18
   - **(b)** 20, 32, 18
   - **(c)** 24, 18, 36
   - **(d)** 4, 8, 16, 20
   - **(e)** 5, 12, 18, 20
   - **(f)** 6, 12, 8, 18
   - **(g)** 135, 175, 65
   - **(h)** 140, 385, 220
   - **(i)** 225, 105, 252

3. Find the **(i)** HCF, **(ii)** LCM and **(iii)** product of the HCF and the LCM for each of the following pairs of numbers.
   - **(a)** 7, 28
   - **(b)** 12, 18
   - **(c)** 12, 35
   - **(d)** 96, 120

   Find also the product of each of these pairs of numbers and compare the result with that in (iii). What do you notice?

*4. The LCM of 6 and a certain number is 24. Find the number. (If there is more than one answer, give the smallest number.)

*5. The HCF of two numbers is 1 and the LCM of these numbers is 91. What are the numbers?

1.7 NUMBER PATTERNS

We can recall that **whole numbers** are the numbers 0, 1, 2, 3, 4, 5, . . ., and that if the number 0 is excluded, the numbers 1, 2, 3, 4, 5, . . . are known as **natural numbers**.

Now among the natural numbers, there are the **odd numbers** (1, 3, 5, 7, 9, 11, . . .) and the **even numbers** (2, 4, 6, 8, 10, . . .). Notice that even numbers can be divided by 2 exactly, but odd numbers cannot. We can show patterns of odd numbers and even numbers by using dots.

For example,

$\begin{matrix} \bullet & \bullet & \bullet & \bullet \\ \bullet & \bullet & \bullet & \end{matrix}$ $\begin{matrix} \bullet & \bullet & \bullet & \bullet \\ \bullet & \bullet & \bullet & \bullet \end{matrix}$

odd number   even number

Numbers which can be represented by dots to form triangular patterns are called **triangular numbers**.

For example,

1   3   6   10

Numbers which can be represented by dots to form square patterns are called **square numbers**.

For example,

1   4   9   16

Notice that these square numbers can be expressed, in index notation, as

$$1^2, 2^2, 3^2, 4^2, \ldots$$

We read these as square of 1, square of 2, square of 3, square of 4 . . . .

Numbers which can be expressed as

$$1^3, 2^3, 3^3, 4^3, \ldots$$

are called **cubic numbers**.

So, 1, 8, 27, 64, . . . are cubic numbers.

We read 1^3 as cube of 1, 2^3 as cube of 2 and so on.

A listing of numbers which follow a certain pattern is called a **sequence**.

Examples
(a)   1, 3, 5, 7, . . . (consecutive odd numbers)
(b)   2, 4, 6, 8, . . . (consecutive even numbers)
(c)   1, 4, 9, 16, . . . (consecutive square numbers)
(d)   1, 3, 6, 10, . . . (consecutive triangular numbers)

MATHSTORY

According to Py-thagorean number lore, odd numbers were considered male and even numbers female.

(e) 1, 4, 7, 10, . . . (beginning with 1 and increasing each step by 3)
(f) 2, 4, 8, 16, . . . (beginning with 2 and doubling each step)
(g) 1, 8, 27, 64, . . . (consecutive cubic numbers)
(h) 3, 6, 9, 12, . . . (consecutive multiples of 3)

The numbers in a sequence are called **terms**. 'Arrow diagrams' may be used to show the relationship between two consecutive terms.

For example,

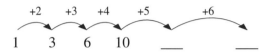

We can continue a sequence when we know its pattern.

Class Activity 5

1. State whether each of the following statements is true or false. If it is false, give an example to show why.
    (a) The sum of two even numbers is even. *True*
    (b) The difference between two unequal even numbers is odd. *false*
    (c) The sum of an even number and an odd number is even.
    (d) The difference between an even number and an odd number is odd.
    (e) The sum of two odd numbers is even.
    (f) The difference between two unequal odd numbers is odd.
    (g) The product of two even numbers is even.
    (h) The product of two odd numbers is even.
    (i) The product of an odd number and an even number is even.

2. Study the following numbers and state which are triangular numbers, which are square numbers and which are cubic numbers. Draw patterns with dots, for part (d), (e) and (g) to show your answer.
    (a) 64   (b) 55   (c) 125
    (d) 49   (e) 36   (f) 625
    (g) 28   (h) 45   (i) 1 225

3. Express each of the triangular numbers 3, 6, 10 and 15 as a sum of consecutive natural numbers. Is it true that every triangular number is the sum of several consecutive natural numbers? *No*

4. Form patterns with matchsticks or toothpicks as shown and then complete the sequences.

1st
pattern

2nd
pattern

3rd
pattern

    (a) Number of matchsticks: 3, 5, 7, ____ , ____

    (b) Number of triangles: 1, 2, 3, ____ , ____

Describe in words the pattern for each sequence.

*5. Notice that a square number can be expressed as a sum of consecutive odd numbers. For example,

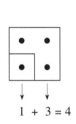   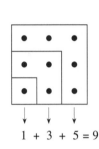   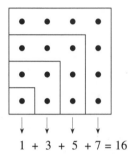

    1 + 3 = 4   1 + 3 + 5 = 9   1 + 3 + 5 + 7 = 16

Find the answers for the following.

    (a) 1 + 3 + 5 + 7 + 9 + 11 + . . . (30 terms) = ____

    (b) 7 + 9 + 11 + 13 + 15 + 17 + . . . (30 terms) = ____

Exercise 1.7 🖎

answers on p. 418

1. Copy and complete each of the following number sequences.

    (a) 1, 4, 9, 16, *27* , *36*   **(b)** 1, 3, 6, 10, ____ , ____

    (c) 1, 4, 7, 10, *13* , *16*   **(d)** 2, 4, 8, 16, ____ , ____

    (e) 5, 11, 17, 23, *29* , *35*   **(f)** 1, 8, 27, 64, ____ , ____

2. Copy and complete each of the following number sequences. For each sequence, describe in words the pattern.

    (a) 2, 7, 12, 17, 22, ____ , ____

    (b) 1, 3, 9, 27, 81, ____ , ____

    (c) 81, 76, 71, 66, 61, ____ , ____

    (d) 3, 9, 7, 13, 11, 17, ____ , ____

    (e) 384, 192, 96, 48, 24, ____ , ____

    (f) 6, 9, 12, 15, ____ , ____

3. Draw the next two patterns and then complete the sequences.

      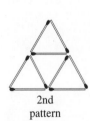   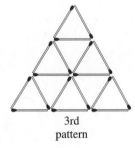

    1st   2nd   3rd

   pattern   pattern   pattern

(a) Number of matchsticks: 3, 9, 18, _29_ , _44_

(b) Number of small triangles: 1, 4, 9, _16_ , _25_

Describe in words the pattern for each sequence.

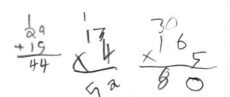

4. Form patterns as shown and then complete the sequences.

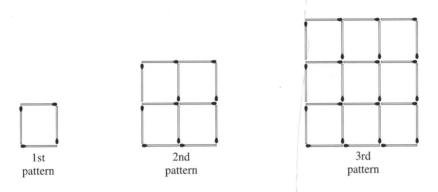

| 1st pattern | 2nd pattern | 3rd pattern |

(a) Number of matchsticks: 4, 12, 24, _52_ , _90_

(b) Number of small squares: 1, 4, 9, _16_ , _25_

Describe in words the pattern for each sequence.

*5. The following three number sequences follow the same pattern.

$$1, 2, 4, \ldots$$
$$3, 6, 12, \ldots$$
$$5, 10, 20, \ldots$$

(a) Describe in words the pattern.

(b) Find the sum of the first three terms of each sequence.

(c) For each sequence, describe in words the relationship between the sum of the first three terms and the first term.

(d) The sum of the first three terms of a number sequence, following this pattern, is 49. Find the three terms.

1.8 VARIABLES

Examples

(a) A calculator is 'programmed' to perform a certain function. For each input number you give, the calculator gives an output number on the display.

Study the list of input and output numbers below.

Input numbers	Output numbers
1	5
2	6
3	7
4	8
.	.
.	.
.	.

A calculator which can perform constant calculation can be preset to show this relationship by pressing $\boxed{4}$ $\boxed{+}$ $\boxed{+}$. Then enter the input number 1 and press $\boxed{=}$ to get the output number 5 and so on.

There are several ways to describe the relationship between the input and the output numbers. The following are some examples.

> The output number is 4 greater than the input number.
> Adding 4 to the input number gives the output number.
> The output number is equal to the input number plus 4.
> If the input number is n, then the output number is $n + 4$.

Expressions like $n + 4$ which consist of numbers and letters related by the four operations are called **algebraic expressions**. The letter n in the expression is referred to as a **variable** because it can have a variety of values. We can find the **value** of the algebraic expression $n + 4$ if we have further information about n. Suppose $n = 37$. Then, replacing n by 37, we have

A variable is a symbol usually a letter, that stands for a number.

$$n + 4 = 37 + 4$$
$$= 41.$$

So the value of $n + 4$ is 41 when n is 37.
This means that when the input number is 37, the output number is 41.

Let us denote the output number as m when the input number is n. So, we write

$$m = n + 4.$$

Thus, for any given value of n, we can find the corresponding value of m. We refer to this as the 'machine rule' the calculator is 'programmed' to obey.

(b) A special calculator is 'programmed' to follow a different machine rule, and the table below shows the input numbers and the corresponding output numbers.

A non-programmable calculator with the ALPHA key can be preset with this 'machine rule' by storing 0 in the variable memory X (or clearing it), followed by entering the formula $X = X + 1 : Y = 2X - 1$. Then press $\boxed{\text{EXE}}$ to display the input 1 and press $\boxed{\text{EXE}}$ to get the output 1. Press $\boxed{\text{EXE}}$ again to display the input 2 and press $\boxed{\text{EXE}}$ to get the output 3 and so on.

Input n	1	2	3	4	5	6	7	8	9	10
Output m	1	3	5	7	9	11	13	15	17	19

Table 1.3

To find the machine rule, we can rewrite the output numbers to show their relationship with the input numbers as follows:

Output m				Input n	
1	=	2	×	1	− 1
3	=	2	×	2	− 1
5	=	2	×	3	− 1
7	=	2	×	4	− 1
.			.		
.			.		
.			.		

From the pattern, we observe that the machine rule is $m = 2 \times n - 1$.

Notice that the output numbers form the sequence of consecutive odd numbers

$$1, 3, 5, 7, 9, \ldots .$$

If the nth term of this sequence is m, we say that the **formula** for the nth term of the sequence is

$$m = 2 \times n - 1,$$

which is the machine rule stated above.

Alternatively, let us study the following dot patterns.

We observe that the number of dots in the nth pattern is 1 dot less than $2 \times n$ dots.

Class Activity 6

1. Copy and complete the table.
   The rule connecting the input n and output m is $m = n + 7$.

Input n	1	2	3	4	5	6	7	8	9	10
Output m	8		10							17

2. Copy and complete the table.
   The rule connecting the input *a* and output *b* is $b = a - 22$.

Input *a*	30	31	32	33	34	35	36	37	38	39	40
Output *b*	8	9	10	11	12	13	14	15	16	17	18

3. Explain how an ordinary scientific calculator can be 'programmed' to obey the machine rules given in questions 1 and 2.

4. For each of the following sequence, find a formula for *m*, the *n*th term of the sequence.
   (a) 3, 6, 9, 12, . . .
   (b) 1, 8, 27, 64, . . .
   (c) 2, 5, 8, 11, . . . (*Hint:* Compare with (a).)
   (d) 97, 94, 91, 88, . . . (*Hint:* Rewrite each term as $100 - \Box$.)

Exercise 1.8

answers on p. 418

1. Copy and complete the table.
   The rule connecting the input *r* and output *s* is $s = 2 \times r$.

Input *r*	1	2	3	4	5	6	7	8	9	10
Output *s*	2		6							20

   Show how the rule $s = 2 \times r$ can be 'programmed' into a scientific calculator.

2. Copy and complete the table.
   The rule connecting the variables *p* and *q* is $q = 2 \times p + 3$.

p	1	2	3	4	5	6	7	8	9	10
q	5			11						23

3. The table shows the input numbers and the corresponding output numbers.

Input *a*	1	2	3	4	5	6	7	8	9	10
Output *b*	8	9	10	11	12	13	14	15	16	17

   Write down the rule connecting the variables *a* and *b*.
   (*Hint:* Rewrite 8 as $1 + 7$, 9 as $2 + 7$, etc.)
   Show how the rule can be 'programmed' into a scientific calculator.

4. The table shows the values of p and the corresponding values of q.

p	1	2	3	4	5	6	7	8	9	10
q	2	5	8	11	14	17	20	23	26	29

Write down the rule connecting p and q.
(*Hint:* Rewrite 2 as $3 \times 1 - 1$, 5 as $3 \times 2 - 1$, etc.)

5. For each of the following number sequences, find a formula for m, the nth term of the sequence.
  (a) 1, 4, 9, 16, . . .   **(b)** 1, 4, 7, 10, . . .
  (c) 2, 4, 6, 8, . . .   **(d)** 5, 11, 17, 23, . . .
  (e) 2, 7, 12, 17, . . .   **(f)** 7, 14, 21, 28, . . .
  (g) 81, 76, 71, 66, . . .   **(h)** 384, 192, 96, 48, . . .

6.

Let M denote the number of matchsticks and T the number of triangles
Find a formula connecting M and T.

7.

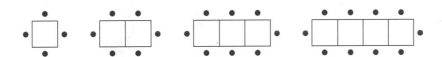

Let S be the number of squares and D the number of dots.
Find a formula connecting S and D.

1.9 BASIC NUMBER LAWS

Look at the following six sentences.
(a) $3 + 2 = 2 + 3$ (b) $(5 \times 4) \times 7 = 5 \times (4 \times 7)$
(c) $7 + 5 = 5 + 7$ (d) $(3 \times 4) \times 6 = 3 \times (4 \times 6)$
(e) $6 + 1 = 1 + 6$ (f) $(6 \times 2) \times 8 = 6 \times (2 \times 8)$

It can be shown that the value of the left-hand side (LHS) of each sentence is equal to the value of the right-hand side (RHS). We say that these sentences are true.

Notice that sentences (a), (c) and (e) belong to one group because they have the same pattern. Letters of the alphabet are used to write pattern sentences. The pattern sentence or general statement for this group is $a + b = b + a$.

Sentences (b), (d) and (f) belong to another group. The general statement for this group is $(a \times b) \times c = a \times (b \times c)$.

Class Activity 7

Verify that the following sentences are true. Classify them into groups and write a general statement for each group.

1.	$7 + 2 = 2 + 7$	**2.**	$13 + 5 = 5 + 13$
3.	$2 + 6 = 6 + 2$	**4.**	$7 + 3 = 3 + 7$
5.	$3 \times 2 = 2 \times 3$	**6.**	$1 \times 5 = 5 \times 1$
7.	$10 \times 1 = 1 \times 10$	**8.**	$7 \times 8 = 8 \times 7$
9.	$(3 + 4) + 5 = 3 + (4 + 5)$	**10.**	$(2 + 3) + 8 = 2 + (3 + 8)$
11.	$(15 + 5) + 4 = 15 + (5 + 4)$	**12.**	$(7 + 8) + 9 = 7 + (8 + 9)$
13.	$(1 \times 2) \times 3 = 1 \times (2 \times 3)$	**14.**	$(5 \times 6) \times 9 = 5 \times (6 \times 9)$
15.	$(3 \times 5) \times 8 = 3 \times (5 \times 8)$	**16.**	$(2 \times 3) \times 4 = 2 \times (3 \times 4)$
17.	$5 \times (3 + 4) = 5 \times 3 + 5 \times 4$	**18.**	$6 \times (8 + 11) = 6 \times 8 + 6 \times 11$
19.	$9 \times (8 + 5) = 9 \times 8 + 9 \times 5$	**20.**	$2 \times (6 + 3) = 2 \times 6 + 2 \times 3$
21.	$(7 + 2) \times 3 = 7 \times 3 + 2 \times 3$	**22.**	$(6 + 5) \times 2 = 6 \times 2 + 5 \times 2$
23.	$(9 + 1) \times 4 = 9 \times 4 + 1 \times 4$	**24.**	$(7 + 5) \times 6 = 7 \times 6 + 5 \times 6$

The general statements obtained in the above class activity describe some basic arithmetic properties. We refer to these as **number laws**. It is useful to know their names for future references.

1. The commutative law of addition:

$$a + b = b + a$$

2. The commutative law of multiplication:

$$a \times b = b \times a$$

3. The associative law of addition:

$$(a + b) + c = a + (b + c)$$

4. The associative law of multiplication:

$$(a \times b) \times c = a \times (b \times c)$$

5. The distributive law of multiplication with respect to addition:

$$a \times (b + c) = (a \times b) + (a \times c)$$
$$(b + c) \times a = (b \times a) + (c \times a)$$

Exercise 1.9 ✍

answers on p. 419

1. Name the number law illustrated by each of the following sentences.
   (a) $2 + 3 = 3 + 2$
   (b) $(2 + 7) + 3 = 2 + (7 + 3)$
   (c) $3 + (2 + 5) = (3 + 2) + 5$
   (d) $7 \times 8 = 8 \times 7$
   (e) $(9 \times 4) \times 3 = 9 \times (4 \times 3)$
   (f) $7 \times (8 \times 5) = (7 \times 8) \times 5$

2. Express each of the following in the form of $(a \times b) + (a \times c)$ or $(b \times a) + (c \times a)$.
   (a) $3 \times (4 + 5)$
   (b) $3 \times (7 + 2)$
   (c) $3 \times (8 + 4)$
   (d) $(5 + 2) \times 4$
   (e) $(3 + 1) \times 7$
   (f) $(7 + 4) \times 11$

3. Copy and complete the following sentences.
   (a) $3 \times \underline{\quad} = 7 \times 3$
   (b) $(7 \times 8) \times 3 = \underline{\quad} \times (8 \times 3)$
   (c) $5 + \underline{\quad} = 6 + 5$
   (d) $\underline{\quad} \times (10 + 3) = (2 \times 10) + (2 \times 3)$
   (e) $(58 + \underline{\quad}) \times 4 = (58 \times 4) + (20 \times 4)$
   (f) $(3 + 4) + \underline{\quad} = 3 + (4 + 5)$

4. Consider the following groups of statements. Check whether they are true, and then write a general statement for each group.
   (a) $5 \times 1 = 1 \times 5 = 5$
   $3 \times 1 = 1 \times 3 = 3$
   $25 \times 1 = 1 \times 25 = 25$
   (b) $8 + 0 = 0 + 8 = 8$
   $5 + 0 = 0 + 5 = 5$
   $11 + 0 = 0 + 11 = 11$

5. By inspection, match each expression in column A with one in column B. Give your reason.

   For example, (a) is equal to (i) by the associative law of addition.

Column A	Column B
(a) $(3 + 2) + 4$	(i) $3 + (2 + 4)$
(b) $5 + (3 + 2)$	(ii) $(4 + 7) \times 2$
(c) $4 \times (3 + 7)$	(iii) $4 \times (6 + 3)$
(d) $(6 + 3) \times 4$	(iv) $5 + (2 + 3)$
(e) $(7 + 4) \times 2$	(v) $(1 + 2) \times 3 + (1 + 2) \times 4$
(f) $(9 \times 3) \times 2$	(vi) $(5 + 4) \times (3 \times 2)$
(g) $(1 + 2) \times (3 + 4)$	(vii) $(4 \times 3) + (4 \times 7)$
(h) $[(5 + 4) \times 3] \times 2$	(viii) $9 \times (3 \times 2)$
(i) $(5 + 3) + 6$	(ix) $6 + (5 + 3)$
(j) $12 + (3 + 5)$	(x) $(12 + 3) + 5$

Chapter Review

1. **Numerals**
   Numerals are symbols used to represent numbers.

2. **Digits**
   Digits are the basic number symbols:

   $$0, 1, 2, 3, 4, 5, 6, 7, 8 \text{ and } 9$$

3. **Place Value**
   Values are assigned to positions occupied by the digits of a numeral. The place value of each position is ten times the place value of the position immediately on its right.

4. **Order of Calculation**
   Expressions without brackets
   • Working from left to right, do multiplication or division before addition or subtraction.

   Expressions with brackets
   • Simplify the expression within the brackets first.
   • If there is more than one pair of brackets, simplify the expression within the innermost pair of brackets first.

5. **Factors and Multiples**
   • Factors of a number divide that number exactly without leaving any remainder.
   • Multiples of a number can be divided exactly by that number.
   Example: $18 = 3 \times 6$
           3 and 6 are factors of 18.
           18 is a multiple of 3 and 6.

6. **Prime Numbers and Composite Numbers**
   • A natural number which has exactly two different factors, 1 and itself, is called a prime number.
   • A natural number which has more than two different factors is called a composite number.
   • The number 1 is neither composite nor prime.
   • Prime factorisation
   Example: $330 = 2 \times 3 \times 5 \times 11$
           i.e. the number is expressed as a product of prime numbers.

7. **Highest Common Factor**
   The HCF of two or more given numbers is the greatest number which is a common factor of these numbers.

8. **Least Common Multiple**
   The LCM of two or more given numbers is the smallest number which is a common multiple of these numbers.

9. **Number Sequence**
   A listing of numbers which follow a certain pattern is called a number sequence, for example,
   $$1, 4, 9, 16, \ldots$$
   $$1, 4, 7, 10, \ldots$$

10. **Basic Number Laws**
    - The commutative law of addition:
      $$a + b = b + a$$
    - The commutative law of multiplication:
      $$a \times b = b \times a$$
    - The associative law of addition:
      $$(a + b) + c = a + (b + c)$$
    - The associative law of multiplication:
      $$(a \times b) \times c = a \times (b \times c)$$
    - The distributive law of multiplication with respect to addition:
      $$a \times (b + c) = (a \times b) + (a \times c)$$
      $$(b + c) \times a = (b \times a) + (c \times a)$$

CHALLENGER 1

1. Find the exact value of each of the following expressions.
   (a) $9 \times 9 + 7$ **(b)** $98 \times 9 + 6$
   (c) $987 \times 9 + 5$ **(d)** $9\,876 \times 9 + 4$
   (e) $98\,765 \times 9 + 3$ **(f)** $987\,654 \times 9 + 2$
   (g) $9\,876\,543 \times 9 + 1$ **(h)** $98\,765\,432 \times 9 + 0$
   (i) $987\,654\,321 \times 9 - 1$ **(j)** $9\,876\,543\,210 \times 9 - 2$
   Explain how you worked out part (j).

2. Is the sum of two consecutive triangular numbers a square number? Give reasons to support your answer.

3. When entering a 4-digit number into a calculator, Ali accidentally placed a '1' in front of the number. How much should he subtract so that he is left with the required number?

4. John accidentally enters $98 \times 3\,429$ into his calculator instead of $98 \times 3\,428$. How much should he subtract in order to get the correct answer?

5. Fatimah accidentally enters $24 \times 8\,868$ into her calculator instead of $24 \times 8\,888$. How much should she add in order to get the correct answer?

6. 4 103 987 526 is a number formed by 10 different digits. Enter this number into your calculator. If you subtract 4 100 000 000 and then add 410 000 000, you will get 413 987 526 on the screen. We say that you have deleted the digit 0, i.e.

$$4\ 103\ 987\ 526 \longrightarrow 413\ 987\ 526.$$
$$\downarrow$$
$$\text{deleted}$$

You can continue to delete the digit 1 like this:

$$413\ 987\ 526 - 410\ 000\ 000 + 40\ 000\ 000 \longrightarrow 43\ 987\ 526$$

You can again continue to delete the digit 2 like this:

$$(43\ 987\ 526 - 26 + 60) \div 10 \longrightarrow 4\ 398\ 756$$

Explain briefly how you can continue to delete the digits 3, 4, 5 and so on.

Problem Solving 1

Get the Right Vertex

Fill in all the circles using all the numbers from 1 to 7 so that the sum of the numbers on each row is 17.

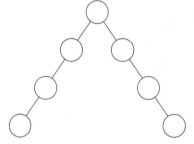

We usually solve puzzles by **trial and error**. This strategy is also called '**guess and check**'. Better puzzle solvers often do their guessing and checking in a systematic manner. They also use their skill in logical reasoning to make 'intelligent guesses'.

To solve this puzzle, you can try placing the numbers 1, 2, 3, . . . systematically at the 'vertex' (middle circle) before completing the other circles. You will probably have discovered that placing odd numbers at the vertex will not work.

The following thinking process will help you make an intelligent guess.

- One of the numbers (1 to 7) must be used twice to get two sums of 17 each, i.e. a total of 34.
- The sum of numbers from 1 to 7 is 28 and so the number 6 must be placed at the vertex since 28 + 6 = 34.

Then, solve the puzzle by trial and error.

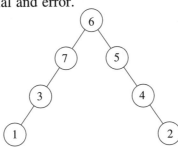

Ask yourself: What if the question is changed to read as follows?

'Fill in all the circles using all the numbers from 1 to 7 so that the sum of the numbers on each row is the same.'

1. **Equal Sums** Fill in the numbers 1, 2, 3, 4, 5 and 6 in the spaces on the diagram so that the numbers along each side of the triangle add up to 10. (You may use each number only once.)

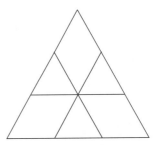

2. **Consecutive Digits** Notice that 12 is the product of the two consecutive numbers 3 and 4 and 12 is also made up of two consecutive digits 1 and 2.
    (a) Use two consecutive digits to form another number such that this number is the product of two consecutive numbers.
    (b) Try using three consecutive digits to form a number such that this number is the product of three consecutive numbers.

3. **Steering Wheel** Fill in all the boxes with all the numbers 1 to 8 so that the sum of numbers in each row and in each circle is the same.

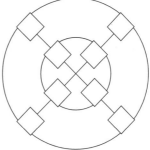

4. **Magic Triangle** Copy the figure. Fill in the circles with numbers 1 to 9 (without repetition) such that the sum of the numbers on each side of the triangle is
    (a) 17,   (b) 20,
    (c) 23.

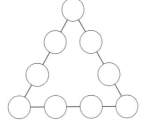

Chapter 2

Fractions, Decimals and Approximation

Chapter Highlights

- Expressing a fraction in its simplest form.
- Converting improper fractions to mixed numbers and vice versa.
- Performing the four operations with fractions and decimals.
- Rounding off a number/quantity to a specified degree of accuracy.
- Converting fractions to decimals and vice versa.
- Making estimations to check reasonableness of answers.

2.1 FRACTIONS

A square region is divided into three equal parts. Each part is one-third of the whole region. Two of these parts are shaded and we say that two-thirds of the whole region is shaded. In symbols, we write one-third as $\frac{1}{3}$ and two-thirds as $\frac{2}{3}$. The symbols $\frac{1}{3}$ and $\frac{2}{3}$ are called **fractions**. In the fraction $\frac{2}{3}$, 2 is called the **numerator** and 3 the **denominator**.

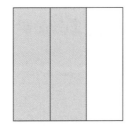

Fig 2.1

Equivalent Fractions

Look at Fig. 2.1 again. If each of the three parts is further divided into two equal parts as shown in Fig. 2.2, then the whole region is divided into 3×2 parts. Among them, 2×2 parts are shaded. We see that $\frac{2 \times 2}{3 \times 2}$, i.e. $\frac{4}{6}$, of the whole region is shaded. We say that $\frac{2}{3}$ and $\frac{4}{6}$ are **equivalent fractions**, and we write $\frac{2}{3} = \frac{4}{6}$.

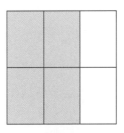

Fig 2.2

Similarly, if each of the three parts in Fig. 2.1 is further divided into three equal parts as shown in Fig. 2.3, then $\frac{2 \times 3}{3 \times 3}$, i.e. $\frac{6}{9}$, is another equivalent fraction of $\frac{2}{3}$. We write $\frac{2}{3} = \frac{6}{9}$.

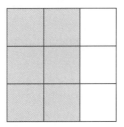

Fig 2.3

So, if each of the parts in Fig. 2.1 is further divided into m equal parts, we have

$$\frac{2}{3} = \frac{2 \times m}{3 \times m}.$$

Taking $m = 2, 3, 4, 5, \ldots$, we can make a list of equivalent fractions of $\frac{2}{3}$ as follows:

$$\frac{2}{3}, \frac{4}{6}, \frac{6}{9}, \frac{8}{12}, \frac{10}{15}, \ldots$$

MATHSTORY

Fractions are written differently over the years.

The ancient Chinese called the denominator 'mother' and the numerator 'son' and would write a fraction of 2 out of 3 as $\frac{3}{2}$.

The Indians would write it as $\frac{2}{3}$.

The Arabs introduced the horizontal bar called vinculum around 700 AD.

Spanish mathematicians used the solidus symbol '/' around 1750.

Using variables, we write the rule for generating equivalent fractions as

$$\frac{a}{b} = \frac{a \times m}{b \times m}.$$

To write equivalent fractions, multiply the numerator and the denominator by the same non-zero factor.

Reduction to Lowest Terms

Look at the fraction $\frac{24}{36}$.

$$\frac{24}{36} = \frac{12 \times 2}{18 \times 2} = \frac{12}{18}$$

We see that $\frac{24}{36}$ is reduced to $\frac{12}{18}$.

We can further reduce $\frac{12}{18}$ in stages until the numerator and the denominator have no common factors other than 1 as follows:

$$\frac{12}{18} = \frac{6 \times 2}{9 \times 2} = \frac{6}{9}$$

$$\frac{6}{9} = \frac{2 \times 3}{3 \times 3} = \frac{2}{3}$$

When 1 is the only non-zero whole number divisor of both the numerator of a fraction, the fraction is reduced to lowest terms.

From the above, we say that $\frac{2}{3}$ is the **simplest form** of $\frac{24}{36}$. We refer to the process of converting a fraction to its simplest form as **reduction to lowest terms**.

In practice, this can be done by cancelling as shown:

$$\frac{24}{36} = \frac{2}{3}$$

Comparison of Fractions

Let us compare the fractions $\frac{4}{8}$ and $\frac{7}{12}$.

List of equivalent fractions from $\frac{4}{8}$ are $\frac{4}{8}, \frac{8}{16}, \mathbf{\frac{12}{24}}, \cdots$

List of equivalent fractions from $\frac{7}{12}$ are $\frac{7}{12}, \mathbf{\frac{14}{24}}, \frac{21}{36}, \cdots$

We choose $\mathbf{\frac{12}{24}}$ to replace $\frac{4}{8}$, and $\mathbf{\frac{14}{24}}$ to replace $\frac{7}{12}$ because $\frac{12}{24}$ and $\frac{14}{24}$ have the same denominator.

So, $\frac{4}{8} < \frac{7}{12}$ because $\frac{12}{24} < \frac{14}{24}$.

Alternatively, we can use the **cross-multiplication method** to compare these fractions:

$$\frac{4}{8} < \frac{7}{12} \text{ since } 4 \times 12 < 7 \times 8$$

Note: '<' means 'is smaller than' and '>' means 'is greater than'.

Improper Fractions and Mixed Numbers

Fig. 2.4 shows 5 parts of the same size. Each part is $\frac{1}{4}$ of a circular region. We write 5 quarters as $\frac{5}{4}$ which means $\frac{1}{4} + \frac{1}{4} + \frac{1}{4} + \frac{1}{4} + \frac{1}{4}$.

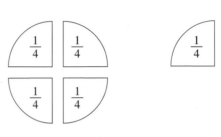

Fig. 2.4

Notice that 4 such parts make a whole.

We write $\frac{5}{4}$ as $1\frac{1}{4}$ which means $1 + \frac{1}{4}$, i.e. 1 whole and 1 quarter.

Numbers like $\frac{3}{4}$, in which the numerator is smaller than the denominator, are called **proper fractions**. Numbers like $\frac{5}{4}$, in which the numerator is greater than the denominator, are called **improper fractions**. Numbers like $1\frac{1}{4}$, which is the sum of a whole number and a fraction, are called **mixed numbers**.

To write a mixed number as an improper fraction, you can multiply the whole number by the denominator and add the numerator. Then write the result over the denominator.

Relationship between Fractions and Division

Examples

(a) Five apples are to be divided into four equal shares. Each share will get one apple first. The remaining one apple is allowed to be cut into 4 equal parts. Then, there will be $1\frac{1}{4}$ apples in each share. So, $5 \div 4 = 1\frac{1}{4} = \frac{5}{4}$. We also refer to $1\frac{1}{4}$ or $\frac{5}{4}$ as the quotient of the division $5 \div 4$.

(b) Suppose 3 oranges are to be shared equally between 4 boys. Let us cut each orange into 4 equal parts and then divide the 12 parts obtained between the 4 boys. Thus, each boy will get 3 parts, i.e. $\frac{3}{4}$ of an orange. So, $3 \div 4 = \frac{3}{4}$.

(c)   What is the meaning of $\frac{3}{1}$? Using division, we have $\frac{3}{1} = 3 \div 1 = 3$. So, we can take $\frac{3}{1}$ to be 3.

Worked Example 1

Which is greater, $\frac{37}{47}$ or $\frac{482}{611}$?

Solution:

Using the cross-multiplication method,

$$37 \times 611 = 22\ 607$$
$$482 \times 47 = 22\ 654$$

So, $37 \times 611 < 482 \times 47$.

Therefore, $\frac{482}{611}$ is greater than $\frac{37}{47}$.

Worked Example 2

Rewrite

(a) $\frac{268}{3}$ in the form of a mixed number,

(b) $12\frac{4}{5}$ in the form of an improper fraction.

Solution:

(a)
$$\begin{array}{r} 89 \\ 3\ \overline{)\ 268} \\ \underline{24} \\ 28 \\ \underline{27} \\ 1 \end{array}$$

Therefore, $\frac{268}{3} = 89\frac{1}{3}$.

(b) $12\frac{4}{5} = 12 + \frac{4}{5}$

$\qquad\quad = \frac{12}{1} + \frac{4}{5}$

$\qquad\quad = \frac{60}{5} + \frac{4}{5}$

$\qquad\quad = \frac{60 + 4}{5}$

$\qquad\quad = \frac{64}{5}$

Note: (b) may be done in fewer steps as follows:

$$12\frac{4}{5} = \frac{12 \times 5 + 4}{5}$$
$$= \frac{64}{5}$$

In this chapter, **all** exercises should be done without using the calculator unless otherwise stated. You may wish to use the calculator to check your answers.

Exercise 2.1   *answers on p. 419*

1. Each of the given figures is divided into equal parts. For each figure, write down the fraction represented by the shaded area.

  (a)   **(b)**   **(c)**

  (d)   **(e)**    **(f)**

2. Each bar is divided into equal parts. Copy and complete the following.

  (a)

    (i) $AC =$ _____ of AB **(ii)** $AD =$ _____ of AB

  (b)

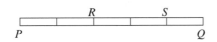

    (i) $PR =$ _____ of PQ **(ii)** $PS =$ _____ of PQ

3. Copy and complete the following.

  (a) $\dfrac{3}{7} = \dfrac{}{56}$ **(b)** $\dfrac{4}{13} = \dfrac{}{78}$ **(c)** $\dfrac{9}{17} = \dfrac{}{187}$

       $\dfrac{7}{8} = \dfrac{}{56}$ $\dfrac{5}{6} = \dfrac{}{78}$ $\dfrac{3}{11} = \dfrac{}{187}$

  (d) $\dfrac{13}{15} = \dfrac{}{105}$ **(e)** $\dfrac{11}{12} = \dfrac{}{156}$ **(f)** $\dfrac{7}{12} = \dfrac{}{180}$

       $\dfrac{9}{7} = \dfrac{}{105}$ $\dfrac{12}{13} = \dfrac{}{156}$ $\dfrac{6}{15} = \dfrac{}{180}$

4. Rewrite each of the following improper fractions as a mixed number.

  (a) $\dfrac{5}{2}$ **(b)** $\dfrac{9}{4}$ **(c)** $\dfrac{15}{2}$

  (d) $\dfrac{18}{5}$ **(e)** $\dfrac{182}{48}$ **(f)** $\dfrac{371}{36}$

  (g) $\dfrac{123}{11}$ **(h)** $\dfrac{246}{13}$ **(i)** $\dfrac{327}{120}$

5. Rewrite each of the following mixed numbers as an improper fraction.

   (a) $2\frac{1}{2}$

   (b) $4\frac{1}{3}$

   (c) $9\frac{3}{11}$

   (d) $11\frac{4}{5}$

   (e) $12\frac{7}{13}$

   (f) $17\frac{5}{16}$

   (g) $64\frac{31}{42}$

   (h) $78\frac{11}{23}$

   (i) $37\frac{47}{121}$

6. Write down the quotients as fractions for the following divisions.

   (a) $7 \div 3$

   (b) $3 \div 5$

   (c) $3 \div 7$

   (d) $11 \div 10$

   (e) $22 \div 8$

   (f) $21 \div 49$

7. Reduce each of the following fractions to its lowest terms.

   (a) $\frac{12}{15}$

   (b) $\frac{5}{30}$

   (c) $\frac{14}{35}$

   (d) $\frac{30}{36}$

   (e) $\frac{21}{49}$

   (f) $\frac{42}{60}$

   (g) $\frac{26}{39}$

   (h) $\frac{135}{165}$

   (i) $\frac{70}{210}$

   (j) $\frac{90}{324}$

   (k) $\frac{630}{672}$

   (l) $\frac{663}{1\ 173}$

8. In each case, which is greater between the two fractions?

   (a) $\frac{2}{3}, \frac{7}{10}$

   (b) $\frac{2}{5}, \frac{15}{36}$

   (c) $\frac{2}{8}, \frac{18}{68}$

   (d) $\frac{10}{12}, \frac{30}{36}$

   (e) $\frac{7}{21}, \frac{14}{40}$

   (f) $\frac{63}{78}, \frac{135}{165}$

9. In each case, determine which fraction is smaller.

   (a) $\frac{3}{8}, \frac{6}{15}$

   (b) $\frac{3}{8}, \frac{1}{2}$

   (c) $\frac{18}{12}, \frac{26}{18}$

   (d) $\frac{36}{31}, \frac{34}{29}$

   (e) $\frac{11}{90}, \frac{16}{135}$

   (f) $\frac{21}{49}, \frac{22}{50}$

10. For each of the following, arrange the fractions in ascending order.

   (a) $\frac{17}{23}, \frac{18}{24}, \frac{20}{27}$

   (b) $\frac{23}{27}, \frac{24}{28}, \frac{27}{32}$

   (c) $\frac{30}{27}, \frac{50}{44}, \frac{49}{43}$

   (d) $\frac{32}{35}, \frac{96}{106}, \frac{47}{53}$

   (e) $\frac{123}{171}, \frac{82}{110}, \frac{500}{342}$

   (f) $\frac{64}{78}, \frac{128}{158}, \frac{184}{234}$

2.2 ADDITION AND SUBTRACTION OF FRACTIONS

Examples

Look at $\dfrac{3}{4} + \dfrac{1}{6}$ and $\dfrac{3}{4} - \dfrac{1}{6}$.

The equivalent fractions of $\dfrac{3}{4}$ are $\dfrac{3}{4}, \dfrac{6}{8}, \mathbf{\dfrac{9}{12}}, \dfrac{12}{16}, \cdots$

The equivalent fractions of $\dfrac{1}{6}$ are $\dfrac{1}{6}, \mathbf{\dfrac{2}{12}}, \dfrac{3}{18}, \dfrac{4}{24}, \cdots$

We choose $\dfrac{9}{12}$ to replace $\dfrac{3}{4}$, and $\dfrac{2}{12}$ to replace $\dfrac{1}{6}$ because $\dfrac{9}{12}$ and $\dfrac{2}{12}$ have the same denominator which is referred to as the **common denominator**.

To perform the operations of addition and subtraction of fractions, we must first rename fractions so that they have the same denominator. Once we have learned to add and subtract fractions and mixed numbers, we will have the tools to solve an assortment of applied problems.

So
$$\begin{aligned}
\frac{3}{4} + \frac{1}{6} &= \frac{9}{12} + \frac{2}{12} \\
&= \frac{9+2}{12} \\
&= \frac{11}{12}
\end{aligned}$$

and
$$\begin{aligned}
\frac{3}{4} - \frac{1}{6} &= \frac{9}{12} - \frac{2}{12} \\
&= \frac{9-2}{12} \\
&= \frac{7}{12}.
\end{aligned}$$

Alternatively, we can use the LCM as the common denominator.

$$\begin{aligned}
\frac{3}{4} + \frac{1}{6} &= \frac{3 \times 3}{4 \times 3} + \frac{1 \times 2}{6 \times 2} \\
&= \frac{9+2}{12} \\
&= \frac{11}{12}
\end{aligned}$$

$$\begin{aligned}
\frac{3}{4} - \frac{1}{6} &= \frac{3 \times 3}{4 \times 3} - \frac{1 \times 2}{6 \times 2} \\
&= \frac{9-2}{12} \\
&= \frac{7}{12}
\end{aligned}$$

2	4, 6
2	2, 3
3	1, 3
	1, 1

LCM $= 2^2 \times 3 = 12$
$12 = 4 \times 3$
$12 = 6 \times 2$

Note: The first step may be done mentally.

39

Worked Example 3

Evaluate $2\frac{1}{4} + 2\frac{1}{3} - 2\frac{2}{5}$.

Solution:

$$2\frac{1}{4} + 2\frac{1}{3} - 2\frac{2}{5} = 2 + \frac{1}{4} + 2 + \frac{1}{3} - 2 - \frac{2}{5}$$

$$= 2 + \frac{1}{4} + \frac{1}{3} - \frac{2}{5}$$

$$= 2 + \frac{15 + 20 - 24}{60}$$

$$= 2 + \frac{11}{60}$$

$$= 2\frac{11}{60}$$

2	4, 3, 5
2	2, 3, 5
3	1, 3, 5
5	1, 1, 5
	1, 1, 1

LCM = $2^2 \times 3 \times 5 = 60$

Note: These examples may be presented in fewer steps if mental calculation is used.

Worked Example 4

Evaluate $89\frac{31}{45} - \left(3\frac{2}{9} - 1\frac{8}{15}\right)$.

Solution:

$$89\frac{31}{45} - \left(3\frac{2}{9} - 1\frac{8}{15}\right) = 89\frac{31}{45} - \left(3\frac{10}{45} - 1\frac{24}{45}\right)$$

$$= 89\frac{31}{45} - \left(2\frac{55}{45} - 1\frac{24}{45}\right)$$

$$= 89\frac{31}{45} - 1\frac{31}{45}$$

$$= 88$$

3	9, 15
3	3, 5
5	1, 5
	1, 1

LCM = $3 \times 3 \times 5 = 45$

Note: Steps done mentally are not shown.

For example, $3\frac{10}{45}$ is replaced by $2\frac{55}{45}$ mentally and the steps omitted are

$$3\frac{10}{45} = 3 + \frac{10}{45} = 2 + 1\frac{10}{45} = 2 + \frac{55}{45} = 2\frac{55}{45}.$$

Exercise 2.2

answers on p. 419

1. Simplify the following.

(a) $\dfrac{3}{8} + \dfrac{1}{4}$

(b) $\dfrac{2}{11} + \dfrac{5}{22}$

(c) $\dfrac{1}{8} + \dfrac{5}{12} + \dfrac{7}{16}$

(d) $\dfrac{4}{5} - \dfrac{8}{15}$

(e) $\dfrac{17}{20} - \dfrac{8}{15}$

(f) $\dfrac{9}{10} - \dfrac{5}{16} - \dfrac{7}{20}$

2. Simplify the following.

(a) $\dfrac{5}{8} + \dfrac{1}{8} - \dfrac{3}{8}$

(b) $\dfrac{7}{9} + \dfrac{1}{9} - \dfrac{5}{9}$

(c) $\dfrac{4}{5} + \dfrac{3}{10} - \dfrac{8}{15}$

(d) $\dfrac{7}{9} + \dfrac{2}{15} - \dfrac{29}{45}$

(e) $\dfrac{3}{8} - \dfrac{3}{4} + \dfrac{11}{12}$

(f) $\dfrac{4}{9} - \dfrac{7}{12} + \dfrac{23}{36}$

3. Simplify the following.

(a) $\dfrac{12}{5} + \dfrac{17}{15}$

(b) $\dfrac{7}{4} + \dfrac{9}{5}$

(c) $\dfrac{11}{3} - \dfrac{12}{5}$

(d) $\dfrac{17}{4} - \dfrac{13}{6}$

(e) $\dfrac{33}{8} + \dfrac{25}{14}$

(f) $\dfrac{31}{9} - \dfrac{19}{15}$

4. Evaluate the following.

(a) $2\dfrac{2}{3} + 4\dfrac{3}{5}$

(b) $3\dfrac{1}{3} - 1\dfrac{1}{5}$

(c) $6\dfrac{1}{9} + 3\dfrac{8}{21}$

(d) $2\dfrac{12}{17} + 4\dfrac{10}{34}$

(e) $5\dfrac{8}{15} - 2\dfrac{8}{25}$

(f) $9\dfrac{5}{14} - 4\dfrac{10}{21}$

5. Evaluate the following.

(a) $3\dfrac{5}{6} + 1\dfrac{1}{2} - 2\dfrac{1}{4}$

(b) $4\dfrac{3}{8} + 2\dfrac{5}{12} - 3\dfrac{1}{6}$

(c) $5\dfrac{1}{2} - 2\dfrac{1}{3} + 1\dfrac{5}{6}$

(d) $2\dfrac{7}{9} + 1\dfrac{2}{3} + 3\dfrac{5}{12}$

(e) $6\dfrac{3}{8} - 2\dfrac{5}{6} - 2\dfrac{1}{4}$

(f) $4\dfrac{3}{4} - 2\dfrac{1}{3} - 1\dfrac{3}{10}$

6. Evaluate the following.

(a) $3\dfrac{17}{18} + \left(4\dfrac{5}{6} - 1\dfrac{7}{9}\right)$

(b) $11\dfrac{7}{18} + \left(12\dfrac{5}{6} + 3\dfrac{7}{9}\right)$

(c) $3\dfrac{11}{12} - \left(4\dfrac{7}{9} - 5\dfrac{3}{8}\right)$

(d) $5\dfrac{8}{9} - \left(15\dfrac{13}{18} - 12\dfrac{5}{6}\right)$

(e) $12\dfrac{5}{6} + \left(5\dfrac{8}{9} - 9\dfrac{13}{18}\right)$

(f) $92\dfrac{8}{35} - \left(41\dfrac{3}{7} - 32\dfrac{17}{20}\right)$

2.3 MULTIPLICATION AND DIVISION OF FRACTIONS

Multiplication

Examples

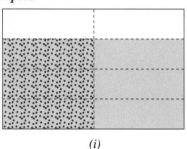 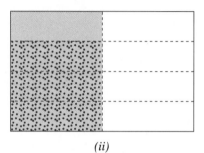

(i)   Fig 2.5   (ii)

(a) Fig. 2.5(i) shows that $\frac{3}{4}$ is coloured and $\frac{1}{2}$ of the part in colour is further shaded. So, $\frac{1}{2}$ of $\frac{3}{4}$ is $\frac{3}{8}$.

Let us write $\frac{1}{2}$ of $\frac{3}{4}$ as $\frac{1}{2} \times \frac{3}{4}$ and $\frac{3}{8}$ as $\frac{1 \times 3}{2 \times 4}$.

Then, we have $\frac{1}{2} \times \frac{3}{4} = \frac{1 \times 3}{2 \times 4}$.

(b) Fig. 2.5(ii) shows that $\frac{1}{2}$ is coloured and $\frac{3}{4}$ of the part in colour is further shaded. So, $\frac{3}{4}$ of $\frac{1}{2}$ is also $\frac{3}{8}$. Again, we have $\frac{3}{4} \times \frac{1}{2} = \frac{3 \times 1}{4 \times 2}$.

These examples suggest the following rule for multiplication of fractions.

> **To do multiplication involving fractions, we multiply the numerators to get the numerator of the product, and multiply the denominators to get the denominator of the product.**

Using variables, we write

$$\frac{a}{b} \times \frac{c}{d} = \frac{a \times c}{b \times d}.$$

Division

Let us study the example below:

$$5 \times 3 = 15$$
$$15 \div 3 = 5$$

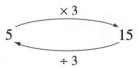

Notice that 'multiplying by 3' changes 5 to 15 but 'dividing by 3' changes 15 to 5 again, i.e. 'dividing by 3' undoes what 'multiplying by 3' does.

We can extend this idea to cases involving fractions. For example, we have

$$\frac{1}{2} \times \frac{3}{4} = \frac{3}{8}.$$

So,

$$\frac{3}{8} \div \frac{3}{4} = \frac{1}{2}.$$

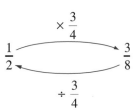

Let us compare this division with the multiplication below:

$$\frac{3}{8} \times \frac{4}{3} = \frac{1}{2}$$

We notice that the divisor $\frac{3}{4}$ and the multiplier $\frac{4}{3}$ are related as follows:

$$\frac{3}{4} \times \frac{4}{3} = 1$$

Two numbers whose product is 1 are called **reciprocals** of each other. Thus, the reciprocal of $\frac{3}{4}$ is $\frac{4}{3}$ and vice versa. We see that 'dividing by $\frac{3}{4}$' is the same as 'multiplying by the reciprocal of $\frac{3}{4}$'. Also, the reciprocal of 4 is $\frac{1}{4}$ since the product of 4 and $\frac{1}{4}$ is 1.

> To find the reciprocal of a fraction, interchange the numerator and denominator. Thus the reciprocal of $\frac{a}{b}$ is $\frac{b}{a}$.

This suggests the following rule for division of fractions.

> **To do division involving fractions, we multiply by the reciprocal of the divisor.**

For example,

$$\frac{3}{8} \div \frac{3}{4} = \frac{3}{8} \times \frac{4}{3}$$
$$= \frac{1}{2}$$

Using variables, we write

$$\frac{a}{b} \div \frac{c}{d} = \frac{a}{b} \times \frac{d}{c}.$$

Worked Example 5
Simplify the following.

(a) $3\frac{2}{5} \times 2\frac{2}{9}$

(b) $1\frac{5}{7} \div 2\frac{2}{11}$

Solution:

(a) $3\dfrac{2}{5} \times 2\dfrac{2}{9} = \dfrac{17}{5} \times \dfrac{20}{9}$

$\qquad\qquad = \dfrac{17 \times 20}{5 \times 9}$

$\qquad\qquad = \dfrac{68}{9}$

$\qquad\qquad = 7\dfrac{5}{9}$

(b) $1\dfrac{5}{7} \div 2\dfrac{2}{11} = \dfrac{12}{7} \div \dfrac{24}{11}$

$\qquad\qquad = \dfrac{12}{7} \times \dfrac{11}{24}$

$\qquad\qquad = \dfrac{12 \times 11}{7 \times 24}$

$\qquad\qquad = \dfrac{11}{14}$

Worked Example 6

Evaluate $\dfrac{6}{21} \div \left(\dfrac{15}{28} + \dfrac{3}{4}\right) \times \dfrac{243}{16}$.

Solution:

$\dfrac{6}{21} \div \left(\dfrac{15}{28} + \dfrac{3}{4}\right) \times \dfrac{243}{16} = \dfrac{6}{21} \div \left(\dfrac{15 + 21}{28}\right) \times \dfrac{243}{16}$

$\qquad\qquad\qquad\qquad\qquad = \dfrac{6}{21} \times \dfrac{28}{36} \times \dfrac{243}{16}$

$\qquad\qquad\qquad\qquad\qquad = \dfrac{27}{8}$

$\qquad\qquad\qquad\qquad\qquad = 3\dfrac{3}{8}$

Exercise 2.3

answers on p. 420

1. Simplify the following.

   (a) $\dfrac{5}{6} \times 14$

   (b) $\dfrac{843}{100} \times 10$

   (c) $\dfrac{19}{12} \times \dfrac{3}{38}$

   (d) $\dfrac{105}{82} \times \dfrac{40}{7}$

   (e) $\dfrac{2}{3} \times \dfrac{4}{5} \times \dfrac{7}{4}$

   (f) $\dfrac{5}{4} \times \dfrac{12}{20} \times \dfrac{3}{7}$

2. Write down the reciprocal of each of the following.

   (a) $\dfrac{3}{5}$

   (b) $\dfrac{3}{8}$

   (c) $\dfrac{7}{8}$

   (d) $\dfrac{9}{10}$

   (e) 5

   (f) 10

   (g) $\dfrac{5}{3}$

   (h) 1

3. Simplify the following.

   (a) $\dfrac{3}{5} \div 5$

   (b) $39 \div \dfrac{26}{7}$

   (c) $\dfrac{21}{12} \div \dfrac{19}{24}$

   (d) $\dfrac{32}{17} \div \dfrac{11}{51}$

   (e) $\dfrac{3}{4} \div \dfrac{5}{6} \div \dfrac{2}{15}$

   (f) $\dfrac{3}{23} \div \dfrac{2}{15} \div \dfrac{30}{115}$

4. Simplify the following.

   (a) $5\dfrac{1}{3} \times 5\dfrac{1}{4}$

   (b) $4\dfrac{4}{5} \times 4\dfrac{3}{8}$

   (c) $3\dfrac{3}{4} \times 1\dfrac{11}{15}$

   (d) $2\dfrac{1}{2} \div 1\dfrac{2}{3}$

   (e) $4\dfrac{2}{3} \div 11\dfrac{2}{3}$

   (f) $7\dfrac{7}{8} \div 2\dfrac{3}{4}$

5. Evaluate the following.

(a) $2\frac{1}{2} \times 3\frac{2}{5} \div \frac{4}{5}$ **(b)** $3\frac{1}{7} \div 2\frac{3}{4} \times \frac{3}{8}$ **(c)** $\frac{3}{4} \times \frac{5}{6} + 3 \times \frac{4}{3}$

(d) $\frac{1}{6} \div \frac{3}{4} \div \left(\frac{3}{8} \div \frac{1}{4}\right)$ **(e)** $\frac{7}{15} \div \frac{22}{12} \times \left(\frac{1}{6} + \frac{2}{3}\right)$ **(f)** $\frac{4}{7} \div \frac{1}{14} \times 2\frac{1}{2} + \frac{5}{2}$

*6. Evaluate the following.

(a) $\dfrac{3 \times 4 - 8}{18 \times 14}$ **(b)** $\dfrac{21 + 3^2}{18 \div 5}$ **(c)** $\dfrac{2 \times 3 - 3 \div 5}{6 \times 7 \div 2}$

(d) $\dfrac{4 \times 8 \div 2}{2 \times 5 - 3}$ **(e)** $\dfrac{5^3 - 14 \times 3}{24 \div 6 - 3}$ **(f)** $\dfrac{2 \times 3 - 1}{31 + 4 \times 3} - 2 \div \frac{3}{4}$

2.4 DECIMALS

Look at the extended place value table below.

Thousands	Hundreds	Tens	Ones	Tenths	Hundredths	Thousandths

Table 2.1

We see that each time we move to the left, the value of the new position is 10 times the value of the previous position. If we move to the right, the value of the new position is $\frac{1}{10}$ the value of the previous position.

Now consider the number 345.

Suppose that we place a 'point' called a **decimal point** after the digit which occupies the 'ones' place, i.e. digit 5. Then, we place a digit, say 7, after the decimal point. We now have 345.7. If digit 9 is placed after digit 7, then we have 345.79.

The table below is the place value table for 345.79.

Thousands	Hundreds	Tens	Ones	Tenths	Hundredths	Thousandths
	3	4	5 .	7	9	

Table 2.2

MATHSTORY

Decimal comes from the latin word 'decimus' meaning 'ten'. It is related to the word 'decimate' — during the Middle Ages, it was a practice to punish the tenth man of any group of soldiers that broke the rules.

In 1580s, Simon Stevin used commas above a number to denote the number of tenths involved. He would write 12 whole 5 tenths and 7 hundredths as 12 5 7.

In 1610s, John Napier introduced the decimal point and he wrote 12.57.

Numbers like 345.79 are said to be written in the decimal form and we may simply refer to them as **decimals**.

The decimal 345.79 is made up of

$$300 + 40 + 5 + \frac{7}{10} + \frac{9}{100}.$$

Simplifying this, we have $345\frac{79}{100}$ or $\frac{34\ 579}{100}$.

Thus, we see that the decimal 345.79 is in fact the fraction $\frac{34\ 579}{100}$.

Shifting of Decimal Point

Study the decimals 0.843, 8.43 and 84.3. How are they related to one another?

We have
$$0.843 = \frac{843}{1\ 000},$$
$$8.43 = \frac{843}{100},$$
and
$$84.3 = \frac{843}{10}.$$

We have 0.843 $\xrightarrow{\times 10}_{\div 10}$ 8.43 because $\frac{843}{1\ 000}$ $\xrightarrow{\times 10}_{\div 10}$ $\frac{843}{100}$

and 0.843 $\xrightarrow{\times 100}_{\div 100}$ 84.3 because $\frac{843}{1\ 000}$ $\xrightarrow{\times 100}_{\div 100}$ $\frac{843}{10}$ and so on.

In general, we have the following rules.

> 1. **To multiply a decimal by 10, 100, . . ., move the decimal point 1 place, 2 places, . . . to the right.**
> 2. **To divide a decimal by 10, 100, . . ., move the decimal point 1 place, 2 places, . . . to the left.**

Addition

The vertical arrangement is a convenient way of adding decimals. The decimal points must be in alignment to keep digits having the same place value in the same column.

Worked Example 7
Calculate 84.01 + 120.92.

Solution:
84.01 + 120.92 = 204.93

```
   84.01
+ 120.92
--------
  204.93
```

Subtraction

Subtraction of decimals may be done in the same way by using the vertical ·arrangement.

Worked Example 8
Calculate 12.4 − 9.56.

Solution:
12.4 − 9.56 = 2.84

$$
\begin{array}{r}
12.4 \\
-\ \ 9.56 \\
\hline
2.84
\end{array}
$$

Multiplication

Worked Example 9
Find 2.31 × 2.3.

Solution:
2.31 × 2.3 = 5.313

$$
\begin{array}{r}
2.3\ 1 \\
\times\quad 2.3 \\
\hline
6\ 9\ 3 \\
4\ 6\ 2\quad \\
\hline
5.3\ 1\ 3
\end{array}
$$

Notice that, in the product, we have marked off three decimal places to obtain the answer 5.313 because the total number of decimal places in 2.31 and 2.3 is three. This fact is illustrated as follows:

$$
\begin{aligned}
2.31 \times 2.3 &= \frac{231}{100} \times \frac{23}{10} \\
&= \frac{5\,313}{1\,000} \\
&= 5.313
\end{aligned}
$$

Remember these steps when multiplying two decimals:

> 1. **Find the product as if they were whole numbers.**
> 2. **Fix the decimal point according to the total number of decimal places in the two numbers.**

Division

We shall first consider the division of decimals by whole numbers.

The word 'division' means 'separation into parts'.

Worked Example 10
Find $0.055\ 5 \div 15$.

Solution:
$0.055\ 5 \div 15 = 0.003\ 7$

$$
\begin{array}{r}
0{\cdot}0037 \\
15\ \overline{)\ 0{\cdot}0555} \\
45 \\
\hline
105 \\
105 \\
\hline
\end{array}
$$

Worked Example 11
Find **(a)** $5.12 \div 6.4$, and **(b)** $0.051\ 2 \div 0.64$.

Solution:

(a) $5.12 \div 6.4 = \dfrac{5.12}{6.4} \begin{array}{l} \leftarrow \text{ dividend} \\ \leftarrow \text{ divisor} \end{array}$

$\qquad\qquad = \dfrac{5.12 \times 10}{6.4 \times 10}$

$\qquad\qquad = \dfrac{51.2}{64}$

$\qquad\qquad = 0.8$

$$
\begin{array}{r}
0.8\ \leftarrow\ \text{quotient} \\
64\ \overline{)\ 51.2} \\
51\ 2 \\
\hline
\end{array}
$$

(b) $0.051\ 2 \div 0.64 = \dfrac{0.051\ 2}{0.64}$

$\qquad\qquad\qquad = \dfrac{0.051\ 2 \times 100}{0.64 \times 100}$

$\qquad\qquad\qquad = \dfrac{5.12}{64}$

$\qquad\qquad\qquad = 0.08$

$$
\begin{array}{r}
0.08 \\
64\ \overline{)\ 5.12} \\
5\ 12 \\
\hline
\end{array}
$$

When we divide a decimal by another decimal we follow these steps:

> 1. **First, convert the divisor to a whole number by multiplying it by 10 or 100 or 1 000, etc. Then, multiply the dividend by the same number. In practice, you may shift the decimal point of the divisor to make it a whole number, and then shift the decimal point of the dividend the same number of places.**
> 2. **Then, use long division to get the answer, making sure that the decimal points of the quotient and the dividend are in alignment.**

Consider dividing 20 by 4. We write $20 \div 4 = 5$. The number 20 being divided is called the **dividend**. The dividing number 4 is called the **divisor** and the answer 5 is called the **quotient**. Thus dividend ÷ divisor = quotient.

Note: In the above examples, the intermediate steps involving fractions may be omitted when the 'rule of shifting decimal' is used.

Exercise 2.4

answer on p. 420

1. Write down the answers when the following are multiplied by 10, 100 and 1 000.
   (a) 0.11
   (b) 0.012
   (c) 8.001
   (d) 95
   (e) 101.35
   (f) 5 683.053

2. Write down the answers when the following are divided by 10, 100 and 1 000.
   (a) 71
   (b) 100.51
   (c) 0.017
   (d) 0.008 4
   (e) 7 088.4
   (f) 452 063.25

3. Do the following additions.
   (a) 0.76 + 29.93
   (b) 33.8 + 9.35
   (c) 28.32 + 32.099 + 1.32
   (d) 21.138 + 9.019 + 123.02

4. Do the following subtractions.
   (a) 82.72 − 61.83
   (b) 31.03 − 3.94
   (c) 13 − 0.13
   (d) 22 − 1.63
   (e) 46.34 − 19.003
   (f) 62.123 − 4.24

5. Evaluate the following.
   (a) 52.7 − 21.07 − 9.8
   (b) 32.1 + 4.26 − 20.07
   (c) 63.123 − 36.74 + 1.2
   (d) 78.007 − 3.26 + 1.713

6. Do the following multiplications.
   (a) 6.03×6
   (b) 40.7×7
   (c) 9.7×2.1
   (d) 26.3×1.3
   (e) $10.3 \times 5.3 \times 11.4$
   (f) $36.4 \times 4.5 \times 3.9$

7. Do the following divisions.
   (a) $46.5 \div 5$
   (b) $13.14 \div 6$
   (c) $32.2 \div 1.4$
   (d) $57.5 \div 0.23$
   (e) $10.56 \div 4.4 \div 48$
   (f) $12.96 \div 3.6 \div 0.012$

8. Evaluate the following.
   (a) $14.7 \div 1.2 \times (8.4 - 3.5)$
   (b) $1.2 + 8.8 \div (0.05 \times 40)$
   (c) $1.8^2 - 0.8^2 \times 3$
   (d) $1.2^3 - 1.2^2 \div 1.2$
   (e) $9.8 \div 1.4^2 \times 2.1$
   (f) $9.8 \div 1.4 \times 1.4 \times 2.1$

2.5 APPROXIMATION

Rounding Off

Examples

(a) Suppose that 16 workers share equally a special bonus of $2 695. How much does each worker get?

Amount each worker gets = $2 695 ÷ 16 = $168.437 5

This answer gives too many digits after the decimal point. To give an **approximation** of the answer, we may round off the answer correct to 2 decimal places as $168.44, since $168.437 5 is closer to $168.44 than $168.43 (see Fig. 2.6).

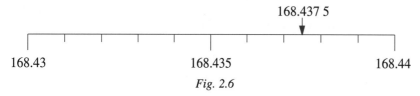

Fig. 2.6

(b) Let us look at Example (a) again. Suppose that we are interested to know about how many dollars each worker will get. Then, we round off the answer correct to the nearest dollar as $168, since 168.437 5 is closer to $168 than to $169 (see Fig. 2.7).

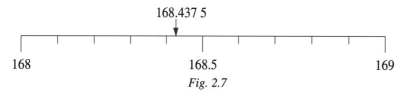

Fig. 2.7

(c) If 10 pencils cost 85 cents, then 1 pencil costs 8.5 cents. 8.5 is exactly halfway between 8 and 9. By convention, we round off 8.5 correct to the nearest larger whole number as 9 (see Fig. 2.8).

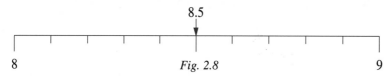

Fig. 2.8

(d) The population of a city is usually rounded off to the nearest 1 000. For example, a city with a population of 351 678 is rounded off as 352 000 because it is nearer to 352 000 than to 351 000 (see Fig. 2.9).

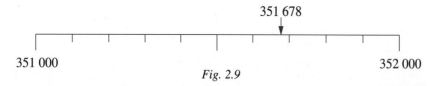

Fig. 2.9

(e) A school population of 1 231 can be rounded off to the nearest 100 as 1 200. This is because 1 231 is nearer to 1 200 than to 1 300 (see Fig. 2.10).

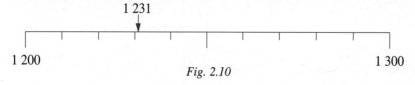

Fig. 2.10

Note: When we round off a given number, we are to discard some of the digits in the given number or replace them with zeros. We refer to these digits as 'unwanted digits'. If the first (considering from left) 'unwanted digit' is 5 or more, we **round up** the given number to a higher value by increasing the previous digit by 1; otherwise we **round down** the given number to a lower value by keeping the previous digit unchanged.

In Example (a),

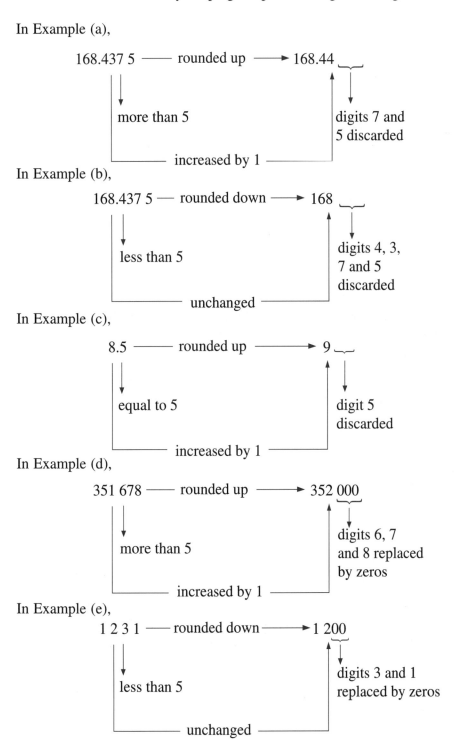

In Example (b),

In Example (c),

In Example (d),

In Example (e),

Remember this:

> **To round off a number, consider the first unwanted digit. If this digit is 5 or more, we round up; otherwise we round down.**

Worked Example 12

Round off the following.

(a) 278.6, correct to the nearest whole number
(b) 2 125, correct to the nearest 10
(c) 43.625, correct to 1 decimal place
(d) 5.523 6, correct to 3 decimal places

Solution:

(a) 278.6 is 279, correct to the nearest whole number.
(b) 2 125 is 2 130, correct to the nearest 10.
(c) 43.625 is 43.6, correct to 1 decimal place.
(d) 5.523 6 is 5.524, correct to 3 decimal places.

Note: In (b), 2 125 is exactly midway between 2 120 and 2 130. By convention, we take 2 125 as 2 130, correct to the nearest 10.

Exercise 2.5a

answers on p. 420

1. For each stick, *A* and *B*, write down the length correct to the nearest cm.

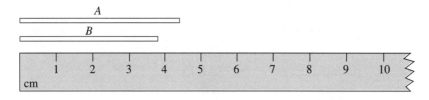

2. For each of the diagrams below, write down the mass correct to the nearest kg.

(a)

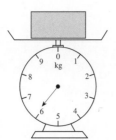

(b)

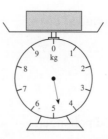

3. For each of the diagrams below, write down the amount of liquid correct to the nearest 10 ml.

(a)

— 50 ml

— 40 ml

— 30 ml

— 20 ml

— 10 ml

(b)

— 50 ml

— 40 ml

— 30 ml

— 20 ml

— 10 ml

4. Round off the following correct to **(i)** the nearest 10, **(ii)** the nearest 100, **(iii)** the nearest 1 000, and **(iv)** the nearest 10 000.
   - **(a)** 451 469
   - **(b)** 675 901
   - **(c)** 872 598
   - **(d)** 965 352
   - **(e)** 810 295
   - **(f)** 404 999

5. Round off the following correct to **(i)** the nearest whole number, **(ii)** 1 decimal place, **(iii)** 2 decimal places, and **(iv)** 3 decimal places.
   - **(a)** 61.235 01
   - **(b)** 29.595 49
   - **(c)** 25.995 49
   - **(d)** 88.319 75
   - **(e)** 63.637 68
   - **(f)** 57.628 3

6. Round off the following correct to **(i)** 2 decimal places, and **(ii)** the nearest whole number.
   - **(a)** $12.312 5
   - **(b)** $45.562 5
   - **(c)** $52.187 5
   - **(d)** $28.812 5
   - **(e)** $288.937 5
   - **(f)** $167.562 5

7. Round off the following correct to **(i)** the nearest 10, **(ii)** the nearest unit indicated, **(iii)** the nearest 1 decimal place, and **(iv)** the nearest 2 decimal places.
   - **(a)** 108.333 333 3 kg
   - **(b)** 124.285 714 3 l
   - **(c)** 146.666 666 7 cm
   - **(d)** 131.428 571 4 m
   - **(e)** 590.588 235 3 g
   - **(f)** 211.818 181 8 km

Significant Figures

Examples

(a) Suppose the distance between *A* and *B* is 0.027 996 km. The place values of some of the digits in the measurement are shown below.

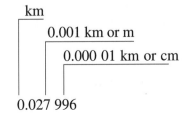

km

0.001 km or m

0.000 01 km or cm

0.027 996

1 km = 1 000 m
1 m = 100 cm

If we want an approximation to tell 'about how many metres (or 0.001 km) there are in this measurement', we round off 0.027 996 km correct to 3 decimal places as 0.028 km, which is equivalent to 28 m. So, we use two digits to tell 'about how many metres (or 0.001 km) the measurement is equal to'. We see that in 0.028, the two digits 2 and 8 are significant digits.

We say that 0.027 996 km is rounded off correct to 2 **significant figures** as 0.028 km. Notice that the first non-zero digit, i.e. 2, is the first significant digit and the zeros in front are not significant digits. Notice also that the rounding off is done with a precision to the nearest metre (or 0.001 km).

We refer to such unit metre or 0.001 km as the **precision unit**.

(b)   Look at the measurement 0.027 996 km again.

If we want an approximation to tell 'about how many centimetres (or 0.000 01 km) there are in this measurement', we round off 0.027 996 km correct to 5 decimal places as 0.028 00 km which is equivalent to 2 800 cm. So, we use four digits to tell 'about how many centimetres (or 0.000 01 km) the measurement is equal to'. Thus, in 0.028 00, the digits 2, 8 and the final two zeros are significant digits.

We say that 0.027 996 km is rounded off correct to 4 significant figures as 0.028 00 km. Again the first non-zero digit, i.e. 2, is the first significant digit. The digits following the digit 2 (including the final zeros) are all significant digits. Here, the precision unit used is the centimetre (or 0.000 01 km).

(c)   The population of a certain city is 2 340 412. It is rounded off correct to the nearest 10 000 as 2 340 000. The precision unit used is 10 000. Since 2 340 000 is 234 × 10 000, there are 234 such 10 000s in 2 340 000. So, we say the population correct to 3 significant figures is 2 340 000.

Suppose we want the population to be rounded off correct to the nearest 1 000. Incidentally, the rounded off number is again equal to 2 340 000. In this case, the precision unit used is 1 000. Since 2 340 000 is 2 340 × 1 000, there are 2 340 such 1 000s in 2 340 000. Thus, we say that 2 340 412 is rounded off as 2 340 000, correct to 4 significant figures.

Remember these:

> In a rounded off **decimal**,
> *   **the first non-zero digit is the first significant digit,**
> *   **the final zeros are significant digits.**

e.g.   0.028 00

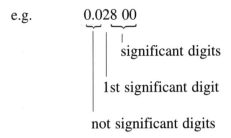

significant digits

1st significant digit

not significant digits

> In a rounded off **whole number**,
> • **the final zeros may or may not be significant digits.**

e.g. 1   2 340 000   (with precision unit of 10 000)

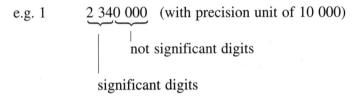

not significant digits

significant digits

e.g. 2   2 340 000   (with precision unit of 1 000)

not significant digits

significant digits

Worked Example 13
Round off the following correct to **(i)** 2 significant figures, and **(ii)** 3 significant figures.
(a) 1 245 km   **(b)** 3 454 l
(c) 3 005 kg   **(d)** 14.04 m
(e) 10.05 cm   **(f)** 0.002 037 km
(g) 0.995 4 m   **(h)** 55 049 kg

Solution:
(a) **(i)** 1 245 km = 1 200 km (correct to 2 significant figures)
      (ii) 1 245 km = 1 250 km (correct to 3 significant figures)

(b) **(i)** 3 454 l = 3 500 l (correct to 2 significant figures)
      (ii) 3 454 l = 3 450 l (correct to 3 significant figures)

(c) **(i)** 3 005 kg = 3 000 kg (correct to 2 significant figures)
      (ii) 3 005 kg = 3 010 kg (correct to 3 significant figures)

(d) **(i)** 14.04 m = 14 m (correct to 2 significant figures)
      (ii) 14.04 m = 14.0 m (correct to 3 significant figures)

(e) **(i)** 10.05 cm = 10 cm (correct to 2 significant figures)
    (ii) 10.05 cm = 10.1 cm (correct to 3 significant figures)

(f) **(i)** 0.002 037 km = 0.002 0 km (correct to 2 significant figures)
    (ii) 0.002 037 km = 0.002 04 km (correct to 3 significant figures)

(g) **(i)** 0.995 4 m = 1.0 m (correct to 2 significant figures)
    (ii) 0.995 4 m = 0.995 m (correct to 3 significant figures)

(h) **(i)** 55 049 kg = 55 000 kg (correct to 2 significant figures)
    (ii) 55 049 kg = 55 000 kg (correct to 3 significant figures)

Worked Example 14

How many significant figures are there in each of the following?
(a) 0.05 m (correct to 2 decimal places)
(b) 104 km (correct to the nearest km)
(c) 250 000 km (correct to the nearest 1 000 km)
(d) 250 000 km (correct to the nearest 10 000 km)

Solution:
(a) There is 1 significant figure in 0.05 m.
(b) There are 3 significant figures in 104 km.
(c) There are 3 significant figures in 250 000 km (correct to the nearest 1 000 km).
(d) There are 2 significant figures in 250 000 km (correct to the nearest 10 000 km).

Exercise 2.5b

answers on p. 421

1. Round off the following correct to **(i)** 2 significant figures, and **(ii)** 3 significant figures.
    (a) 1 324 km   **(b)** 5 406 km   **(c)** 4 007 km
    (d) 6 020 km   **(e)** 7 995 l **(f)** 4.462 m
    (g) 15.37 m   **(h)** 20.92 m   **(i)** 50.04 cm
    (j) 0.023 45 km   **(k)** 0.000 564 2 km   **(l)** 0.982 5 km
    (m) 0.995 1 km   **(n)** 64 056 kg   **(o)** 74 034 kg

2. How many significant figures are there in each of the following? (Each measurement is made correct to the nearest number of decimal places indicated in the brackets.)
    (a) 0.06 m (2)   **(b)** 1.30 g (2)   **(c)** 0.030 g (3)
    (d) 34.04 kg (2)   **(e)** 10.00 (2)   **(f)** 23.003 (3)

3. How many significant figures are there in each of the following? (Each measurement is made correct to the nearest unit concerned.)
   (a) 155 g   **(b)** 3 652 km   **(c)** 401 kg
   (d) 4 000 kg   **(e)** 26 s   **(f)** 46 min

4. How many significant figures are there in each of the following?
   (a) 120 m (nearest 10 m)   **(b)** 35 000 km (nearest 100 km)
   (c) 45 000 km (nearest 1 000 km)   **(d)** 500 000 km (nearest 10 000 km)
   (e) 102 000 km (nearest 100 km)   **(f)** 204 040 km (nearest 10 km)

5. Evaluate the following correct to **(i)** 2 significant figures, and **(ii)** 3 significant figures.
   (a) 0.76 + 1.234 + 10.2   **(b)** 28.23 − 1.324 − 8.148
   (c) 34.5 + 10.78 − 0.49   **(d)** 734 × 3.25 + 170.5
   (e) 71.4 + 35.1 ÷ 12   **(f)** 4.21 ÷ 21.05 × 0.457 1

2.6 CONVERSIONS BETWEEN FRACTIONS AND DECIMALS

The conversion of a fraction to a decimal is carried out by division. Sometimes, the division goes on and on and the quotient has a recurring pattern, for example,

$$\frac{27}{110} = 27 \div 110$$
$$= 0.245\ 45 \dots$$

$$\begin{array}{r} 0.2454 \\ 110\overline{)27.00000} \\ \underline{22\ 0} \\ 5\ 00 \\ \underline{4\ 40} \\ 600 \\ \underline{550} \\ 500 \\ \underline{440} \\ 600 \end{array}$$

You can always add zeros to the right of a decimal number without changing its value.

Notice that the division is not exact. There is always a remainder. (After some steps, we come to the same remainder.) It is clear that the set of digits '45' in the quotient repeats endlessly. Thus, we write the quotient 0.245 45. . . as $0.2\dot{4}\dot{5}$. We indicate the repeating set '45' by placing a dot above each of the digits.

Note: When there are more than two digits in a repeating set, we place dots above the first and last digits. For example, 26 ÷ 111 = 0.234 234 . . . = $0.\dot{2}3\dot{4}$.

In practice, we usually take an approximate value for the quotient by rounding off instead of using a recurring decimal. The following examples illustrate the method of rounding off.

For example, to find $27 \div 110$ correct to 1 decimal place, we carry out the division to 2 decimal places and then round off.

$$
\begin{array}{r}
0.24\ldots \\
110\,\overline{)\,27.00} \\
22\ 0 \\
\hline
5\ 00 \\
4\ 40 \\
\hline
60
\end{array}
$$

Now, 0.24 is rounded off as 0.2, correct to 1 decimal place.
So, $27 \div 110$ is 0.2 (correct to 1 decimal place).

Similarly, to find $27 \div 110$ correct to 2 decimal places, we carry out the division to 3 decimal places and then round off.

$$
\begin{array}{r}
0.245\ldots \\
110\,\overline{)\,27.000} \\
22\ 0 \\
\hline
5\ 00 \\
4\ 40 \\
\hline
600 \\
550 \\
\hline
50
\end{array}
$$

Now, 0.245 is rounded off as 0.25, correct to 2 decimal places.
So, $27 \div 110$ is 0.25 (correct to 2 decimal places).

Note: Alternatively, we can write $27 \div 110$ as $2.7 \div 11$ and then proceed to do the division.

Worked Example 15
Express

(a) $\dfrac{3}{11}$ as a recurring decimal,

(b) $\dfrac{1}{13}$ as a decimal, correct to 3 decimal places.

Solution:

(a) $\dfrac{3}{11} = 3 \div 11$

$\qquad = 0.\dot{2}\dot{7}$

$$
\begin{array}{r}
0.2727\ldots \\
11\,\overline{)\,3.0000} \\
2\ 2 \\
\hline
80 \\
77 \\
\hline
30 \\
22 \\
\hline
80 \\
77 \\
\hline
3
\end{array}
$$

(b) $\dfrac{1}{13} = 1 \div 13$

$\qquad = 0.077$ (correct to 3 decimal places)

$$
\begin{array}{r}
0.0769\ldots \\
13\,\overline{)\,1.0000} \\
\underline{91} \\
90 \\
\underline{78} \\
120 \\
\underline{117} \\
3
\end{array}
$$

Worked Example 16

Convert the following fractions into decimals.

(a) $\dfrac{12}{25}$ **(b)** $\dfrac{1}{125}$

Solution:

(a) $\dfrac{12}{25} = 12 \div 25$

$\qquad = 0.48$

(b) $\dfrac{1}{125} = 1 \div 125$

$\qquad = 0.008$

$$
\begin{array}{r}
0.48 \\
25\,\overline{)\,12.00} \\
\underline{10\,0} \\
2\,00 \\
\underline{2\,00} \\
\end{array}
$$

Alternative solution:

(a) $\dfrac{12}{25} = \dfrac{12 \times 4}{25 \times 4}$

$\qquad = \dfrac{48}{100} = 0.48$

(b) $\dfrac{1}{125} = \dfrac{1 \times 8}{125 \times 8}$

$\qquad = \dfrac{8}{1\,000} = 0.008$

$$
\begin{array}{r}
0.008 \\
125\,\overline{)\,1.000} \\
\underline{1\,000} \\
\end{array}
$$

Worked Example 17

Convert the following decimals into fractions.

(a) 0.08 **(b)** 2.125

Solution:

(a) $0.08 = \dfrac{8}{100} = \dfrac{2}{25}$

(b) $2.125 = \dfrac{2\,125}{1\,000} = \dfrac{17}{8}$

Worked Example 18

Calculate the following.

(a) $1\dfrac{1}{4} + 2.5 \times \dfrac{3}{5}$ **(b)** $2.4 \div \left(7\dfrac{1}{5} - \dfrac{9.6}{1.5} \right)$

Solution:

(a) $1\dfrac{1}{4} + 2.5 \times \dfrac{3}{5} = 1\dfrac{1}{4} + 2\dfrac{1}{2} \times \dfrac{3}{5}$

$\qquad\qquad\qquad\quad = 1\dfrac{1}{4} + \dfrac{5}{2} \times \dfrac{3}{5}$

$\qquad\qquad\qquad\quad = 1\dfrac{1}{4} + 1\dfrac{1}{2}$

$\qquad\qquad\qquad\quad = 2\dfrac{3}{4}$

(b) $2.4 \div \left(7\frac{1}{5} - \frac{9.6}{1.5} \right) = \frac{24}{10} \div \left(\frac{36}{5} - \frac{96}{15} \right)$

$$= \frac{24}{10} \div \left(\frac{36 - 32}{5} \right)$$

$$= \frac{24}{10} \times \frac{5}{4}$$

$$= 3$$

Alternative solution:

(a) $1\frac{1}{4} + 2.5 \times \frac{3}{5} = 1.25 + 2.5 \times 0.6$

$$= 1.25 + 1.50$$

$$= 2.75$$

(b) $2.4 \div \left(7\frac{1}{5} - \frac{9.6}{1.5} \right) = 2.4 \div \left(7.2 - \frac{3.2}{0.5} \right)$

$$= 2.4 \div (7.2 - 6.4)$$

$$= 2.4 \div 0.8$$

$$= 3$$

Note: 1. You can give your answer either as a fraction or a decimal unless otherwise stated in the question.

2. You should be able to convert simple fractions to decimals mentally and vice versa.

For example, $\frac{1}{2} = 0.5$, $\frac{1}{4} = 0.25$, $\frac{1}{5} = 0.2$, $\frac{1}{8} = 0.125$,

$\frac{3}{4} = 0.75$, $\frac{3}{5} = 0.6$, etc.

Worked Example 19

Arrange the following in ascending order.

$$\frac{7}{12}, \frac{5}{9}, 0.52, 0.516$$

Solution:

$\frac{7}{12} = 0.583 \ldots$

$\frac{5}{9} = 0.555 \ldots$

Therefore, the required order is

$0.516, 0.52, \frac{5}{9}, \frac{7}{12}$.

$$\begin{array}{r} 0{\cdot}583 \ldots \\ 12 \overline{)\ 7{\cdot}000} \\ 6\,0 \\ \hline 1\,00 \\ 96 \\ \hline 40 \\ 36 \\ \hline 4 \end{array} \qquad \begin{array}{r} 0{\cdot}555 \ldots \\ 9 \overline{)\ 5{\cdot}000} \\ 4\,5 \\ \hline 50 \\ 45 \\ \hline 50 \\ 45 \\ \hline 5 \end{array}$$

Exercise 2.6

answers on p. 421

1. Convert the following decimals into fractions. Give your answers in the lowest terms.
    (a) 0.375
    (b) 0.016
    (c) 3.2
    (d) 0.000 1
    (e) 0.005
    (f) 1.004

2. Convert the following fractions into decimals.
    (a) $\dfrac{1}{2}$
    (b) $\dfrac{3}{8}$
    (c) $\dfrac{11}{25}$
    (d) $\dfrac{1}{5}$
    (e) $\dfrac{13}{52}$
    (f) $\dfrac{18}{25}$

3. Express each of the following as a recurring decimal.
    (a) $\dfrac{2}{11}$
    (b) $\dfrac{1}{6}$
    (c) $\dfrac{1}{9}$
    (d) $\dfrac{1}{3}$
    (e) $\dfrac{2}{9}$
    (f) $\dfrac{13}{66}$
    (g) $\dfrac{27}{37}$
    (h) $\dfrac{99}{101}$

4. Express the following as decimals correct to (i) 2 decimal places, and (ii) 3 decimal places.
    (a) $\dfrac{2}{13}$
    (b) $\dfrac{11}{23}$
    (c) $\dfrac{12}{19}$
    (d) $\dfrac{13}{17}$
    (e) $\dfrac{21}{23}$
    (f) $\dfrac{103}{222}$

5. For each of the following, arrange the fractions and/or decimals in ascending order.
    (a) $\dfrac{2}{5}, \dfrac{3}{7}, 0.43, 0.419$
    (b) $0.39, 0.411, \dfrac{5}{11}, \dfrac{3}{8}$
    (c) $\dfrac{3}{7}, \dfrac{3}{8}, \dfrac{4}{9}, \dfrac{6}{13}$
    (d) $\dfrac{5}{9}, \dfrac{7}{15}, \dfrac{9}{20}, \dfrac{11}{21}$

6. Simplify the following. Give your answers either in fractions or decimals.
    (a) $2\dfrac{1}{5} + 2.6$
    (b) $3.2 - 1\dfrac{1}{4}$
    (c) $1.75 + 1\dfrac{1}{5} \times 0.25$
    (d) $2\dfrac{1}{4} + 0.6 \div \dfrac{2}{5}$
    (e) $4\dfrac{1}{2} \times 3.25 \div \left(1.2 - \dfrac{3}{4}\right)$
    (f) $2.5 \div 1\dfrac{1}{4} \times \left(\dfrac{4}{5} + 1.125\right)$

7. Simplify the following, giving your answers in decimals correct to 1 decimal place.

(a) $\dfrac{0.312 \times 0.02}{0.8 \times 0.05}$

(b) $\dfrac{0.16 \times 1.24}{0.14 \times 0.02}$

(c) $\dfrac{56.4 \times 0.27}{0.03 \times 40}$

(d) $\dfrac{31.88 \times 2.12}{24.8 \times 11.2}$

8. Evaluate the following, giving your answers in decimals correct to 2 decimal places.

(a) $\dfrac{1.2^2 \times 3.1 - 1.3}{3.1 \times 1.5 + 2.3}$

(b) $\dfrac{3.2 \times 1.2 \div 1.25}{3.5 - 1.3^2}$

(c) $\dfrac{1.2 \times 1.3}{3.6} + \dfrac{2.7}{1.2}$

(d) $\dfrac{3.7 \div 2.5}{3.3} - \dfrac{1}{0.11}$

2.7 ESTIMATION

Sometimes, it is useful to check your calculations by making a quick estimation.

One practical use of estimation is estimating the costs of items. One thing for sure, you need to know whether you have enough money when paying to avoid all the embarassment!

Examples

(a) Consider $59.67 - 24.265 + 11.32$.

59.67 is about 60, 24.265 is about 20 and 11.32 is about 10. The answer is about $60 - 20 + 10$, i.e. 50. The exact answer is 46.725.

Suppose, by mistake, we obtain 24.085 as the answer. After making a comparison of this with the estimation which is 50, we know that 24.085 is not a reasonable answer.

Note: The symbol '≈' which means 'is approximately equal to' may be used. We may write, for example, $11.32 \approx 10$, $24.265 \approx 20$, etc.

(b) Consider $58.75 \times 47.5 \div 44.65$.

$58.75 \approx 60$, $47.5 \approx 50$ and $44.65 \approx 40$. The answer $\approx \dfrac{60 \times 50}{40}$, i.e. 75. The exact answer is 62.5.

Suppose, by mistake, we obtain 6.25 as the answer. Since the estimated answer is 75, we suspect that this answer is wrong.

Worked Example 20
Make an estimation and then select the correct answer in each of the following cases.

(a) 0.145×5.42

Answers: (i) 0.785 9   (ii) 7.859
(iii) 78.59   (iv) 785.9

(b) 26.34 + 152.312 − 92.123
    Answers: **(i)** 62.823   **(ii)** 86.529
            (iii) 628.23   **(iv)** 865.29

(c) 26.8 ÷ 1.25
    Answers: **(i)** 0.214 4   **(ii)** 2.144
            (iii) 21.44   **(iv)** 214.4

Solution:

(a) $0.145 \approx 0.1$, $5.42 \approx 5$ and so the product ≈ 0.5. The correct product is therefore (i), i.e. 0.785 9.

(b) $26.34 \approx 30$, $152.312 \approx 150$ and $92.123 \approx 90$. The answer $\approx 30 + 150 - 90$, i.e. 90. The answer is therefore (ii), i.e. 86.529.

(c) $26.8 \approx 27$, $1.25 \approx 1$ and so the quotient ≈ 27. The correct quotient is therefore (iii), i.e. 21.44.

Exercise 2.7

answers on p. 421

1. Make an estimation and then select the correct answer in each case.

    (a) 8.65 − 28.28 + 118.36
        Answers: **(i)** 138.73   **(ii)** 137.99
                (iii) 98.73   **(iv)** 9.873

    (b) 99.25 − 9.25 × 8.24
        Answers: **(i)** 741.6   **(ii)** 91.628
                (iii) 23.03   **(iv)** 2.303

    (c) 82.45 × 9.78
        Answers: **(i)** 80.636 1   **(ii)** 806.361
                (iii) 8 063.61   **(iv)** 80 636.1

    (d) 205.4 × 66.4
        Answers: **(i)** 136 385.6   **(ii)** 13 638.56
                (iii) 136.385 6   **(iv)** 13.638 56

    (e) 30.03 × 0.065
        Answers: **(i)** 1.951 95   **(ii)** 19.519 5
                (iii) 195.195   **(iv)** 1 951.95

    (f) 0.310 02 ÷ 0.025
        Answers: **(i)** 1 240.08   **(ii)** 124.008
                (iii) 12.400 8   **(iv)** 1.240 08

(g) $151.5 \div 0.96$

    Answers: **(i)** 1 578.125   **(ii)** 157.812 5

                (iii) 15.781 25   **(iv)** 1.578 125

(h) $8\,486.2 \div 1.25$

    Answers: **(i)** 6 788.96   **(ii)** 678.896

                (iii) 67.889 6   **(iv)** 6.788 96

(i) $0.234\,2 \div 0.025$

    Answers: **(i)** 936.8   **(ii)** 93.68

                (iii) 9.368   **(iv)** 0.936 8

(j) $33.34 \times 16.01 \div 25.5$

    Answers: **(i)** 20.932 29   **(ii)** 209.322 9

                (iii) 2 093.229   **(iv)** 20 932.29

2. Study the following. Some of the answers may be incorrect. Make an estimation to identify those which are obviously wrong. Then, use a calculator to obtain the correct answers. Give your answers correct to 2 decimal places.

(a) $\dfrac{4.426 \times 7.201^2}{20.34} = 49.94$ **(b)** $\dfrac{12.316 \times 4.123^2}{3.621} = 57.82$

(c) $\dfrac{13 \times 6.993}{2.3 \times 2} = 79.05$ **(d)** $\dfrac{47 \times 9.072}{6.3 - 0.8} = 66.88$

(e) $\dfrac{45 \times 11.8^2}{15.1 \times 4.8} = 86.45$ **(f)** $\dfrac{5.3 \times 12.4^2}{11.3 \times 5.6} = 403.86$

(g) $9.62 \times 1.58 + 1.143 \times 3.81 = 62.27$

(h) $10.32 \times 14.3 - 9.51 \times 2.1 = 127.61$

(i) $\dfrac{7.2^2 + 5.6^2}{4.4^2 - 3.2^2} = 55.28$ **(j)** $\dfrac{9.8^2 + 6.7^2}{5.6^2 - 4.6^2} = 13.82$

(k) $\dfrac{7.24 + 8.43^2}{4.321} = 119.07$ **(l)** $\dfrac{9.45 \times 9.23^2}{2.81 \times 2} = 573.01$

3. Use your calculator to evaluate the following. Give your answers correct to 2 decimal places. It is advisable to check your answers by estimation.

(a) $2.3 \times \left(13.6 + \dfrac{0.5}{3.6}\right)$ **(b)** $46.4 \times \left(\dfrac{1.2}{0.1} - 2.6\right)$

(c) $13.4 \times \left(22.6 - \dfrac{2.4}{1.4}\right) \div 1.15$ **(d)** $\dfrac{0.125}{6.2 \times 4.1} + \dfrac{1.23}{2.5}$

(e) $\dfrac{11.6}{1.2} - \dfrac{21.52}{2.6 \times 2.8}$ **(f)** $\dfrac{3.2}{14.2} \times \dfrac{4.3}{0.8} - \dfrac{1.2}{7.1} \times \dfrac{32.5}{56.1}$

(g) $\dfrac{12.1}{1.7} - \dfrac{5.32}{2.6} - \dfrac{4.2}{3.2} \times \dfrac{0.7}{1.3}$ **(h)** $\dfrac{0.312 \times 0.015}{0.8 \times 0.007}$

(i) $\dfrac{56.5 \times 0.52}{0.03 \times 4.1}$

(j) $\dfrac{1.06 \times 1.25}{0.4 \times 0.12}$

(k) $\dfrac{0.25^2 + 2.3^2}{5.3^2 - 2.4^2}$

(l) $\dfrac{1.3^2 - 0.3^2}{1.12^2 - 0.14^2}$

(m) $\dfrac{2.683^2 + 3.033^2}{2.881^2 - 2.366^2}$

(n) $\dfrac{1.983^3 - 1.721^3}{2.569^2 - 2.098^2}$

Chapter Review

1. **Operations with Fractions**
   - To add and subtract with fractions:
     (a) Find the LCM for the denominators.
     (b) Add or subtract the like fractions.

     Examples: $\dfrac{1}{3} + \dfrac{2}{5} = \dfrac{5+6}{15} = \dfrac{11}{15}$

     $\dfrac{3}{4} - \dfrac{2}{5} = \dfrac{15-8}{20} = \dfrac{7}{20}$

   - To multiply with fractions:
     (a) Multiply the numerators to get the numerator of the product.
     (b) Multiply the denominators to get the denominator of the product.

     Example: $\dfrac{4}{5} \times \dfrac{2}{7} = \dfrac{8}{35}$

   - To divide by a fraction:
     Multiply by the reciprocal of the divisor.

     Example: $\dfrac{3}{5} \div \dfrac{7}{8} = \dfrac{3}{5} \times \dfrac{8}{7} = \dfrac{24}{35}$

2. **Operations with Decimals**
   - To multiply a decimal by 10, 100, 1 000, . . ., move the decimal point one place, two places, three places, . . . to the right.

     Examples: $21.23 \times 10 = 21\,2.3 = 212.3$

     $21.23 \times 100 = 21\,23. = 2\,123$

     $21.23 \times 1\,000 = 21\,230. = 21\,230$

- To divide a decimal by 10, 100, 1 000, . . ., move the decimal point one place, two places, three places, . . . to the left.

  Examples: $21.23 \div 10 = 2 \overset{\frown}{.\,1} 23 = 2.123$

  $21.23 \div 100 = \overset{\frown}{.\,2\,1} 23 = 0.212\,3$

  $21.23 \div 1\,000 = \overset{\frown}{.\,0\,2\,1} 23 = 0.021\,23$

- To multiply a decimal by a decimal:
  (a) Find the product as with whole numbers.
  (b) Fix the decimal point according to the total number of decimal places in the two numbers.
  Example: $2.31 \times 2.3 = 5.313$

- To divide a decimal by a decimal:
  (a) Convert the divisor to a whole number.
  (b) Move the decimal point in the dividend the same number of places to the right as in the divisor.

3. **Conversion between Fractions and Decimals**
   - To convert a decimal to a fraction:
     (a) Express the decimal as a fraction with 10, 100, 1 000, . . . as denominator.
     (b) Reduce the fraction to its lowest terms.

     Example: $0.08 = \dfrac{8}{100} = \dfrac{2}{25}$

   - To convert a fraction to a decimal:
     Divide the numerator of the fraction by its denominator.

     Example: $\dfrac{12}{25} = 12 \div 25 = 0.48$

4. **Rounding Off Numbers**
   - To round off numbers:
     Consider the first (considering from left) unwanted digit. If this digit is 5 or more, we round up, otherwise we round down.
     Example: $7 \div 8 = 0.875 = 0.9$ (correct to 1 decimal place)

5. **Significant Figures**
   - In a rounded off decimal, the first non-zero digit in the recorded measurement is considered as the first significant digit and the final zeros are significant digits.
     Examples: 0.000 13 mm

     first significant digit

     not significant digits

0.20 mm (correct to the nearest 0.01 mm)

significant zero

- In a rounded off whole number, the final zeros may or may not be significant digits.

  Examples:

  2 340 000 (correct to the nearest 10 000)

  not significant zeros

  2 340 000 (correct to the nearest 1 000)

  not significant zeros

  significant zero

CHALLENGER 2

1. Calculate the following mentally.

   (a) $4.5 \times \dfrac{1}{4} + 2.5 \times \dfrac{1}{4} + 3 \times \dfrac{1}{4}$

   (b) $4.5 \times \dfrac{1}{4} + 2.5 \times 0.25 + 3 \times 0.5 \times \dfrac{1}{2}$

   (c) $4.5 \div 4 + 2\dfrac{1}{2} \times 0.25 + 1\dfrac{1}{2} \times \dfrac{1}{2}$

   (d) $3.85 \times 47.3 + 52.7 \times 3.85$

   (e) $1.25 \times 0.32 \times 0.25$

   (f) $38.7 \times 17 \div 51$

   (g) $27 \times 31 + 28 \times 31 + 69 \times 55$

   Explain your thinking process.

2. 0.000 000 000 025 is denoted by $0.\underbrace{00 \ldots 0}_{10 \text{ zeros}}25$.

   Find

   (a) $0.\underbrace{00 \ldots 0}_{1\,997 \text{ zeros}}4 + 0.\underbrace{00 \ldots 0}_{1\,997 \text{ zeros}}25$

   (b) $0.\underbrace{00 \ldots 0}_{1\,997 \text{ zeros}}4 - 0.\underbrace{00 \ldots 0}_{1\,997 \text{ zeros}}25$

   (c) $0.\underbrace{00 \ldots 0}_{1\,997 \text{ zeros}}4 \times 0.\underbrace{00 \ldots 0}_{1\,997 \text{ zeros}}25$

   (d) $0.\underbrace{00 \ldots 0}_{1\,997 \text{ zeros}}4 \div 0.\underbrace{00 \ldots 0}_{1\,997 \text{ zeros}}25$

3. Find the exact answer for each of the following.

   (a) $9 \times 0.\dot{6}$ **(b)** $9 \times 0.\dot{2}$

   (c) $99 \times 0.\dot{2}\dot{7}$ **(d)** $99 \times 0.\dot{1}\dot{8}$

   [*Hint:* Write $9 \times 0.\dot{6} = (10 - 1) \times 0.\dot{6} = 10 \times 0.\dot{6} - 0.\dot{6}$]

4. Convert the following to fractions.

   (a) $0.\dot{6}$ **(b)** $0.\dot{2}$

(c) $0.2\dot{7}$ **(d)** $0.1\dot{8}$

(e) $1.\dot{3}$ **(f)** $2.\dot{7}$

(g) $0.24\dot{5}$ **(h)** $0.1\dot{9}\dot{6}$

5. The fractions $\dfrac{1}{7}$ and $\dfrac{1}{8}$ form a special pair such that their product is equal to their difference, that is,

$$\frac{1}{7} \times \frac{1}{8} = \frac{1}{7} - \frac{1}{8}.$$

Write down 5 pairs of fractions with this property.

6. Simplify the following.

(a) $\dfrac{1}{2} - \dfrac{1}{3} + \dfrac{1}{3} - \dfrac{1}{4} + \dfrac{1}{4} - \dfrac{1}{5} + \dfrac{1}{5} - \dfrac{1}{6} + \dfrac{1}{6} - \dfrac{1}{7}$

(b) $\dfrac{1}{2} \times \dfrac{1}{3} + \dfrac{1}{3} \times \dfrac{1}{4} + \dfrac{1}{4} \times \dfrac{1}{5} + \dfrac{1}{5} \times \dfrac{1}{6} + \dfrac{1}{6} \times \dfrac{1}{7}$

(c) $\dfrac{1}{7} - \dfrac{1}{8} + \dfrac{1}{8} - \dfrac{1}{9} + \dfrac{1}{9} - \dfrac{1}{10} + \dfrac{1}{10} - \dfrac{1}{11} + \dfrac{1}{11} - \dfrac{1}{12}$

(d) $\dfrac{1}{7} \times \dfrac{1}{8} + \dfrac{1}{8} \times \dfrac{1}{9} + \dfrac{1}{9} \times \dfrac{1}{10} + \dfrac{1}{10} \times \dfrac{1}{11} + \dfrac{1}{11} \times \dfrac{1}{12}$

(e) $\dfrac{1}{2} \times \dfrac{1}{3} + \dfrac{1}{3} \times \dfrac{1}{4} + \dfrac{1}{4} \times \dfrac{1}{5} + \ldots + \dfrac{1}{99} \times \dfrac{1}{100}$

Problem Solving 2

Bookfair

At a bookfair, Bala spent \$3 less than $\dfrac{3}{5}$ of his money on mathematics books and \$3 more than $\dfrac{3}{4}$ of his remaining money on other books. He still had \$3 left. How much money did he have at first?

Let us represent Bala's money before and after buying the mathematics books by bars A and B respectively. The shaded part represents the amount of money spent.

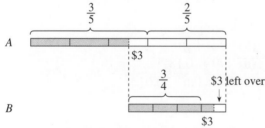

From the diagram, we have as follows:

$\frac{1}{4}$ of bar B is \$6.

So, bar B is \$6 × 4, i.e. \$24.

Bar B is $\frac{2}{5}$ of bar A plus \$3.

So, $\frac{2}{5}$ of bar A is \$24 − \$3, i.e. \$21.

Therefore, bar A is \$21 × $\frac{5}{2}$, i.e. \$52.50.

The strategy used here is **use model**.

Alternatively, we may use the strategies **use arrow diagram** and **work backwards** as follows:

Bala's money at first
$$\boxed{} \xrightarrow{\times \frac{2}{5}} \boxed{} \xrightarrow{+ \$3} \boxed{} \xrightarrow{\times \frac{1}{4}} \boxed{} \xrightarrow{- \$3} \boxed{\$3}$$

To work backwards, we reverse the arrows and use the inverse operation.

$$\boxed{\$52.50} \xleftarrow{\div \frac{2}{5}} \boxed{\$21} \xleftarrow{- \$3} \boxed{\$24} \xleftarrow{\div \frac{1}{4}} \boxed{\$6} \xleftarrow{+ \$3} \boxed{\$3}$$

So, Bala had \$52.50 at first.

 **Problems...**

1. **Savings** John spent \$24 of his savings on a watch and $\frac{1}{5}$ of the remainder on a T-shirt. He still had $\frac{2}{3}$ of his savings left. How much were his savings at first?

2. **Which Cost More?** Ali spent \$3 less than $\frac{3}{5}$ of his money on a book and \$3 more than $\frac{3}{4}$ his remaining money on a pen. He still had 50 cents left. Which items cost more between the book and the pen?

3. **Mixed Numbers** Replace each box by the number 1 or 2 or 3 to form mixed numbers, so that the following mathematical sentences are true.

    (a) $\square\frac{\square}{\square} \times \frac{2}{3} = \square\frac{\square}{\square}$

    (b) $\square\frac{\square}{\square} \times 1\frac{2}{5} = \square\frac{\square}{\square}$

4. **Repeated Divisions** How many times is $\frac{1}{3}$ used repeatedly to make the following mathematical sentence true?

$$\frac{1}{3} \div \frac{1}{3} \div \frac{1}{3} \div \ldots \div \frac{1}{3} = 81$$

Chapter 3

Arithmetic Problems

Chapter Highlights

- Converting units of measure.
- Solving simple and multi-step word problems.
- Making estimation of quantities in practical situations.

3.1 UNITS OF MEASURE

Measurement of a quantity involves a number and a unit of measure.

Long ago, people did not have the types of instruments that we use today for measurement. Early units of measure were crude as they were based on body units. For example, the distance from a man's elbow to the tip of his middle finger is called a **cubit**. The distance from a man's nose to the tip of his middle finger when his arm is outstretched is called a **yard**. A cubit is about half a yard.

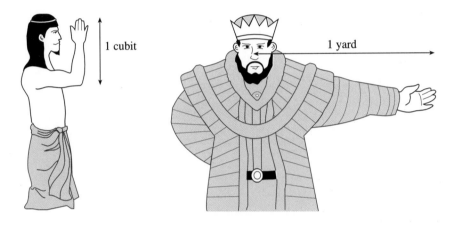

Fig. 3.1

As different body units were used by different people, they saw the need to standardise units of measure.

Some standard units used nowadays are as follows:

Mass	1 tonne	= 1 000 kilograms (kg)
	1 kilogram (kg)	= 1 000 grams (g)
	1 gram (g)	= 1 000 milligrams (mg)
Length	1 kilometre (km)	= 1 000 metres (m)
	1 metre (m)	= 100 centimetres (cm)
	1 centimetre (cm)	= 10 millimetres (mm)
Capacity	1 litre (l) = 1 000 millilitres (ml)	
Time	1 hour (h)	= 60 minutes (min)
	1 minute (min)	= 60 seconds (s)

Note: The 24-hour clock can also be used, e.g. 05 30 means 5.30 a.m. and 18 15 means 6.15 p.m.

MATHSTORY

The metric system was proposed in France in 1670 by Gabriel Mouton. However, it was only in 1790 that the French Academy of Sciences brought various groups together to develop the system. Members of the Academy chose $\frac{1}{10\,000\,000}$ of the distance from the equator to the North Pole on a meridian through Paris as the basic unit of length and called it the metre (m). In 1983, the metre was redefined as the distance travelled by light in a vacuum during $\frac{1}{299\,792\,458}$ second.

Class Activity 1

1. Which of the units – mm, cm, m, km, g, kg, tonne, h, min, s, m*l* or *l* – are commonly used for the following?
    (a) The distance of the shortest route from Katong to Jurong.
    (b) The length of your index finger.
    (c) The height of your house.
    (d) The distance from the earth to the sun.
    (e) The width of your desk.
    (f) The length of your school field.
    (g) The height of your classroom.
    (h) The thickness of your book.
    (i) The length of your book.
    (j) The length of a grain of rice.
    (k) The mass of a man.
    (l) The mass of an exercise book.
    (m) The mass of a bicycle.
    (n) The mass of an eraser.
    (o) The mass of a ship.
    (p) The capacity of a soft drink bottle.
    (q) The capacity of a cup.
    (r) The capacity of a petrol tank in a car.
    (s) The capacity of a test tube.
    (t) The capacity of a bath tub.
    (u) The time to complete a 100-metre race by a runner.
    (v) The time required to boil an egg.
    (w) The time to travel from Singapore to Kuala Lumpur by car.
    (x) The time a man works in his office.

2. Ali gives the following answers to a set of questions. Are the answers sensible? State 'Yes' or 'No' for each.
    (a) The length of a mathematics textbook is 20 m.
    (b) A baby girl weighs 50 kg.
    (c) The height of a coconut tree is 200 cm.
    (d) An average person sleeps 8 h a night.
    (e) The capacity of a thermos flask is 20 *l*.
    (f) An ordinary drinking glass can hold 250 m*l* of water.
    (g) A kettle of cold water takes 15 s to boil.
    (h) A man takes 10 min to walk 1 km.

3. Complete the table.

Weighing scale	Mass	Weighing scale	Mass
(a)	_____	**(b)**	_____
(c)	_____	**(d)**	_____
(e)	_____	**(f)**	_____

4. Complete the table.

Time sequence	12-hour clock	24-hour clock
(a)	7.15 a.m.	07 15
(b)	_____	_____
(c)	12.00 noon	_____
(d)	_____	_____
(e)	12.00 midnight	_____
(f)	_____	03 55

Conversion of Units

Worked Example 1

Express
(a) 13.7 g in kg,
(b) 3 465 g in kg and g,
(c) 25 kg 322 g in g.

Solution:

(a)   1 000 g = 1 kg

$$1 \text{ g} = \frac{1}{1\ 000} \text{kg}$$

$$\therefore \quad 13.7 \text{ g} = \left(13.7 \times \frac{1}{1\ 000}\right) \text{kg}$$

$$= 0.013\ 7 \text{ kg}$$

(b) $$1 \text{ g} = \frac{1}{1\ 000} \text{ kg}$$

$$\therefore \ 3\ 465 \text{ g} = \left(3\ 465 \times \frac{1}{1\ 000}\right) \text{kg}$$

$$= 3.465 \text{ kg}$$

$$= 3 \text{ kg } 465 \text{ g}$$

(c)   1 kg = 1 000 g
        25 kg = (25 × 1 000) g
            = 25 000 g
$\therefore$ 25 kg 322 g = (25 000 + 322) g
            = 25 322 g

Worked Example 2

Express
(a) 1.2 km in m,
(b) 2.1 m in cm,
(c) 42.5 m in km,
(d) 723 cm in m and cm.

Solution:

(a)   1 km = 1 000 m
$\therefore$ 1.2 km = (1.2 × 1 000) m
            = 1 200 m

(b)   1 m = 100 cm
$\therefore$ 2.1 m = (2.1 × 100) cm
            = 210 cm

(c)   1 000 m = 1 km

$$1 \text{ m} = \frac{1}{1\ 000} \text{ km}$$

$$\therefore \quad 42.5 \text{ m} = \left(42.5 \times \frac{1}{1\ 000}\right) \text{km}$$

$$= 0.042\ 5 \text{ km}$$

(d)   100 cm = 1 m

$$1 \text{ cm} = \frac{1}{100} \text{ m}$$

$$\therefore \quad 723 \text{ cm} = \left(723 \times \frac{1}{100}\right) \text{m}$$

$$= 7.23 \text{ m}$$

$$= 7 \text{ m } 23 \text{ cm}$$

Worked Example 3

Express

(a) 24 minutes in seconds, **(b)** 4 hours in minutes,

(c) 200 seconds in minutes and seconds.

Solution:

(a) $\quad$ 1 min = 60 s $\qquad\qquad$ **(b)** $\quad$ 1 h = 60 min

$\quad\therefore\quad$ 24 min = (24 × 60) s $\qquad\qquad\therefore\quad$ 4 h = (4 × 60) min

$\qquad\qquad$ = 1 440 s $\qquad\qquad\qquad\qquad$ = 240 min

(c) $\qquad\qquad$ 60 s = 1 min

$\qquad\qquad\qquad$ 1 s = $\dfrac{1}{60}$ min

$\quad\therefore\quad$ 200 s = $\left(200 \times \dfrac{1}{60}\right)$ min

$\qquad\qquad\qquad$ = $\dfrac{200}{60}$ min

$\qquad\qquad\qquad$ = $3\dfrac{20}{60}$ min

$\qquad\qquad\qquad$ = 3 min 20 s

Exercise 3.1 $\qquad\qquad\qquad\qquad$ *answers on p. 422*

1. Express the following in the units required.
   - **(a)** 2.5 m in cm
   - **(b)** 1 cm in m
   - **(c)** 7.6 cm in m
   - **(d)** 3.8 km in m
   - **(e)** 1 m in km
   - **(f)** 11.8 m in km
   - **(g)** 2 km in cm
   - **(h)** 1 mg in g
   - **(i)** 5.5 mg in g
   - **(j)** 1 g in kg
   - **(k)** 3.3 g in kg
   - **(l)** 8.5 kg in mg
   - **(m)** 3.5 tonnes in kg
   - **(n)** 2 570 kg in tonnes
   - **(o)** 4.5 kg in g
   - **(p)** 20 m*l* in *l*
   - **(q)** 2.6 *l* in m*l*
   - **(r)** 35 min in s
   - **(s)** 3 h in min
   - **(t)** 2 h in s
   - **(u)** 690 min in h

2. Express the following in the units required.
   - **(a)** 5 252 g in kg and g
   - **(b)** 4 211 g in kg and g
   - **(c)** 3 215 m in km and m
   - **(d)** 1 268 m in km and m
   - **(e)** 462 cm in m and cm
   - **(f)** 801 cm in m and cm
   - **(g)** 6 523 m*l* in *l* and m*l*
   - **(h)** 6 h in min
   - **(i)** 215 s in min and s
   - **(j)** 121 min in h and min
   - **(k)** 2 h 5 min in s
   - **(l)** 1 h 20 min 3 s in s
   - **(m)** 4 625 s in h, min and s
   - **(n)** 3 679 s in h, min and s

3.2 SIMPLE WORD PROBLEMS

Worked Example 4

Zhiming mixed 2 *l* of syrup with 18 *l* of water to make soft drinks. Then he poured the mixture into 5 jugs. He sold all the drinks at $2 per jug and made a profit of $7.

(a) How many litres of soft drinks did he make?

(b) How many litres of soft drinks were there in each jug?

(c) How much money did he get?

(d) What was the cost price of the soft drinks?

(e) How many parts of water were used to mix with one part of syrup?

Solution:

(a) Total number of litres of soft drinks = 2 + 18 = 20

(b) Number of litres of soft drinks in each jug = 20 ÷ 5 = 4

(c) Amount of money received = 5 × $2 = $10

(d) Cost price of the soft drinks = $10 − $7 = $3

(e) Number of parts of water used = 18 ÷ 2 = 9

Exercise 3.2

answers on p. 422

No calculators may be used.

1. One dozen identical ball-point pens cost $24.
   (a) What was the cost of 1 ball-point pen?
   (b) How much would 30 such pens cost?
   (c) How many such pens could you buy with $30?

2. Mr Li works for five days a week. He starts work at 09 00, has his lunch at 12 30 and continues to work from 13 30 to 17 00.
   (a) How many hours does he work before his lunch?
   (b) How many hours does he work after his lunch?
   (c) How many hours does he work a day?
   (d) How many hours does he work a week?
   (e) If he is paid $8 an hour, how much does he earn a week?
   (f) For how many weeks must he work in order to earn $1 120?

3. John is now 32 years old. He got married 7 years ago. His sister, Ann, got married 3 years earlier than he when she was 21 years old.
   (a) How old was John when he got married?
   (b) How old was Ann when John got married?
   (c) How old is Ann now?

4. The capacity of a mug is 1 l. A mug holds 3 l of milk less than a jug. A jug holds 2 l of milk more than a bottle. The total cost of a jug, a mug and a bottle of milk is $10.50.
   (a) What is the capacity of the jug?
   (b) What is the capacity of the bottle?
   (c) What is the total capacity of the three containers?
   (d) How much does the milk cost per litre?

5. 85 workers of a garment factory received the same monthly salary. $\frac{2}{5}$ of the workers worked overtime and each of them earned $300 extra per month. The factory paid a total of $112 200 as salaries and overtime payment.
   (a) How many workers worked overtime?
   (b) How much was paid by the factory as overtime payment?
   (c) How much was paid by the factory as salaries?
   (d) How much was the monthly salary paid to each worker?

6. Mrs Li bought 90 m of cloth to make 5 curtains. 15 m of the cloth cost $60.
   (a) What was the cost of 1 m of cloth?
   (b) How much did she pay for 90 m of cloth?
   (c) How much cloth did she need for 1 curtain?
   (d) How much cloth did she use if she made only 3 curtains?
   (e) How much was the cost of cloth for 1 curtain?

7.

Station	Time						
A	13 05	13 33	13 55	14 02	14 11	14 55	15 00
B	13 26		14 15	14 22	14 32	15 15	15 23
C	13 41	14 41	14 49	14 55	15 18	15 49	15 55
D	14 51	15 36		15 45	16 17		16 45
E			16 13	16 15	16 45	17 13	17 15
F	15 31	16 37			17 50		

The above is a time table for seven buses travelling from station A.
(a) How many of the buses stop at station D?
(b) How many of the buses stop at both stations B and E?
(c) How long does it take the 13 55 bus to reach station E?
(d) What is the longest time it takes for a bus to travel from station A to station F?
(e) A man arrives at station B at 14 18. At what time will he arrive at station E if his bus is on time?

8.

Fare in cents

Travel time in minutes (Exclude transfer and waiting time.)

Town K	50	50	50	60	90	80	70	80	90	100	100
	Town J	50	50	50	80	70	60	70	90	90	100
2		Town I	50	50	80	60	60	60	80	80	90
4	2		Town H	50	70	50	50	50	70	80	80
6	4	2		Town G	50	50	60	90	100	100	110
15	12	10	8		Town F	50	50	70	90	90	100
11	9	7	5	4		Town E	50	70	80	90	90
9	7	5	3	5	2		Town D	50	50	60	70
10	8	6	4	12	9	7		Town C	50	50	50
14	12	10	8	16	12	11	4		Town B	50	50
16	14	12	10	18	14	12	6	2		Town A	50
18	16	14	12	20	16	14	8	4	2		Town A

The above is part of the time table of a fast train.

For example, town *J* to town *E*: fare – 60 cents, travel time – 7 minutes.

(a) How long does it take to travel from town *J* to town *D*?

(b) Between which 2 towns is the travelling time the longest?

(c) Peter has to travel from town *K* to town *D* to meet his friend. Then, both of them plan to visit the park in town *I*. How much will they spend on the train fare altogether?

(d) Ranjit boarded the train at town *H* at 08 15 to go to his office in town *A*. When will he arrive at town *A*?

(e) At what rate in cents per minutes was Ranjit charged for his trip?

9. 19 teams took part in an inter-school soccer tournament. The chart below shows the result of the first round.

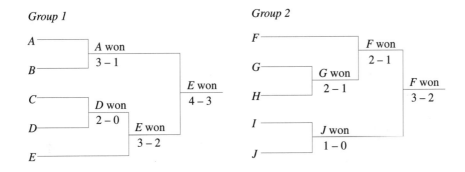

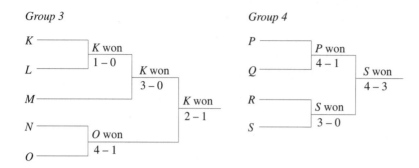

Study the chart and answer the questions below.
(a) Name the champion team in each group that will go into the second round.
(b) How many games did each champion team play?
(c) What is the goal average scored by each group champion?

10. The group champions in the 1st round (refer to question 9 above) meet in the 2nd round. The chart below shows the result of the second round.

Away match

		E	F	K	S
Home match	E		3 – 2	4 – 1	6 – 0
	F	3 – 0		1 – 1	4 – 2
	K	5 – 4	3 – 1		3 – 2
	S	5 – 5	1 – 2	0 – 1	

Notice that E and F played each other twice. When E played its home match (i.e. at E's ground) against F, the result was 3 – 2, meaning E scored 3 goals and F scored 2 goals. In other words, E won the home match. When E played its away match (i.e. at F's ground), the result was 3 – 0, meaning F scored 3 goals and E did not score. In other words, E lost the away match.

Study the chart and answer the following questions.
(a) What was the score when E played its home match against K? Who won the game?
(b) What was the score when S played its away match against E? Who won the game?
(c) How many games did each team play altogether in this round?
(d) How many goals were scored for E in this round?
(e) How many goals were scored against E in this round?

11. In the second round, points were awarded to decide the best two teams which would enter the final. The rule for awarding points was as follows: 2 points for a match won, 1 point for a match drawn and no point for a match lost. (Net gain in goals may be used as tie-breaker.)

    (a) Study the result chart in question 10, and then copy and complete the following chart.

	No. of matches won	No. of matches drawn	No. of matches lost	No. of goals scored for	No. of goals scored against	No. of points awarded
E	3	1	2	22	16	7
F						
K						
S						

    (b) Which two teams entered the final round to decide the winner?
    (c) Which team scored the most number of goals?
    (d) Which team scored the least number of goals?
    (e) How many goals were scored against the best team?

3.3 MULTI-STEP WORD PROBLEMS

Example

Daud earned some pocket money by working during his school holidays. He worked 8 days in a departmental store which paid him $18 a day and 7 days in a fast-food centre which paid him $15 a day. He bought a present which cost $54 for his mother and spent a 3-day vacation in Malaysia with the rest of his money. What was his average expenditure per day in Malaysia?

We can solve this problem step by step as follows:

Amount earned in departmental store	= $18 × 8
	= $144
Amount earned in fast-food centre	= $15 × 7
	= $105
Total amount earned	= $144 + $105
	= $249
Amount left after buying the present	= $249 − $54
	= $195
Average expenditure per day in Malaysia	= $195 ÷ 3
	= $65

Using combined operations, we can present the solution of a multi-step problem like this:

Average expenditure per day = ($18 × 8 + $15 × 7 − $54) ÷ 3
$$= \$65$$

Worked Example 5

A man bought 580 oranges at 25 cents each. He selected 430 larger oranges and sold them at 35 cents each. The rest were sold at 15 cents each. Find his profit.

Solution:

Let the cost of oranges be denoted by C, the money received from the sale of larger and smaller oranges be L and S respectively.

$$C = \$0.25 \times 580 \qquad L = \$0.35 \times 430 \qquad S = \$0.15 \times (580 - 430)$$
$$= \$145.00 \qquad\qquad = \$150.50 \qquad\qquad = \$22.50$$

$$\text{Profit} = L + S - C$$
$$= \$150.50 + 22.50 - \$145.00$$
$$= \$28.00$$

Alternative solution:

$$\text{Profit} = \$0.35 \times 430 + \$0.15 \times (580 - 430) - \$0.25 \times 580$$
$$= \$28.00$$

Worked Example 6

Mr Wu left some money for his 3 sons. The eldest son received $\frac{2}{5}$ of it, the second received $\frac{3}{8}$ of it and the youngest received $27. How much money did Mr Wu leave for his sons?

Solution:

Let the amount of money left by Mr Wu be denoted by A.

$$\text{Youngest son's share} = \left(1 - \frac{2}{5} - \frac{3}{8}\right) \text{ of } A$$

$$= \frac{9}{40} \text{ of } A$$

$$\frac{9}{40} \text{ of } A = \$27$$

$$\frac{1}{40} \text{ of } A = \$27 \times \frac{1}{9}$$

$$\therefore \quad A = \$27 \times \frac{1}{9} \times 40$$

$$= \$120$$

Alternative solution:

$$A = \$27 \div \left(1 - \frac{2}{5} - \frac{3}{8}\right) = \$27 \div \frac{9}{40}$$

$$= \$27 \times \frac{40}{9}$$

$$= \$120$$

Note: Checking of answers is a good habit. This can be done as 'rough work' even though it is not required as part of the solution.

Exercise 3.3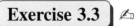

answers on p. 422

1. The table shows the temperature measured at noon in a town for a certain week.

Days	Sun	Mon	Tue	Wed	Thur	Fri	Sat
Temp. in °C	24.5	23.8	22.4	25.6	26.0	23.1	24.0

Find the average temperature at noon for that week.

2. The temperature of a liquid is 25°C. After heating the liquid for 10 seconds, the temperature reads 35°C. Find the average increase in temperature in 1 second.

3. A man worked 7 days a week for 4 weeks. He was paid $45 per day on Sundays and $30 per day on weekdays. What was his total pay?

4. A man bought 12 bags of rice at $50 per bag. Find his net profit if he paid $15 for transport and sold all the rice for $650?

5. In 1 minute, machine A can pack 152 packets of biscuits and machine B can pack 205 packets of biscuits. How many packets of biscuits can both machines pack in 2 hours?

6. The cost of making a cake is $3. If the baker wishes to make a profit of $5 per cake and the cake is to be cut into 16 pieces, what is the selling price of each piece?

7. A man bought 10 cartons of oranges. There were 30 oranges in each carton. He kept 50 for his friends and sold the rest. At what price did he sell each of these oranges if he sold them all for $45?

8. Sue's mother bought 5 lemons at $0.25 each, $\frac{1}{2}$ kg of mutton at $8.36 per kg and 2.5 l of milk at $0.85 per $\frac{1}{2}$ l. How much money did she spend altogether?

9. The cost of 6 mangoes was the same as the cost of 2 durians. Paul bought 3 mangoes and 4 durians for $30. Find the cost of one mango.

10. The admission tickets to an exhibition were priced at $5 for an adult and $2 for a child. A family of 3 adults and 4 children visited the exhibition. What would be the change if a $50 note was used to buy the tickets?

11. A transport company delivered 120 vases at a cost of $2 per vase. It had to pay $15 for each vase that was broken during the transport. It received a payment of $165 after the delivery. How many vases were broken?

12. Mrs Hua had 2 ten-dollar notes, 1 five-dollar note, 7 one-dollar coins and 8 ten-cent coins. She bought a fish for $5.60, a piece of cake for $1.25, a bag of rice for $7.30 and a chicken for $6.60. How much money had she left?

13. 3 brothers share a sum of money. The eldest gets $\frac{3}{5}$ of it and the youngest gets $\frac{1}{10}$ of it. If the eldest gets $108, how much will the others get?

14. Henry made 200 tarts. He sold $\frac{2}{5}$ of them and gave $\frac{1}{4}$ of the remainder to his friend. How many tarts had he left?

15. In a school hall, $\frac{2}{5}$ of the chairs are red, $\frac{3}{7}$ are blue and the rest are yellow. If there are 24 yellow chairs, how many chairs are blue?

16. Peter, Ali, Mingfa and Sunny share the cost of a present. Peter pays $\frac{1}{6}$ of the bill and the rest of the cost is shared equally by the other 3 friends. What fraction of the bill does Sunny pay?

17. A shopkeeper orders a special brand of coffee powder to be delivered to him. A packet of this coffee powder cost $2. These packets are packed into containers which cost $3 each. Each container can hold 30 packets. A van delivers 60 containers of this coffee powder to the shop and charges $20 for transport. How much does the shopkeeper pay altogether?

18. Ganesan worked in a gift shop and was paid $4 an hour. He worked 5 days a week for 6 weeks and was given $2 transport allowance a day. He earned a total of $780. How many hours did he work per day during the 6 weeks?

19. A tin of oil is $\frac{3}{5}$ full. 3.5 l of oil is required to fill it completely. If 1 full tin of oil costs $28, how much does $\frac{3}{4} l$ of this oil cost?

*20. A man bought 20 boxes of apples at $16 per box. There were 64 apples in each box. A total of 30 apples were found to be rotten and could not be sold. If he wanted to make a profit of $55, how much should he sell each apple?

*21. Meifang bought 200 eggs for $15.20. Some of the eggs were broken and discarded. He sold the remaining eggs at 12 cents each. Altogether, he made a profit of $7.60. How many eggs were discarded?

*22. John worked 7 hours per day on 5 weekdays and earned $140 for the 5 days work. He also worked 4 hours per day on Saturday and Sunday and his hourly pay was twice that of a weekday. He went for a holiday with all that he had earned and spent an average of $50 a day. If he still had $54 left, how many days did he spend on his holiday?

*23. Kassim spent $\frac{3}{5}$ of his salary and saved the rest. $\frac{5}{8}$ of what he spent was on food. He spent $600 more on food than on all other items combined. How much did he save?

*24. At 10 15, a heating device was switched on and the temperature of a liquid when heated increased 2.5°C every minute. At 10 35, the heating device was switched off and at the same time a cooling device was switched on so that the temperature of the liquid decreased at a uniform rate. At 11 05, the temperature of the liquid was 12.5°C higher than that at 10 15. When was the temperature 12.5°C higher than that at 11 05?

3.4 ESTIMATION IN DAILY LIFE SITUATIONS

Examples

(a) Suppose you wish to buy five articles costing $1.55, $1.90, $2.00, $1.85 and $1.75. Without calculating the total cost, how would you quickly decide whether a $10 note is sufficient to pay for the articles? To find out, you examine the cost of each article. Since no article costs more than $2, the total cost should be less than $10.

(b) Suppose a man wants to drive from town *A* to town *B*. To decide the least amount of petrol that his car will need to reach the other town, he must consider
(i) the distance from town *A* to town *B*,
(ii) how far his car can go on 1 litre of petrol.

If the distance to travel is 85 km and his car can travel about 10 km on 1 litre of petrol, his car will need about 8.5 litres of petrol. If he puts 9 litres in his car tank, he knows that he will reach the other town with some petrol to spare.

(c) A section of a book shelf has a measurement of 65 cm by 25 cm by 35 cm as shown. Suppose a teacher wishes to keep the exercise books in this section. To estimate how many exercise books she can put in the section, she has to consider
   (i)   the thickness of each exercise book,
   (ii) the length and width of each exercise book.

If each exercise book is 0.5 cm thick, 20 cm wide and 25 cm long, she can put three piles of about 70 exercise books each in the section, i.e. about 210 exercise books.

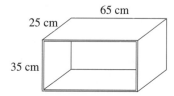

Class Activity 2

1. (a) Suppose you are asked to estimate the number of candidates that a school hall can accommodate for an examination. Do you have to consider
   (i)   the floor area of the hall,
   (ii) the space occupied by the desk and chair for each candidate,
   (iii) the allowance for space between the candidates to prevent dishonest activities as well as to allow the invigilators to move around,
   (iv) the space for the chief invigilator's table?

   (b) The sketch on the right shows how a hall of a certain school is to be arranged for an examination. If the length and width of the hall are 30 m and 20 m respectively, estimate the number of candidates that the hall can accommodate.

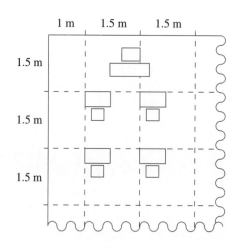

2. **(a)** Suppose your class is going on a picnic and you are asked to estimate how much bread is required. Do you have to consider
   (i) the number of pupils in your class who are going,
   (ii) the number of meals in which bread is served,
   (iii) the number of servings per meal per pupil,
   (iv) the number of slices per serving?

   (b) Estimate how many loaves of bread is required to serve 40 pupils so that each pupil will have 3 meals with 1 serving for each meal, assuming that 5 servings can be made from 1 loaf of bread.

3. Estimate the number of classroom desks that you would stack up to reach the ceiling of your classroom.

4. Estimate the number of cups of water to fill a teapot and the number of teapots of tea required to serve 200 pupils allowing one cup for each pupil.

5. Estimate the number of words in your mathematics textbook.

6. If you can write 8 words on one line in your exercise book, estimate the number of words that you can write in your exercise book.

7. Estimate the number of books in your school library.

8. Estimate the length and breadth of your school field.

9. Estimate the time you would take to walk round your school field once.

10. A bottle contains about 1 kg of soya beans. Suggest a method you would use to estimate the number of beans in the bottle.

Chapter Review

1. **Simple Word Problems**

   The problem consists of several parts. Each part is a one-step problem. To solve the problem, we identify the relevant information for each part and solve each part of the given problem.

2. **Multi-step Word Problems**

   The problem consists of several missing parts. Each part is itself a one-step problem. To solve the given problem, we identify the missing parts and solve them, step by step, until we reach the solution to the given problem.

CHALLENGER ❸

1. Siti had $\frac{2}{3}$ as much money as Rani. If Siti spent $\frac{3}{4}$ of her money and Rani spent $\frac{4}{5}$ of her money, what fraction of Rani's remainder was Siti's remainder?

2. Albert had $120 more than Benny. Each day, Albert spent $24 and Benny spent $18. After Albert spent all his money, Benny still had $120. How much money had each at first?

3. Menghui and Meili had $8 altogether. If Menghui spent $\frac{1}{3}$ of his money and Meili spent $1.50, then they would have the same amount left. Find the original amount of money each had at first.

4. A country club has 1 150 members. $\frac{1}{5}$ of the men and $\frac{1}{4}$ of the ladies do not play golf. A total of 250 members do not play golf. How many men play golf?

5. A, B and C are three groups of pupils. If group A is $\frac{1}{3}$ of the total number of pupils in the three groups, group B has 5 pupils more than group A and group C has $\frac{3}{5}$ as many pupils as group B, find the original number of pupils in each group.

6. Ali bought 5 packets of sweets and Mary bought 3 packets of sweets. The cost was the same for each packet. These 8 packets of sweets were shared equally between Ali, Mary and John. John had to pay 40 cents for his share of sweets. How much of the 40 cents should be paid to Ali and to Mary?

Problem Solving 3

Chess Tournament

In a chess tournament, each competitor is to play with every other competitor once only. If there are 12 players, how many games are played?

We use the strategy **make a systematic list**.

Let the 12 players be A, B, C, . . . and L.

AB, AC, AD, AE, AF, AG, AH, AI, AJ, AK, AL _____   11 games

BC, BD, BE, BF, BG, BH, BI, BJ, BK, BL _____   10 games

CD, CE, CF, CG, CH, CI, CJ, CK, CL _____   9 games

.   _____   .

.   _____   .

.   _____   .

JK, JL _____   2 games

KL _____   1 game

Total number of games $= 1 + 2 + 3 + 4 + \ldots + 11$
$$= 66$$

Alternatively, we use the strategies **simplify the problem**, **use diagram** and **look for pattern**.

Thinking process

Suppose only 5 players are involved.
Use drawing to find the number of games.
Then, study the pattern and extend the pattern to find the number of games when 12 players are involved.

Now, let the players be A, B, C, $\ldots$ and L.

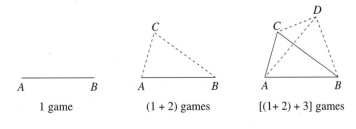

A B A B A B

1 game $(1 + 2)$ games $[(1 + 2) + 3]$ games

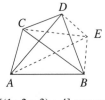

$[(1 + 2 + 3) + 4]$ games
... and so on.

From the above pattern, we see that
total number of games played by the 12 people
$$= 1 + 2 + 3 + 4 + 5 + 6 + 7 + 8 + 9 + 10 + 11 = 66$$

Another way is to **use tabulation** and then **look for pattern**.

	A	B	C	D	E	F	G	H	I	J	K	L
A	✗	✔	✔	✔	✔	✔	✔	✔	✔	✔	✔	✔
B		✗	✔	✔	✔	✔	✔	✔	✔	✔	✔	✔
C			✗	✔	✔	✔	✔	✔	✔	✔	✔	✔
D				✗	✔	✔	✔	✔	✔	✔	✔	✔
E					✗	✔	✔	✔	✔	✔	✔	✔
F						✗	✔	✔	✔	✔	✔	✔
G							✗	✔	✔	✔	✔	✔
H								✗	✔	✔	✔	✔
I									✗	✔	✔	✔
J										✗	✔	✔
K											✗	✔
L												✗

The symmetrical pattern suggests that the number of boxes marked with '✔' is equal to $\frac{1}{2}$ of the total number of boxes excluding those marked '✗', i.e. $(12 \times 12 - 12) \div 2$ which is 66.

Problems...

1. **Soccer Tournament**   11 teams take part in an inter-school soccer tournament. Each team is to play with every other team twice, one match is played at home ground and the other away. How many matches are to be played?

2. **Handshakes**   There are 10 boys in a party. If each boy shakes hands with every other boy once, how many handshakes are made?

3. **Triangular and Square Numbers**   △ represents a triangular number.
   ☐ represents a square number.
   Copy and complete the following.

   (a) $2 \times \triangle{3} + \square = \triangle{10}$ **(b)** $2 \times \triangle + \boxed{9} = \triangle$

   (c) $2 \times \triangle + \square = \triangle{21}$ **(d)** $2 \times \triangle + \square = \square$

   (e) $2 \times \square + \square = \triangle$ **(d)** $2 \times \triangle + \triangle = \square$

4. **Missing Operations** Insert the four operations and brackets, where necessary, to make the following sentences true. The first 3 are done. Check whether they are correct.

(a) $(1 + 2) \div 3 = 1$
(b) $1 \times 2 + 3 - 4 = 1$
(c) $1 \div 2 \times 3 \times 4 - 5 = 1$
(d) $1\ 2\ 3\ 4\ 5\ 6 = 1$
(e) $1\ 2\ 3\ 4\ 5\ 6\ 7 = 1$
(f) $1\ 2\ 3\ 4\ 5\ 6\ 7\ 8 = 1$
(g) $1\ 2\ 3\ 4\ 5\ 6\ 7\ 8\ 9 = 1$

Real Numbers

Chapter Highlights

- Using integers in practical situations.
- Performing calculations with integers.
- Finding the square roots and cube roots of given numbers using prime factorisation.
- Recognising rational and irrational numbers.
- Performing calculations with rational numbers.
- Performing mental calculations using various strategies.

4.1 NEGATIVE NUMBERS

MATHSTORY

The Chinese are thought to have been the first to use the idea of a negative number as early as 300 BC. However, it was not until the 1500s that negative numbers were made use of. Negative numbers were often thought of as 'false numbers' or 'incorrect numbers'.

Look at the following mathematical sentence.

$$10 - 12 = \square$$

This does not make sense if we think of concrete objects such as marbles because we do not take away 12 marbles from 10 marbles.

Let us think of the following situation.

Suppose John has $10 and he wishes to buy a book which costs $12. John has to borrow $2 in order to buy the book. We use a **negative number** –2 to describe the amount borrowed and we write

$$10 - 12 = -2.$$

When we say 'John has –2 dollars left', we actually mean 'John owes people 2 dollars'. There are many situations in which negative numbers are used.

Examples

(a) The temperature 10°C below zero may be recorded as –10°C.

(b) A water level 2 m below sea level may be represented as –2 m from sea level.

(c) We may say 'a gain of –200 dollars' when we mean 'a loss of 200 dollars'.

(d) To describe changes in temperatures, we may say 'a fall of –5°C' when we mean 'a rise of 5°C'.

Class Activity 1

1. Copy and complete the following.
   (a) If –5°C represents five degrees Celsius below the freezing point (i.e. zero degree), then five degrees Celsius above the freezing point is represented by _____.

   (b) If two metres above sea level is recorded as +2 m, then –3 m means three metres _____ sea level.

   (c) In a building, if a storey five levels above the ground floor is represented by +5, then a basement two levels below the ground floor is represented by _____.

(d) If five minutes before midnight is represented by –5 minutes from midnight, then ten minutes after midnight is represented by _____ from midnight.

(e) If +2 km from a given point means two kilometres due east of the given point, then –4 km from the given point means four kilometres due _____ of the given point.

(f) If a turning of +30° means a turning of 30° anticlockwise, then a turning of –30° means a turning of 30° _____.

2. Copy and complete the following.
(a) A gain of –30 dollars means a loss of _____ dollars.

(b) A loss of –20 dollars means a _____ of 20 dollars.

(c) A credit of –150 dollars means a debit of _____ dollars.

(d) A deposit of –150 dollars means a withdrawal of _____ dollars.

(e) A descent of –10 m means an ascent of _____.

(f) 4 steps backward means _____ steps forward.

(g) An income of –100 dollars means an expenditure of _____ dollars.

(h) A boat is rowed –2 km downstream means it is rowed _____ upstream.

Integers

Let us look at the number line in Fig 4.1

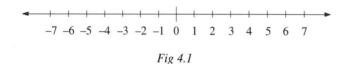

Fig 4.1

The set of integers is the set of whole numbers and their negatives.

The whole numbers 1, 2, 3, 4, . . . are referred to as **positive integers** and the negative whole numbers –1, –2, –3, –4, . . . as **negative integers**. We refer to all the numbers . . . –4, –3, –2, –1, 0, 1, 2, 3, 4, . . . as integers. Notice that the set of integers includes the integer 0 which is neither positive nor negative. Notice also that the points that represent the integers on the number line are equally spaced.

Note: Positive integers 1, 2, 3, 4, . . . are sometimes written, for emphasis, as +1, +2, +3, +4, ...

Order of Integers

Integers are arranged according to the order of size on the number line so that for any two integers, the smaller integer always lies to the left of the larger integer (refer to Fig. 4.1). For example, 3 lies to the left of 5 and so we know that 3 is less than 5. −3 lies to the left of −1 and so −3 is less than −1.

The symbol '<' which means 'is less than' may be used for writing the order of size of integers as follows:

$$\ldots -4 < -3 < -2 < -1 < 0 < 1 < 2 < 3 < 4 < 5 \ldots$$

The symbol '>' which means 'is greater than' can also be used for writing the order. If we use this symbol, we get

$$\ldots 5 > 4 > 3 > 2 > 1 > 0 > -1 > -2 > -3 > -4 \ldots$$

Numerical Value

The **numerical value** of an integer is the value represented by the numeral, irrespective of the sign. Thus, the numerical value of the negative integer −12 is 12 and the numerical value of the positive integer 9 is 9 itself. Notice that although −12 is less than 9, the numerical value of −12 is larger than the numerical value of 9 and we say that −12 is **numerically** larger than 9.

Note: The term 'numerical value' is also known as **'absolute value'**.

Exercise 4.1

answers on p. 422

1. Draw a diagram of the number line and mark dots on it to indicate the following integers.

    5, −8, 0, −1, 6, 9, −3

2. In each case, replace the box by '>' or '<'.
   - **(a)** 5 ☐ 3
   - **(b)** 7 ☐ −4
   - **(c)** −8 ☐ −1
   - **(d)** 125 ☐ −3
   - **(e)** 0 ☐ 4
   - **(f)** 6 ☐ −8
   - **(g)** −3 ☐ −12
   - **(h)** 0 ☐ −9
   - **(i)** −12 ☐ 10

3. Write down the numerical value of each of the following integers.
   - **(a)** −5
   - **(b)** 7
   - **(c)** 0
   - **(d)** −7
   - **(e)** 18
   - **(f)** −18

4. Between −14 and 12, **(a)** which is larger, and **(b)** which is numerically larger?

5. Between –14 and –18, **(a)** which is smaller, and **(b)** which is numerically smaller?

6. Between –25 and 24, **(a)** which has a greater value, and **(b)** which has a greater absolute value?

7. Between –15 and –16, **(a)** which has a smaller value, and **(b)** which has a smaller absolute value?

8. Copy and complete the following number patterns.
   (a) 4, 3, 2, 1, 0, ____, ____, ____
   (b) 2, 4, 6, 8, ____, ____, ____
   (c) –8, –6, –4, –2, ____, ____, ____
   (d) –4, ____, –2, –1, 0, ____, ____, ____
   (e) –6, –3, ____, ____, 6, ____
   (f) –2, ____, ____, ____ (decreasing each step by 1)
   (g) –5, ____, ____, ____ (decreasing each step by 2)
   (h) –4, ____, ____, ____ (decreasing each step by 2)
   (i) 3, ____, ____, ____, ____ (decreasing each step by 1)
   (j) –3, ____, ____, ____, ____ (decreasing each step by 1)
   (k) 9, ____, ____, ____, ____ (decreasing each step by 3)
   (l) –9, ____, ____, ____, ____ (increasing each step by 3)

4.2 ADDITION AND SUBTRACTION OF INTEGERS

The temperature in the desert region can drop as much as 40°C from noon to midnight. For example, at noon the temperature can be as high as 35°C and at midnight it can drop to 5°C below zero.

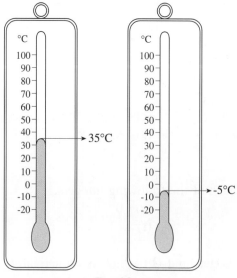

Fig. 4.2

We can describe this situation by using a subtraction sentence:

$$35 - 40 = -5$$

Similarly, to describe a rise of 25°C from –10°C to 15°C, we write

$$-10 + 25 = 15.$$

The following class activity will help you discover some rules for doing addition and subtraction of integers.

Class Activity 2

1. Copy the vertical scale and the table. Then, use the vertical scale to help you complete the table.

15
10
5
0
–5
–10
–15

Original temperature	Change	New temperature	Mathematical sentence
5°C	rise 3°C	8°C	5 + 3 = 8
2°C	rise 9°C		2 + 9 = ☐
5°C	fall 3°C		5 – 3 = ☐
5°C	fall 8°C		5 – 8 = ☐
–5°C	rise 12°C		–5 + 12 = ☐
–8°C	rise 5°C		–8 + 5 = ☐
–5°C	fall 3°C		–5 – 3 = ☐

2. Copy and complete the following.
    (a) 'A rise of –8°C' means 'a fall of 8°C'.
        So 'adding –8' is interpreted as 'subtracting ____'.
    (b) 'A fall of –9°C' means 'a rise of 9°C'.
        So 'subtracting –9' is interpreted as 'adding ____'.

3. Copy the number line. Then, use it to help you complete the mathematical sentences that follow.

–15   –10   –5   0   5   10   15

(a) 8 + 6 = ☐   (b) 3 + 10 = ☐
(c) –5 + (–6) = ☐   (d) –8 + (–3) = ☐
(e) –12 + 9 = ☐   (f) 7 + (–9) = ☐
(g) –9 + 14 = ☐   (h) 11 + (–8) = ☐

4. Is each of the following statements true or false? Give an example to illustrate your answer.

    (a) To add two negative integers, we find the sum of their numerical values and take the negative sign for the answer.

    (b) Given that a negative integer is numerically larger than a positive integer, to add these two integers, we find the difference between their numerical values and take the negative sign for the answer.

    (c) Given that a positive integer is numerically larger than a negative integer, to add these two integers, we find the difference between their numerical values and take the positive sign for the answer.

5. Rewrite the following subtraction sentences as addition sentences. Then, write down the answers.

    (a) $8 - (-6) = \square$ **(b)** $3 - (-10) = \square$

    (c) $-5 - 6 = \square$ **(d)** $-8 - 3 = \square$

    (e) $-12 - (-9) = \square$ **(f)** $7 - 9 = \square$

    (g) $-9 - (-14) = \square$ **(h)** $11 - 8 = \square$

From the above class activity, we have learnt that we can perform addition and subtraction with integers on the number line by interpreting

> - **'adding a negative integer' as 'subtracting a positive integer',**
> - **'subtracting a negative integer' as 'adding a positive integer'.**

In symbols, if n is a natural number, we write as follows:

$$+ (-n) = -n$$
$$- (-n) = +n$$

We can also add integers using the following rules.

> **1. To add two negative integers, we find the sum of their numerical values and take the negative sign for the answer.**
>
> **2. To add two integers of different signs, we find the difference between their numerical values and take the same sign as that of the numerically larger integer for the answer.**

In symbols, if a and b are natural numbers, we write as follows:

$$-a + (-b) = -(a + b)$$
$$-a + b = -(a - b) \text{ if } a > b$$
$$-a + b = b - a \text{ if } b > a$$

To add two positive integers, we simply add them like natural numbers.

To perform subtraction of integers we can convert the subtraction sentence to an addition sentence and then carry out the addition using the addition rules for integers. For example,

$$3 - (-4) = 3 + 4 = 7$$
$$-5 - 6 = -5 + (-6) = -11$$

Worked Example 1

Calculate the following.

(a) $-62 + (-12)$

(b) $62 + (-52)$

(c) $62 + (-78)$

(d) $-70 - 31$

Solution:

(a) $-62 + (-12) = -(62 + 12)$
$$= -74$$

(b) $62 + (-52) = 62 - 52$
$$= 10$$

(c) $62 + (-78) = -(78 - 62)$
$$= -16$$

(d) $-70 - 31 = -70 + (-31)$
$$= -(70 + 31)$$
$$= -101$$

Note: In (d), the step '$= -70 + (-31)$' may be omitted as it can be done mentally.

Worked Example 2

Calculate the following.

(a) $567 - 625$

(b) $-421 - (-342)$

(c) $122 - 362 - 102$

(d) $301 - 966 + 665$

Solution:

(a) $567 - 625 = -(625 - 567)$
$$= -58$$

(b) $-421 - (-342) = -421 + 342$
$$= -(421 - 342)$$
$$= -79$$

(c) $122 - 362 - 102 = -(362 - 122) - 102$
$$= -240 - 102$$
$$= -(240 + 102)$$
$$= -342$$

(d) $301 - 966 + 665 = 301 + 665 - 966$
$$= 966 - 966$$
$$= 0$$

Note: In (a), the step '= 567 + (–625)' is omitted.
In (c), the steps '122 + (–362)' and '– 240 + (–102)' are omitted.
In (d), we view 301 – 966 + 665 as 301 + (–966) + 665 and use regrouping for easy computation.

Worked Example 3
An aeroplane was flying at a height of 2 000 m. In order to clear a mountain, it had to climb a further height of 2 000 m. After that, it descended 3 000 m and flew for some time before it climbed another 2 000 m again to avoid a thunder-storm. What was its height then?

Solution:
2 000 m + 2 000 m + (–3 000) m + 2 000 m = 3 000 m
Its height then was 3 000 m.

Note that you must not use the calculator to do your exercises in this chapter unless otherwise stated. You should, however, use the calculator to check your answers. For example, to check the answer for –421 – (–342), we proceed with the calculator as follows:

$$\boxed{(-)}\ 421\ \boxed{-}\ \boxed{(-)}\ 342\ \boxed{EXE}$$

Notice that the brackets in (–342) need not be keyed.

For a different calcu-lator, the 'keying order' may appear as 421 $\boxed{+/-}$ $\boxed{-}$ 342 $\boxed{+/-}$ $\boxed{=}$.

Exercise 4.2

answers on p. 423

1. Draw a number line, then use it to help you do the following.
   (a) 9 + (–5)   (b) 5 + (–7)   (c) –2 + (–5)

2. Do the following.
   (a) –7 + 16   (b) –3 + (–9)   (c) 15 + (–19)
   (d) –21 + 16   (e) –5 + (–20)   (f) –7 + 7
   (g) –5 + (–2)   (h) 5 + (–10)   (i) –7 + 5
   (j) 3 + (–7)   (k) –23 + (–13)   (l) –45 + 18
   (m) 27 + (–32)   (n) –38 + 81   (o) 55 + (–42)
   (p) –37 + 37   (q) –64 + (–64)   (r) –129 + 107

3. Do the following.
   (a) 7 – 3   (b) 5 – 8   (c) –5 – 8
   (d) –5 – 3   (e) 8 – (–3)   (f) 5 – (–7)
   (g) –6 – (–8)   (h) –8 – (–4)   (i) –34 – (–74)
   (j) –52 – (–31)   (k) 38 – (–8)   (l) –45 – (–12)
   (m) –24 – (–32)   (n) 82 – (–18)   (o) 14 – (–56)
   (p) –92 – (–92)   (q) 107 – 128   (r) –351 – (–101)

4. Evaluate the following.
   (a) 24 – (–12)   (b) –156 – 342
   (c) 342 – (–32)   (d) 765 – (–342)
   (e) –(–682) + 402   (f) –345 + (–284)
   (g) 354 – (–404)   (h) 432 – (–135)
   (i) 426 – (–12) + 28   (j) 255 – (–122) – 201
   (k) –(–234) – 111 – 182   (l) 365 + (–182) – (–222)
   (m) 562 – (–100) – 201   (n) –(–800) + (–510) – (120)
   (o) –285 – (–124) – (–321)   (p) –379 – (–128) – (–251)

5. Copy and complete the following table.

Original temperature	Change	New temperature	Mathematical sentence
5°C	–3°C	2°C	5 + (–3) = 2
12°C	+10°C	22°C	
15°C	–13°C		
15°C	–18°C		
–8°C	+14°C		
–18°C	+ 9°C		
–21°C	–13°C		

6. Copy and complete the following table.

John has some cheques(C) and bills(B) in a box		Total amount in the box ($)	Mathematical sentence
C: $10	B: $15	–5	10 + (–15) = –5
C: $25	B: $17	8	
C: $7	B: $10		
B: $25	C: $18		
B: $18	C: $25		
C: $16	C: $17		
B: $19	B: $25		

7. Copy and complete the following table.

John has some cheques(C) and bills(B) in a box			Total amount ($)	A cheque(C) or a bill(B) is taken out	Amount of money left ($)	Mathematical sentence
C $10	C $30	B $16	24	C: $30	–6	24 – 30 = –6
B $37	C $15	C $10	–12	C: $10	–22	
C $52	B $10	B $12		B: $12		
C $25	B $15	B $20		B: $15		
C $33	C $15	B $10		C: $15		
C $20	B $42	B $18		B: $18		

8. The table below shows a company's profits and losses for the first six months of a certain year.

January	$5 000	profit	April	$1 000	profit
February	$2 000	profit	May	$4 000	profit
March	$6 000	loss	June	$3 000	loss

   (a) Use positive and negative integers to show these income figures.
   (b) What is the total income for the six-month period?
   (c) What is the total income for the first three months of the year?
   (d) Find the total income for this four-month period: March, April, May and June.

9. At noon, the temperature of a certain place registered 35°C. At 01 00 the next day, the temperature was –5°C. What was the difference in the temperature? It was found that the temperature after 01 00 further decreased by 0.5°C every hour. What was the temperature at 04 00?

10. A missile travelling at an altitude of 13 000 m makes a climb of 5 000 m followed by a descent of 3 000 m.
   (a) Represent the final altitude of the missile as a sum of positive and negative integers.
   (b) What is the altitude of the missile after the descent?

4.3 MULTIPLICATION OF INTEGERS

Examples

(a) If John puts 9 cheques for $8 each in a box, then he puts $8 × 9 in the box. By how much does the money in the box increase?

We interpret 8 × 9 as '8 is multiplied by 9', i.e. $\underbrace{8 + 8 + \ldots + 8}_{9 \text{ terms}}$. So, the money in the box increases by $72.

(b) If John puts – 9 cheques for $8 each in a box, then he puts $8 × (–9) in the box. By how much does the money in the box increase?

It does not make sense to interpret 8 × (–9) as $\underbrace{8 + 8 + \ldots + 8}_{-9 \text{ terms}}$.

Let us first interpret 'John puts –9 cheques in a box' as 'John takes away 9 cheques from a box'. Then, we interpret 'John puts $8 × (–9) in the box' as 'John takes away $8 × 9 from the box'. So, the money in the box decreases by $72. We can also say that the money in the box increases by $(–72).

In short, we interpret 8 × (–9) as –(8 × 9).

(c) If John puts 9 bills of $8 each in a box, then he puts $(–8) × 9 in the box. By how much does the money in the box increase?

We interpret –8 × 9 as '–8 is multiplied by 9', i.e. $\underbrace{(-8) + (-8) + \ldots + (-8)}_{9 \text{ terms}}$ which is equal to $\underbrace{-(8 + 8 + \ldots + 8)}_{9 \text{ terms}}$. So, the money in the box increases by $(–72).

In short, we interpret –8 × 9 as – (8 × 9).

(d) If John puts –9 bills of $8 each in a box, then he puts $(–8) × (–9) in the box. By how much does the money in the box increase?

We first interpret 'John puts –9 bills in a box' as 'John takes away 9 bills from a box'. Then, we interpret 'John puts $(–8) × (–9) in the box' as 'John takes away $(–8) × 9 from the box'. So, the money in the box decreases by $(–72). This means that the money in the box increases by $72.

In short, we interpret –8 × (–9) as 8 × 9.

The above examples suggest the following rules for multiplication of integers.

> **1. To multiply two integers of the same sign, we take the positive sign for the answer.**
>
> **2. To multiply two integers of different signs, we take the negative sign for the answer.**

In symbols, if a and b are natural numbers, we write as follows:

$$a \times b = a \times b$$
$$-a \times (-b) = a \times b$$
$$a \times (-b) = -(a \times b)$$
$$-a \times b = -(a \times b)$$

Note: The products $a \times 0$, $-a \times 0$, $0 \times a$ and $0 \times (-a)$ are zero.

Squares and Square Roots

We know that $4 \times 4 = 16$. This can be written as $4^2 = 16$. We say that 16 is the **square** of 4 and 4 is the **square root** of 16.

16 is also the square of -4 since $(-4)^2 = -4 \times (-4) = 16$. Thus, -4 is also the square root of 16. This means that 16 has a positive square root 4 and a negative square root -4. We indicate the positive square root of 16 as $\sqrt{16}$, and the negative square root of 16 as $-\sqrt{16}$.

To find the square root of a square number, we can use the **prime factorisation method**. For example, to find the positive square root of 196, we prime factorise 196 as follows:

$$\begin{aligned} 196 &= 2 \times 2 \times 7 \times 7 \\ &= (2 \times 7) \times (2 \times 7) \\ &= (2 \times 7)^2 \\ &= 14^2 \end{aligned}$$

Therefore, $\sqrt{196} = 14$.

Cubes and Cube Roots

We know that $2 \times 2 \times 2 = 8$. This can be written as $2^3 = 8$. We say that 8 is the **cube** of 2 and 2 is the **cube root** of 8. We indicate the cube root of 8 as $\sqrt[3]{8}$.

The cube of -2 is -8 since $(-2) \times (-2) \times (-2) = -8$, and the cube root of -8 is -2 which we write as $\sqrt[3]{-8} = -2$.

To find the cube root of a cubic number, we can use the **prime factorisation method**. For example, to find $\sqrt[3]{216}$, we prime factorise 216 as follows:

$$216 = 2 \times 2 \times 2 \times 3 \times 3 \times 3$$
$$= (2 \times 3) \times (2 \times 3) \times (2 \times 3)$$
$$= (2 \times 3)^3$$
$$= 6^3$$

Therefore, $\sqrt[3]{216} = 6$.

Class Activity 3

1.

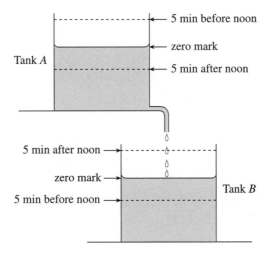

In the above diagram, water is made to flow from tank A to tank B (both tanks are of the same size) so that in 1 minute the water level in tank A drops 2 cm while the water level in tank B rises 2 cm. A zero mark is made on each tank to indicate the level of water at noon.

Copy and fill in the blanks with the correct answers.
(a) If 5 minutes after noon is represented by +5 minutes from noon, then 5 minutes before noon is represented by ____ minutes from noon.

(b) If x cm above zero is represented by +x cm from zero, then x cm below zero is represented by ____ cm from zero.

(c) If the water level in tank A changes at –2 cm/min, then the water level in tank B changes at ____ cm/min.

(d) At 5 minutes after noon, the water level in tank A is $5 \times (-2)$ or –10 cm, that is, the water level is ____ cm below zero.

(e) At 5 minutes before noon, the water level in tank A is $-5 \times (-2)$ or 10 cm, that is, the water level is ____ cm above zero.

(f) At 5 minutes after noon, the water level in tank B is 5×2 or 10 cm, that is, the water level is _____ cm above zero.

(g) At 5 minutes before noon, the water level in tank B is -5×2 or -10 cm, that is, the water level is _____ cm below zero.

2. Mary says that since the square roots of 16 are 4 and -4, then the square roots of -16 are -4 and 4. Do you agree? Why?

3. Use a calculator to find the value of $3.162\ 277\ 66 \times 3.162\ 277\ 66$.

   Can you say the square of $3.162\ 277\ 66$ is 10? Why?

   Can you say the positive square root of 10 is $3.162\ 277\ 66$? Why?

4. Consider $-a = -1 \times a$.
   By choosing a suitable integer to replace a, verify the following.
   (a) $-(-2) = 2$ **(b)** $-(-5) = 5$
   (c) $-[-(-4)] = -4$ **(d)** $-\{-[-(-7)]\} = 7$

Worked Example 4
Calculate the following.
(a) -51×16 **(b)** $27 \times (-18)$
(c) $-95 \times (-26)$ **(d)** $0 \times (-72)$

Solution:
(a) $-51 \times 16 = -(51 \times 16)$ **(b)** $27 \times (-18) = -(27 \times 18)$
$\qquad\qquad\quad = -816$ $= -486$

(c) $-95 \times (-26) = 95 \times 26$ **(d)** $0 \times (-72) = 0$
$\qquad\qquad\qquad = 2\ 470$

Worked Example 5
Find the positive square root of 324.

Solution:
$$324 = 2 \times 2 \times 3 \times 3 \times 3 \times 3$$
$$= (2 \times 3 \times 3)^2$$
$$= 18^2$$
$$\therefore \quad \sqrt{324} = 18$$

To check the answer with a calculator, we key

$$\boxed{\sqrt{}}\ \ 324\ \ \boxed{\text{EXE}}\quad \text{or}\quad 2\ \ \boxed{\sqrt[x]{}}\ \ 324\ \ \boxed{\text{EXE}}\ .$$

Worked Example 6

Find the cube root of −1 728.

Solution:

$$1\ 728 = 2 \times 2 \times 2 \times 2 \times 2 \times 2 \times 3 \times 3 \times 3$$
$$= (2 \times 2 \times 3)^3$$
$$= 12^3$$
$$\therefore \ \sqrt[3]{-1\ 728} = -12$$

To check the answer with a calculator, we key

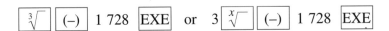

Exercise 4.3

answers on p. 423

1. Find the products of the following.
   - **(a)** $3 \times (-5)$
   - **(b)** $4 \times (-1)$
   - **(c)** $-3 \times (-2)$
   - **(d)** $0 \times (-3)$
   - **(e)** -5×0
   - **(f)** 18×11
   - **(g)** $-14 \times (-7)$
   - **(h)** $-7 \times (-2) \times 3$
   - **(i)** $-3 \times 4 \times (-5)$
   - **(j)** $5 \times (-2) \times 7$
   - **(k)** $3 \times (-8) \times 0$
   - **(l)** $-7 \times (-3) \times (-2)$
   - **(m)** $-5 \times (-8) \times (-3)$
   - **(n)** $-2 \times (-3) \times (-4) \times (-5)$
   - **(o)** $-3 \times 4 \times (-8) \times (-7)$
   - **(p)** $-2 \times 0 \times 3 \times (-5)$
   - **(q)** $-12 \times (-11) \times (-321)$
   - **(r)** $-25 \times (-26) \times 123$
   - **(s)** $-16 \times (-123) \times (-37)$
   - **(t)** $-214 \times (-15) \times (-125)$
   - **(u)** $13 \times (-10) \times (-301)$
   - **(v)** $45 \times (-14) \times 377$
   - **(w)** $6 \times (-18) \times (-7)$
   - **(x)** $-27 \times 8 \times (-15)$
   - **(y)** $5 \times (-19) \times (-102)$
   - **(z)** $-25 \times 6 \times (-200)$

2. Find the value of each of the following.
   - **(a)** 15^2
   - **(b)** $(-45)^2$
   - **(c)** 106^2
   - **(d)** $(-312)^2$

3. Find the square roots of each of the following numbers.
   - **(a)** 121
   - **(b)** 256
   - **(c)** 625
   - **(d)** $1\ 225$

4. Evaluate the following.
   - **(a)** $\sqrt{441}$
   - **(b)** $-\sqrt{576}$
   - **(c)** $-\sqrt{4\ 624}$
   - **(d)** $\sqrt{7\ 396}$

5. Find the value of each of the following.
   - **(a)** 11^3
   - **(b)** $(-25)^3$
   - **(c)** $(-30)^3$
   - **(d)** 42^3

6. Find the cube root of each of the following numbers.
   (a) 125
   (b) −1 728
   (c) −8 000
   (d) 12 167

7. Find the value of each of the following.
   (a) $\sqrt[3]{512}$
   (b) $\sqrt[3]{-1\ 331}$
   (c) $\sqrt[3]{9\ 261}$
   (d) $\sqrt[3]{-15\ 625}$

8. Check questions 1 to 7 with a calculator. Show the 'keying order' for questions 4 and 7.

9. Calculate the following.
   (a) $-(-32) \times (-12)^2$
   (b) $31^2 \times [-(-31)]$
   (c) $13^3 \times \{-[-(-30)]\}$
   (d) $-\{-[-(-23)]\} \times [-(-71)^3]$

4.4 DIVISION OF INTEGERS

Division is the reverse process of multiplication.
For example, the 'arrow diagram' illustrates that

'−7 multiplied by 6 is −42' and
'−42 divided by 6 is −7'.

Look at the following 'arrow diagrams'.

These 'arrow diagrams' suggest the following rules for division of integers.

> **1. To divide one integer by another integer of the same sign, we take the positive sign for the answer.**
>
> **2. To divide one integer by another integer of a different sign, we take the negative sign for the answer.**

In symbols, if a and b are natural numbers, we write as follows:

$$a \div b = a \div b$$
$$-a \div (-b) = a \div b$$
$$-a \div b = -(a \div b)$$
$$a \div (-b) = -(a \div b)$$

Note: The quotients of $0 \div a$ and $0 \div (-a)$ are zero. The quotients of $a \div 0$ and $(-a) \div 0$ are meaningless.

Worked Example 7
Evaluate the following.
(a) $-984 \div 8$ (b) $598 \div (-13)$
(c) $-1\,932 \div (-23)$ (d) $0 \div (-328)$

Solution:
(a) $-984 \div 8 = -(984 \div 8)$ (b) $598 \div (-13) = -(598 \div 13)$
$\qquad\qquad = -123$ $\qquad\qquad\qquad = -46$

(c) $-1\,932 \div (-23) = 1\,932 \div 23$ (d) $0 \div (-328) = 0$
$\qquad\qquad\qquad = 84$

Exercise 4.4

answers on p. 424

Evaluate the following.

1. $-8 \div 4$ 2. $-24 \div 6$
3. $-45 \div 9$ 4. $9 \div (-3)$
5. $42 \div (-7)$ 6. $0 \div (-18)$
7. $72 \div (-6)$ 8. $-9 \div (-3)$
9. $-32 \div (-8)$ 10. $-72 \div (-9)$
11. $-123 \div 3$ 12. $-456 \div 6$
13. $448 \div (-8)$ 14. $207 \div (-9)$
15. $-244 \div (-4)$ 16. $-560 \div (-5)$
17. $-504 \div (-9)$ 18. $576 \div (-24)$
19. $384 \div (-32)$ 20. $-144 \div (-12)$
21. $-345 \div (-15)$ 22. $-252 \div 18$

23. $-220 \div 22$ **24.** $237 \div (-79)$
25. $-168 \div (-42)$ **26.** $-713 \div 31 \div (-23)$
27. $325 \div (-13) \div [-(-5)]$ **28.** $-112 \div (-4)^2 \div 7$
29. $616 \div [-(-11)] \div (-28)$ **30.** $-384 \div 96 \div [-(-4)]$

4.5 REAL NUMBERS

Rational Numbers

Let us take a look at the number line again.

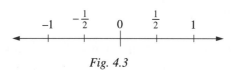

Fig. 4.3

The rational numbers are all fractions formed by dividing pairs of integers (except dividing by zero).

We know that the point midway between 0 and 1 represents the fraction $\frac{1}{2}$.

We can also choose a point midway between 0 and -1 to represent $-\frac{1}{2}$ (see Fig. 4.3).

Examples

(a) Consider $-2, -1\frac{3}{4}, -1\frac{1}{4}, -1, -\frac{3}{4}, 0, \frac{3}{4}, 1$ and 2.

These numbers can be represented on the number line as shown in Fig. 4.4.

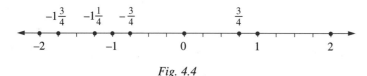

Fig. 4.4

(b) Consider -1.25.

$$-1.25 = -1\frac{1}{4}$$

Thus, -1.25 is represented by the same point as $-1\frac{1}{4}$ on the number line (see Fig. 4.4).

(c) Consider $\frac{-3}{-4}$.

$$\frac{-3}{-4} = -3 \div (-4)$$
$$= 3 \div 4$$
$$= \frac{3}{4}$$

Thus, $\dfrac{-3}{-4}$ is represented by the same point as $\dfrac{3}{4}$ on the number line (see Fig. 4.4).

(d) Consider $\dfrac{-3}{4}$ and $\dfrac{3}{-4}$.

$$\frac{-3}{4} = -3 \div 4$$

$$= -\frac{3}{4}$$

$$\frac{3}{-4} = 3 \div (-4)$$

$$= -\frac{3}{4}$$

Thus, both $\dfrac{-3}{4}$ and $\dfrac{3}{-4}$ are represented by the same point as $-\dfrac{3}{4}$ on the number line (see Fig. 4.4).

Notice that all integers, fraction, mixed numbers and decimals (terminating and recurring) can be represented on the number line. We refer to all these numbers as **rational numbers**. For example, $2, 0, -1, \dfrac{3}{4}, -\dfrac{3}{4}, -1\dfrac{3}{4}$, and -1.25 are rational numbers.

You will find that all rational numbers can be expressed in the form of $\dfrac{a}{b}$ or $-\dfrac{a}{b}$, where a and b are whole numbers and $b \neq 0$.

Examples

(a) $2 = \dfrac{2}{1} = \dfrac{a}{b}$, where $a = 2$ and $b = 1$.

(b) $0 = \dfrac{0}{1} = \dfrac{a}{b}$, where $a = 0$ and $b = 1$.

(c) $-1 = -\dfrac{1}{1} = -\dfrac{a}{b}$, where $a = 1$ and $b = 1$.

(d) $-1\dfrac{3}{4} = -\dfrac{7}{4} = -\dfrac{a}{b}$, where $a = 7$ and $b = 4$.

(e) $-1.25 = -1\dfrac{1}{4} = -\dfrac{5}{4} = -\dfrac{a}{b}$, where $a = 5$ and $b = 4$.

Irrational Numbers

Mathematicians have found that numbers such as $\sqrt{2}$ and $\sqrt{3}$ are not rational numbers because they cannot be expressed in the form of $\dfrac{a}{b}$ or $-\dfrac{a}{b}$, where a and

The most famous irrational number is π, which is the ratio of the circumference of any circle to its diameter.

b are whole numbers and $b \neq 0$. We refer to these non-rational numbers as **irrational numbers**.

Although the value of $\sqrt{2}$ is usually given as 1.414, it is only an approximate value. The actual value is 1.414 213 56 . . . . The numeral continues without end and without a repeating pattern. Notice that the irrational number $\sqrt{2}$ is greater than 1.4 and less than 1.5. Thus, the point representing $\sqrt{2}$ must be on the number line somewhere between 1.4 and 1.5. In fact, all irrational numbers as well as rational numbers can be represented on the number line. The set of all rational and irrational numbers is referred to as the set of **real numbers**. We may call the number line, for emphasis, the **real number line**.

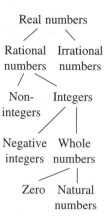

Worked Example 8
Calculate the following.

(a) $-\dfrac{3}{5} + \dfrac{1}{4}$

(b) $\dfrac{1}{2} - \left(-\dfrac{2}{3}\right)$

Solution:

(a) $-\dfrac{3}{5} + \dfrac{1}{4} = \dfrac{1}{4} - \dfrac{3}{5}$

$= \dfrac{5 - 12}{20}$

$= \dfrac{-7}{20}$

$= -\dfrac{7}{20}$

(b) $\dfrac{1}{2} - \left(-\dfrac{2}{3}\right) = \dfrac{1}{2} + \dfrac{2}{3}$

$= \dfrac{3 + 4}{6}$

$= \dfrac{7}{6}$

$= 1\dfrac{1}{6}$

Worked Example 9
Calculate the following.

(a) $\dfrac{3}{4} \times \left(-\dfrac{1}{2}\right)$

(b) $-\dfrac{5}{21} \div (-50)$

Solution:

(a) $\dfrac{3}{4} \times \left(-\dfrac{1}{2}\right) = -\dfrac{3}{8}$

(b) $-\dfrac{5}{21} \div (-50) = -\dfrac{5}{21} \times \left(-\dfrac{1}{50}\right)$

$= \dfrac{5 \times 1}{21 \times 50}$

$= \dfrac{1}{210}$

Exercise 4.5 ✍

answers on p. 424

1. State which of the following sentences are true.
   (a) The product of two negative rational numbers is positive.
   (b) The product of a negative rational number and zero is zero.
   (c) The product of zero and a negative rational number is negative.
   (d) The product of a negative rational number and a positive rational number is always negative.
   (e) If the product of two rational numbers is positive, then one of them is positive and the other is negative.
   (f) If the product of two rational numbers is positive, then both numbers are positive.

2. Calculate the following. Give your answers in the simplest forms.
   (a) $-\dfrac{1}{2} + \dfrac{1}{3}$
   (b) $-\dfrac{3}{4} + \left(-\dfrac{1}{2}\right)$
   (c) $-\dfrac{9}{16} + \dfrac{9}{16}$
   (d) $\dfrac{1}{4} + \left(-\dfrac{2}{3}\right)$
   (e) $-\dfrac{9}{7} + \left(-\dfrac{4}{9}\right)$
   (f) $-3\dfrac{3}{5} + \dfrac{9}{10}$

3. Calculate the following. Give your answers in the simplest forms.
   (a) $\dfrac{2}{7} - \left(-\dfrac{1}{3}\right)$
   (b) $-\dfrac{4}{5} - \left(-\dfrac{4}{5}\right)$
   (c) $\dfrac{3}{2} - \left(-\dfrac{2}{3}\right)$
   (d) $-\dfrac{2}{11} - \left(-\dfrac{1}{3}\right)$
   (e) $\dfrac{21}{25} - \left(-\dfrac{23}{50}\right)$
   (f) $-\dfrac{25}{72} - \dfrac{15}{36}$

4. Calculate the following.
   (a) $-\dfrac{2}{3} \times \left(-\dfrac{3}{4}\right)$
   (b) $-\dfrac{14}{15} \times \left(-\dfrac{6}{7}\right)$
   (c) $\dfrac{9}{18} \times \left(-\dfrac{9}{4}\right)$
   (d) $\dfrac{15}{4} \times \left(-\dfrac{1}{2}\right)$
   (e) $-\dfrac{35}{6} \times \left(-\dfrac{10}{21}\right)$
   (f) $-\dfrac{2\,148\,214}{5\,732\,195} \times 0$

5. Calculate the following.
   (a) $-\dfrac{2}{3} \div \left(-\dfrac{4}{7}\right)$
   (b) $-\dfrac{3}{5} \div \dfrac{9}{5}$
   (c) $-\dfrac{18}{5} \div \dfrac{3}{10}$
   (d) $-5 \div \left(-\dfrac{3}{4}\right)$
   (e) $-\dfrac{3}{7} \div (-3)$
   (f) $27 \div \left(-\dfrac{15}{7}\right)$

6. Write each of the following rational numbers in the form of $\dfrac{a}{b}$ or $-\dfrac{a}{b}$, where a and b are positive integers.
   (a) $\dfrac{-2}{3}$
   (b) $\dfrac{4}{-5}$
   (c) $\dfrac{3}{-7}$
   (d) $\dfrac{5}{-16}$
   (e) $-\dfrac{3}{-7}$
   (f) $\dfrac{-4}{9}$

(g) $\dfrac{-5}{-24}$ **(h)** $\dfrac{-7}{20}$ **(i)** $\dfrac{-9}{-10}$

(j) $-\dfrac{8}{-15}$ **(k)** $\dfrac{-84}{-11}$ **(l)** $\dfrac{-678}{5}$

7. Copy and write '>' or '<' in the boxes to make the sentences true.

     (a) $-1 \,\square\, -2$ **(b)** $-\dfrac{3}{4} \,\square\, \dfrac{1}{2}$

     (c) $-2\dfrac{4}{5} \,\square\, -2\dfrac{1}{2}$ **(d)** $2\dfrac{3}{4} \,\square\, -4\dfrac{1}{4}$

     (e) $-2.3 \,\square\, 1.4$ **(f)** $3.6 \,\square\, -4.4$

     (g) $-5.5 \,\square\, -2.8$ **(h)** $-8.6 \,\square\, -1.1$

8. $\dfrac{1}{7}, \dfrac{3}{10}, 1.2, 0.\dot{2}\dot{7}, 0.24\dot{5}, \sqrt{4}, \sqrt{3}, \sqrt{8}, \sqrt{5}, \sqrt{\dfrac{1}{4}}$

     From the above, list
     (a) the rational numbers,
     (b) the irrational numbers.

9. Use a calculator to find, correct to 4 significant figures, the values of the following.

     (a) $\sqrt{2}$ **(b)** $\sqrt{3}$ **(c)** $\sqrt{6}$

     (d) $\sqrt{2} \times \sqrt{3}$ **(e)** $\sqrt{18}$ **(f)** $\sqrt{18} \div \sqrt{3}$

     (g) $\sqrt[3]{2}$ **(h)** $\sqrt[3]{3}$ **(i)** $\sqrt[3]{6}$

     (j) $\sqrt[3]{2} \times \sqrt[3]{3}$ **(k)** $\sqrt[3]{12}$ **(l)** $\sqrt[3]{12} \div \sqrt[3]{6}$

4.6 ORDER OF CALCULATION

The convention for computation of rational numbers is the same as that for whole numbers. That is, working from left to right, do multiplication or division before addition or subtraction; but when brackets are used, simplify the expression within the brackets first.

Worked Example 10
Evaluate the following.

(a) $7 \times 8 + 6 \times (-9)$ **(b)** $-\dfrac{1}{2} \div \left(\dfrac{1}{4} + 1\dfrac{1}{8} \right)$

Solution:
(a) $7 \times 8 + 6 \times (-9) = 56 + (-54)$
$$= 2$$

(b) $-\dfrac{1}{2} \div \left(\dfrac{1}{4} + 1\dfrac{1}{8}\right) = -\dfrac{1}{2} \div \left(\dfrac{2}{8} + \dfrac{9}{8}\right)$

$$= -\dfrac{1}{2} \div \left(\dfrac{11}{8}\right)$$

$$= -\dfrac{1}{2} \times \dfrac{8}{11}$$

$$= -\dfrac{4}{11}$$

Worked Example 11
Calculate the following.

(a) $-52 + [(-23) + 32] \times (-11)$ **(b)** $-\dfrac{2}{3} + \left[\left(-\dfrac{1}{6}\right) + \dfrac{2}{3}\right] \div \left(-\dfrac{1}{4}\right)$

Solution:
(a) $-52 + [(-23) + 32] \times (-11) = -52 + 9 \times (-11)$

$$= -52 + (-99)$$

$$= -151$$

(b) $-\dfrac{2}{3} + \left[\left(-\dfrac{1}{6}\right) + \dfrac{2}{3}\right] \div \left(-\dfrac{1}{4}\right) = -\dfrac{2}{3} + \left[\left(-\dfrac{1}{6}\right) + \dfrac{4}{6}\right] \div \left(-\dfrac{1}{4}\right)$

$$= -\dfrac{2}{3} + \dfrac{3}{6} \div \left(-\dfrac{1}{4}\right)$$

$$= -\dfrac{2}{3} + \dfrac{1}{2} \times (-4)$$

$$= -\dfrac{2}{3} - 2$$

$$= -2\dfrac{2}{3}$$

Exercise 4.6 ✎   *answers on p. 424*

Evaluate the following.

1. $[34 + 21 + (-12)] \times 5$
2. $[5 + (-18)] + [24 + (-30)] \times (-7)$
3. $\{[12 - (-8)] \times 2 + 3\} \times 4$
4. $-15 \times [13 + (-8)] \times 23$
5. $237 - 48 \times (-35) + (-59)$
6. $-85 + (-92 + 78) \times (-15)$
7. $-18 \times (-15) + 28 - (-39)$
8. $48 - 34 + 29 \times [43 - (-32)]$

9. $52 - (-23) + (-24) \times [78 + (-68)]$

10. $75 \times (-23) - [43 + (-12)]$

11. $(-19 + 52) \times (-23) - (-42)$

12. $24 + (-57) - 28 \times [53 + (-48)]$

13. $[32 + (-21)] \times [-15 + 16]$

14. $(178 - 168) \times (-12) - [-150 + 120] \times 3$

15. $\{56 - [28 + (-26)] \times 12\} + 86$

16. $248 + 84 - [36 + (-78)] \times 3 + (-29)$

17. $-\left[\dfrac{1}{2} + \left(-\dfrac{1}{8}\right)\right] \times \dfrac{3}{4} + \dfrac{3}{8}$

18. $\left[\left(\dfrac{5}{6} - \dfrac{1}{3}\right) \div 1\dfrac{1}{3} + \dfrac{1}{2}\right] \div \left(-\dfrac{2}{3}\right)$

19. $\left[-\dfrac{1}{5} + \left(-\dfrac{1}{10}\right)\right] \div \left[\dfrac{1}{2} - \left(-\dfrac{1}{4}\right)\right] \div \dfrac{1}{6}$

20. $-\dfrac{1}{2} + \left[\left(-\dfrac{1}{8}\right) \times \dfrac{1}{4} - \left(-\dfrac{1}{2}\right) - \dfrac{1}{4}\right] \div \dfrac{1}{8}$

4.7 MENTAL CALCULATIONS

If you have mastered the addition and subtraction facts within 20 and the multiplication tables up to 10×10, you should be able to do mental calculations with some practice.

The following are some useful strategies for mental calculations and estimations.

Recalling Facts

Recalling the following facts can sometimes make mental calculations easier.

$\dfrac{1}{2} = 0.5$	$\dfrac{1}{10} = 0.1$	$25 = \dfrac{100}{4}$
$\dfrac{1}{4} = 0.25$	$\dfrac{1}{5} = \dfrac{2}{10} = 0.2$	$125 = \dfrac{1\,000}{8}$
$\dfrac{3}{4} = 0.75$	$\dfrac{1}{50} = \dfrac{2}{100} = 0.02$	$\dfrac{1}{3} \approx 0.33$
$\dfrac{1}{8} = 0.125$	$5 = \dfrac{10}{2}$	$\dfrac{2}{3} \approx 0.67$

Recall: The sign '$\approx$' means 'is approximately equal to'.

MATHSTORY

Mrs Shakuntala Devi of India used mental mathematics to multiply the numbers 7 686 369 774 870 and 2 465 099 745 729. She got the correct answer in a short time of 28 seconds.

Examples

(a) Find 0.53×130.

Thinking process

$0.5 \times 130 = \dfrac{130}{2} = 65$

$0.03 \times 130 = 3 \times 1.3 = 3.9$

Required answer = $65 + 3.9$
$\qquad\qquad\qquad = 68.9$

(b) Find 0.135×240.

Thinking process

$0.125 \times 240 = \dfrac{1}{8} \times 240 = 30$

$0.01 \times 240 = 2.4$

Required answer = $30 + 2.4$
$\qquad\qquad\qquad = 32.4$

(c) Find $7\ 216 \times 125$.

Thinking process

$125 = \dfrac{1\ 000}{8}$

Required answer = $7\ 216 \times \dfrac{1\ 000}{8}$
$\qquad\qquad\qquad = 902\ 000$

(d) Find $2\ 163 \div 5$.

Thinking process

$5 = \dfrac{10}{2}$

Required answer = $2\ 163 \times \dfrac{2}{10}$
$\qquad\qquad\qquad = 216.3 \times 2$
$\qquad\qquad\qquad = 432.6$

(e) Estimate $0.67 \div 0.32$.

Thinking process

$0.67 \approx \dfrac{2}{3}$

$0.32 \approx \dfrac{1}{3}$

Required answer $\approx \dfrac{2}{3} \times \dfrac{3}{1}$
$\qquad\qquad\quad \approx 2$

(f) Estimate 26×119.

Thinking process

$26 \approx 25$

$119 \approx 120$

Required answer $\approx 25 \times 120$
$\qquad\qquad\quad \approx 25 \times 4 \times 30$
$\qquad\qquad\quad \approx 3\ 000$

Grouping

Examples

(a) Find $8 + 3 + 2 + 7$.

Thinking process

$$\overset{\displaystyle 10}{8 + 3 + 2 + 7}$$
$$\underset{\displaystyle 10}{}$$

Required answer = $10 + 10 = 20$

(b) Find $6 + 7 + 6 + 4 + 8$.

Thinking process

$$6 + 7 + 6 + 4 + 8$$
$$\quad 6 + 1 \qquad 6 + 6$$

Required answer = $6 \times 5 + 1$
$\qquad\qquad\qquad = 31$

(c) Find $125 \times 123 \times 2 \times 8 \times 15$.

Thinking process

$(125 \times 8) \times (15 \times 2) \times 123$

$\quad\quad \downarrow \quad\quad\quad\quad \downarrow$

$\quad\quad 1\,000 \quad\quad\quad 30$

Required answer = $1\,000 \times 30 \times 123$
$\qquad\qquad\qquad = 3\,690\,000$

(d) Find $32 - 79 + 25 - 30 + 85$.

Thinking process

$(32 - 30) + (85 - 79) + 25$

$\quad\quad \downarrow \quad\quad\quad\quad \downarrow$

$\quad\quad 2 \quad\quad\quad\quad\quad 6$

Required answer = $2 + 6 + 25$
$\qquad\qquad\qquad = 33$

(e) Find $32 \times 13 \div 16 \div 26 \times 25$.

Thinking process

$$\frac{\cancel{32}^{2} \times \cancel{13} \times 25}{\cancel{16} \times \cancel{26}_{\cancel{2}}}$$

Required answer = 25

Note: View the questions as

$$32 \times 13 \times \frac{1}{16} \times \frac{1}{26} \times 25.$$

(f) Estimate $33 + 54 + 48 + 69$.

Thinking process

$$\overset{\approx 100}{\overbrace{33 + 54 + 48\ \ 69}}$$
$$\underset{\approx 100}{}$$

Required answer $\approx 100 + 100$
$\qquad\qquad\qquad \approx 200$

(g) Estimate $192 + 209 + 128 + 270$.

Thinking process

$$\underset{\approx 400}{\underbrace{192 + 209}} + \underset{\approx 400}{\underbrace{128 + 270}}$$

Required answer $\approx 400 + 400$
$\qquad\qquad\qquad \approx 800$

(h) Estimate $371 + 59 - 18 - 369$.

Thinking process

$$\overset{\approx 40}{\overbrace{371 + 59 - 18 - 369}}$$
$$\underset{\approx 0}{}$$

Required answer $\approx 0 + 40$
$\qquad\qquad\qquad \approx 40$

Decomposing

Examples

(a) Find 8×99.
Thinking process
$8 \times 100 - 8 \times 1$

Required answer = $800 - 8$
$\qquad\qquad\qquad = 792$

(b) Find 112×12.
Thinking process
$100 \times 12 + 12 \times 12$

Required answer = $1\,200 + 144$
$\qquad\qquad\qquad = 1\,344$

(c) Find $989 + 462 + 103$.

Thinking process

$$
\begin{array}{rr}
1\,000 & -11 \\
100 & +\,3 \\
+\quad 462 & \\
\hline
1\,562 & -\,8 = 1\,554
\end{array}
$$

or

$$989 \xrightarrow{\;+400\;} \boxed{1\,389} \xrightarrow{\;+60\;} \boxed{1\,449}$$
$$\xrightarrow{\;+2\;} \boxed{1\,451} \xrightarrow{\;+100\;} \boxed{1\,551} \xrightarrow{\;+3\;} \boxed{1\,554}$$

Required answer = 1 554

(d) Find $4\frac{3}{4} \times 6$.

Thinking process

$$4 \times 6 + \frac{3}{4} \times 6 = 24 + \frac{9}{2}$$

Required answer $= 28\frac{1}{2}$

Exercise 4.7

answers on p. 424

Do the following mentally.

1. Find

   (a) $\frac{1}{4}$ of $72,

   (b) $\frac{3}{4}$ of $104,

   (c) $1\frac{1}{4}$ of $832,

   (d) 0.55×44,

   (e) 0.145×64,

   (f) 0.09×256.

2. Find

   (a) $4\,920 \times 125$,

   (b) $525 \div 25$,

   (c) $3\,128 \times 5$,

   (d) $112 \div 125$,

   (e) 824×25,

   (f) $7\,325 \div 5$.

3. Find

   (a) $7 + 4 + 5 + 3 + 8 + 6$,

   (b) $7 + 8 + 7 + 9 + 4 - 15$,

   (c) $6 + 7 - 9 + 3 + 6 - 10$,

   (d) $24 - 34 + 42 - 21 + 39$,

   (e) $15 \times 25 \times 2 \times 114 \times 4$,

   (f) $42 \times 72 \div 7 \div 12 \times 125$.

4. Find

   (a) 7×99,

   (b) 124×12,

   (c) $992 + 528 + 107$,

   (d) $721 + 315 + 243$,

   (e) $321 - 175 + 412$,

   (f) $2\frac{5}{6} \times 4$,

   (g) 15×112,

   (h) $1\frac{1}{5} \div \frac{3}{10}$.

5. Estimate
  (a) 24×121,
  (b) $28 + 35 + 68 + 71$,
  (c) $0.26 \div 0.124$,
  (d) $315 + 298 + 289$,
  (e) 0.52×0.24,
  (f) 126×7.9.

Chapter Review

1. Integers
  • The natural numbers 1, 2, 3, 4, . . . are referred to as positive integers and their opposites –1, –2, –3, –4, . . . as negative integers.
  • We refer to all numbers . . . , –4, –3, –2, –1, 0, 1, 2, 3, 4, . . . as integers.

2. General Rules on the Four Operations with Integers
  • Adding and subtracting with integers:
    (a) $+ (-n) = -n$
    (b) $- (-n) = +n$
    (c) $-a - b = -(a + b)$
    (d) $a - b = -(b - a)$
    (e) $- b + a = a + (-b)$

  • Multiplying with integers:
    (a) $-a \times b = -(a \times b)$, where a and b are natural numbers.
    (b) $-a \times (-b) = a \times b$, where a and b are natural numbers.
    (c) $a \times (-b) = -(a \times b)$, where a and b are natural numbers.
    (d) When multiplying one integer by another of the same sign, the result takes a positive sign, otherwise it takes a negative sign.

  • Dividing with integers:
    (a) $-a \div b = - (a \div b)$
    (b) $-a \div (-b) = a \div b$
    (c) $a \div (-b) = -(a \div b)$
    (d) When dividing one integer by another of the same sign, the result takes a positive sign, otherwise it takes a negative sign.

3. Squares, Square Roots, Cubes and Cube Roots
  • Squares and square roots
    Example: $4^2 = 16$
      16 is the square of 4 and 4 is the square root of 16, i.e. $\sqrt{16} = 4$.
  • Cubes and cube roots
    Example: $3^3 = 27$
      27 is the cube of 3 and 3 is the cube root of 27, i.e. $\sqrt[3]{27} = 3$.

4. **Real Numbers**

- All rational numbers can be expressed in the form of $\frac{a}{b}$ or $-\frac{a}{b}$, where a and b are whole numbers and $b \neq 0$.

- $\sqrt{2}$ and $\sqrt{3}$ are irrational numbers because they cannot be expressed in the form $\frac{a}{b}$ or $-\frac{a}{b}$, where a and b are whole numbers and $b \neq 0$.

- The set of all rational and irrational numbers is the set of real numbers.

5. **Order of Calculation**

- The convention of computation of rational numbers is the same as that for natural numbers, that is, do multiplication or division before addition or subtraction working from left to right; but when brackets are used, simplify the expression within the brackets first.

CHALLENGER 4

1. If a is a negative integer, then
    (a) $10 + a > 10,$
    (b) $10 + a < 10,$
    (c) $10 - a > 10,$
    (d) $10 - a < 10,$
    (e) $10 \times a > 10,$
    (f) $10 \times a < 10,$
    (g) $10 + a > a,$
    (h) $10 + a < a,$
    (i) $10 - a > a,$
    (j) $10 - a < a,$
    (k) $10 \times a > a,$
    (l) $10 \times a < a.$
    Is each of the above sentences true? If not, give a reason.

2. State whether each of the following is true or false.

    (a) $\left(-\frac{5}{4}\right) > \frac{1}{\left(-\frac{5}{4}\right)} > -\frac{1}{\left(-\frac{5}{4}\right)} > -\left(-\frac{5}{4}\right)$

    (b) $-\left(-\frac{5}{4}\right) > \frac{1}{\left(-\frac{5}{4}\right)} > -\frac{1}{\left(-\frac{5}{4}\right)} > \left(-\frac{5}{4}\right)$

    (c) $\left(-\frac{5}{4}\right) < \frac{1}{\left(-\frac{5}{4}\right)} < -\frac{1}{\left(-\frac{5}{4}\right)} < -\left(-\frac{5}{4}\right)$

    (d) $\left(-\frac{5}{4}\right) < \frac{1}{\left(-\frac{5}{4}\right)} < -\left(-\frac{5}{4}\right) < -\frac{1}{\left(-\frac{5}{4}\right)}$

3. Which of the following has the largest absolute value?

    (a) $\dfrac{1}{\left(-\frac{123}{456}\right)}$

    (b) $\dfrac{1}{\left(-\frac{124}{457}\right)}$

(c) $\dfrac{1}{\left(-\dfrac{125}{458}\right)}$ **(d)** $\dfrac{1}{\left(-\dfrac{122}{455}\right)}$

4. If $a < b < 0$, which of the following is true and which is false?

(a) $\dfrac{1}{a} > \dfrac{1}{b}$ **(b)** $\dfrac{a}{b} < 1$

(c) $\dfrac{a}{b} > 1$ **(d)** $ab < 1$

5. a, b and c are positive integers such that $a > b > c$. If the average value of these integers is 8 and $b = 5$, find
    (a) the greatest possible value of a,
    (b) the smallest possible value of a.

6. a, b, c and d are integers such that $a \neq b \neq c \neq d$. If the product of these four integers is 9, find the sum of the four integers.

Problem Solving 4

Basketball Tournament

17 teams took part in a basketball tournament which was played in a 'knock-out' system (i.e. only the team that wins will play on). How many games were played before the champion team was declared?

One easy strategy is **use diagram**.

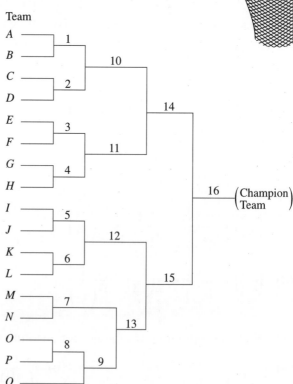

Altogether, 16 games were played.

Alternatively, we reword the problem by modifying the last question as follows:
(a) How many teams were knocked out?
(b) Write down the number of matches played.

Thinking process

(a) Since only one team survived at the end of the tournament, the number of teams that were knocked out was 17 − 1, i.e. 16.

(b) Since one team was knocked out after every match played, the number of matches played in the tournament was 16.

The strategy used here is **restate a problem in another way**.

 **Problems...**

1. **Badminton Championship**   20 students took part in a school badminton singles championship which was played in a knock-out system. How many matches were played before a girl champion and a boy champion emerged? (The boys and girls played separately.)

2. **Friendly Match**   The G&G Club invited the W&W Club for a basketball friendly match. After the match, each of the 10 players of the G&G team shakes hands with each of the 11 players of the W&W team, and after that the 11 players of the W&W team shook hands to congratulate each other for winning the match. How many handshakes were made altogether?

3. **Chocolate Bar**   A chocolate bar is made up of 4×6 single pieces. How many breaks are needed to break the bar into 24 pieces, each break is made by taking one block and breaking it into two along a straight line?

4. **Corner Numbers**   The diagram shows a part of a number chart which consists of numbers 1 to 100. If you were to draw a square enclosing 49 numbers, so that the sum of the numbers at the four corners is 216, what numbers would be at the four corners?

1	2	3	4	5	6	7	8	9	10
11	12	13	14	15	16	17	18	19	20
21	22	23	24	25	26	27	28	29	30
31	32	33	34	35	36	37	38	39	40
41	42	43	44	45	46	47	48	49	50

REVISION EXERCISE 1

Revision 1A   *(answers on p. 424)*

1. Write completely as product of prime factors each of the following.
   (a) 384
   (b) 555
   (c) 1 045
   (d) 2 048

2. Find the smallest number which when divided by 15 or 20 leaves
   (a) no remainder,   (b) a remainder 1,   (c) a remainder 2.

3. Which is a better buy, the medium tin or the large tin? Give your reasons.

4. Express
   (a) 14.7 g in kg,
   (b) 116 minutes in hours and minutes.

5. Copy and complete the following.

   (a) $\left(-\dfrac{1}{4}\right) + \dfrac{1}{4} + \left(\dfrac{5}{-21} \times \dfrac{42}{\square}\right) = 1$

   (b) $\left(\dfrac{3}{-28}\right) + \left(\dfrac{-6}{\square}\right) = 0$

   (c) $\dfrac{7}{38} \times \left(\dfrac{\square}{-21}\right) + \dfrac{3}{2} + \dfrac{5}{2} = 3$

   (d) $\left(\dfrac{-5}{19}\right) + \left(\dfrac{-10}{-38}\right) - \left[\dfrac{4}{15} \times \dfrac{\square}{-12} \times 2\right] = 2$

6. Copy and fill in the blank in each case with < or >.
   (a) 5 ____ 3
   (b) −2 ____ −1
   (c) −4 ____ 0
   (d) 6 ____ −8
   (e) −16 ____ −17
   (f) $(-1) \times (-2)$ ____ $1 \times (-3)$
   (g) $13 + 4 \times 5$ ____ $(-4) \times 20$
   (h) $3 \times 6 + 4 - 2$ ____ $6 \times (-3) + 4 \times 2$

7. Evaluate the following.
   (a) $192 + 48 - \{[36 + (-78)] \times 8 + (-92)\}$
   (b) $(187 - 168) \times (-21) - [(-150) + 141] \times 3$

8. Estimate the value of $\dfrac{5.96}{2.02}$ to 1 significant figure. Using this result, estimate the value of $\dfrac{596}{0.202}$.

9. The admission tickets to an exhibition were priced at $4 for an adult and $2 for a child. A family of 3 adults and 4 children visited the exhibition. What would be the change if a $100 was used to buy the tickets?

10. Henry bought 3 tins of biscuits and 5 cans of baked beans for $14. Find the cost of 1 can of baked beans if 1 tin of biscuits cost the same as 3 cans of beans.

Revision 1B   *(answers on p. 425)*

1. **(a)** Express 1 155 as a product of prime numbers.
   (b) Write down the largest factor of 1 155 other than 1 155 itself.

2. Find the LCM of the following.
   (a) 32, 12
   (b) 5, 9, 12, 16
   (c) 52, 28, 20
   (d) 15, 25, 10, 35

3. For each of the following, calculate the product or quotient, correct to 3 decimal places.
   (a) 72.342×84.5
   (b) 11.001×5.428
   (c) $\dfrac{23}{3}$
   (d) $\dfrac{103}{17}$

4. Bulan Avenue is $120\dfrac{5}{8}$ m long. Bintang Avenue is $\dfrac{4}{5}$ of the length of Bulan Avenue. Mata Hari Avenue is $\dfrac{11}{8}$ of Bintang Avenue. Find the difference in length between Bulan Avenue and Mata Hari Avenue.

5. Put the correct numbers in the boxes.

   (a)
   ```
      6 □ 2 3
   -  1 5 □ 5
   ─────────────
      □ 8 7 □
   ```

   (b)
   ```
        □ 4 □
   +    8 7 6
   ─────────────
      1 2 □ 1
   ```

6. Taking noon as zero hour and the hour as the unit, use directed numbers to denote the following times.
   (a) 11 30
   (b) 15 00
   (c) 23 30
   (d) 06 00
   (e) 03 30

7. Evaluate the following.
   (a) $-\{[456 - (-122)] \times 4\} - 192$
   (b) $[(-21) - (-221)] \times [(-151) + (162)] \times 4$

8. The bottle contains 150 m*l* of medicine. Peter is advised by the doctor to take it for 1 week. If 1 spoonful contains 6 m*l* of medicine, how much medicine is left after he has followed the doctor's advice?

one spoonful
3 times
a day

Dr A.K.Ong

9. Find $\dfrac{1.584 \times 0.14}{0.2 \times 4.5}$ as a decimal numeral, correct to 2 decimal places.

10. Find the value of $\dfrac{10.9 \times 0.642}{2.190}$, giving your answer correct to 1 significant figure.

Revision 1C   *(answers on p. 425)*

1. What number must be divided by 6 to make 8?

2. Find the smallest number which when divided by
   (a)   16 or 24 or 34 leaves a remainder 1,
   (b)   20 or 42 or 63 leaves a remainder 11,
   (c)   5 or 10 or 22 or 35 leaves a remainder 3.

3. Write down the largest of the three numbers.
   (a) $\dfrac{22}{7}, \dfrac{25}{8}, 3.13$ (b) $\dfrac{1}{4}, \dfrac{1}{3}, 0.22$

   (c) $\dfrac{5}{8}, \dfrac{6}{11}, 0.71$ (d) $\dfrac{9}{13}, \dfrac{11}{19}, 0.62$

   (e) $\dfrac{15}{7}, \dfrac{23}{11}, 2.23$

4. The total mass of a basket and the durians in it is $55\dfrac{5}{9}$ kg. If the mass of the basket is $\dfrac{1}{25}$ of the total mass, what is the mass of the durians?

5. Copy and complete the following number patterns.
   (a)   18, 13, _____, 3, _____, _____
   (b)   _____, –38, –24, _____, 4, _____

6. A point X is 500 m above sea level and a point Y is 20 m below sea level. Taking the sea level as zero metre, denote these two heights by directed numbers. How much higher is X than Y?

7. Do the following.
   (a) $\dfrac{2}{3} + \left(-\dfrac{3}{4}\right)$ (b) $\dfrac{4}{5} + \dfrac{7}{12}$ (c) $\dfrac{13}{28} + \dfrac{7}{14} - \left(-\dfrac{8}{21}\right)$

   (d) $-\dfrac{3}{25} + \left(-\dfrac{4}{15}\right)$ (e) $-\dfrac{23}{32} - \dfrac{15}{24}$

8. Evaluate the following.
   (a) $[(248 + 24) \times 3 - 12] \times 15 - 3 \times (-12 - 124)$
   (b) $-15 + 2 \times [(-38 - 10) \times (-8) + 5] - (-17 - 19)$
   (c) $\{[(32 - 29) \times (-4) + 5] \times 6 + (-2)\} - (12 + 8 + 7)$

9. What number when multiplied by 7 gives 882?

10. The cost of 6 apples is the same as the cost of 2 oranges. Peter bought 3 apples and 5 oranges for $3. Find the cost of 1 orange.

Revision 1D   *(answer on p. 425)*

1. Determine which of the following numbers are prime numbers.
   - (a) 87
   - (b) 131
   - (c) 157
   - (d) 201
   - (e) 437
   - (f) 1 331

2. Find the HCF of the following.
   - (a) 384, 124, 64
   - (b) 250, 60, 45
   - (c) 42, 28, 63, 98
   - (d) 180, 95, 120, 350

3. Evaluate $2.4 \div \left(5\frac{1}{5} - \frac{5.2}{1.3}\right)$.

4. A length of $12\frac{2}{3}$ m is cut away from a rope whose length is $23\frac{1}{4}$ m. How long is $\frac{3}{5}$ of the remainder in metres?

5. What must be added to
   - (a) (+7) to get (+1),
   - (b) (–8) to get (–2),
   - (c) (+5) to get 0,
   - (d) (–18) to get (–22),
   - (e) (+21) to get (+50)?

6. Do the following.
   - (a) $\left(-\frac{6}{11}\right) \times \frac{5}{18}$
   - (b) $\frac{27}{52} \times \frac{13}{135}$
   - (c) $\frac{49}{892} + \left(\frac{-84}{223}\right)$
   - (d) $\frac{98}{-125} \div \left(-\frac{63}{60}\right)$
   - (e) $\frac{21}{462} \times \left(\frac{165}{-81} \div \frac{125}{135}\right)$
   - (f) $7\frac{1}{7} \times \frac{14}{15}$
   - (g) $11\frac{7}{11} \times \left(\frac{15}{-86}\right) \times \left(5\frac{1}{24}\right) \times 2 \times \frac{11}{6}$
   - (h) $7\frac{5}{16} \div 62\frac{1}{48}$
   - (i) $\frac{51}{64} \div 7\frac{7}{16}$

7. Evaluate the following.
   - (a) $-\{[346 + (-265)] \times 4\} + 22$
   - (b) $\{296 - [281 + (-125)] \times 11\} + 68$
   - (c) $[(-91) + 52] \times (-12) - (-129)$

8. Put brackets in the following to make the equation true.
   (a) $8 + 5 \times 9 - 6 \div 3 = 43$
   (b) $10 + 2 \times 3 - 8 + 16 \div 4 = 4$

9. A man worked 6 days a week for 3 weeks. He was paid $25 a day on weekdays and twice as much on Saturdays. What was his total pay?

10. A man bought 20 boxes of oranges at $30 per box. There were 50 oranges in each box. 50 oranges were found to be rotten and could not be sold. If he wanted to make a profit of $65, how much would he charge for one orange?

Revision 1E   *(answers on p. 425)*

1. What is the remainder when 3 462 is divided by 7?

2. Evaluate $0.2 \times 0.3 \div 0.001$ 2.

3. The masses of Jiaming, Aminah and Samy are $35\frac{3}{5}$ kg, $32\frac{2}{5}$ kg and $39\frac{1}{2}$ kg respectively. What is their total mass?

4. If +1 m is 1 m above sea level and –1 m is 1 m below sea level, use directed numbers to denote the heights of the following.
   (a) A rest-house which is 120 m above sea level.
   (b) A tunnel which is 50 m below sea level.
   (c) A helicopter which is seen 200 m above sea level.
   (d) A ship which is sailing at sea level.

5. Evaluate the following.
   (a) $(42 + 21 - 8) \times 15$
   (b) $[6 + (-9)] - [24 + (-20)] \times (-2)$
   (c) $\{[13 - (-8)] \times 4 + 3\} \times (-4)$

6. Refer to the diagram. Find the cost of
   (a) each fountain pen,
   (b) each ball-point pen,
   (c) the mechanical pencil.

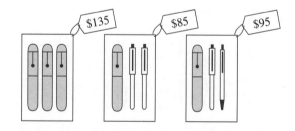

7. Evaluate $\dfrac{0.24 \times 14.3}{5.2}$.

8. Express 0.027 684
   (a) as a decimal, correct to 3 decimal places,
   (b) as a decimal, correct to 4 significant figures.

9. Peter mixed 3 *l* of syrup with 21 *l* of water to make soft drinks. He poured the mixtures into 8 bottles and sold them for $3 per bottle and made a profit of $12. What was the cost price per litre of the mixtures?

10. A man worked 5 days a week for 4 weeks and was paid $5 an hour. In addition, he was paid a transport allowance of $2 a day. He earned a total of $640. How many hours per day did he work for the 4 weeks?

MISCELLANEOUS EXERCISE 1

(answers on p. 426)

1.

> **M & M VARIETY SHOW**
> Performances daily at 7.45 pm
> FROM 7th TO 21st DECEMBER
> Tickets: Adults $11
>   Children $5.50
> Performance ends at 10.20 pm

   (a) How many performances were there?
   (b) How long did a performance last?
   (c) If 263 adults and 160 children bought tickets for a performance, calculate the total cost of their tickets.

2. Write down the smallest 3-digit number which is divisible by 5 and 9.

3. Pick two numbers from the following such that their product is divisible by 6.

   31, 35, 45, 71, 82

4. A number when divided by 2, 3 or 5 has a remainder 1. What is this number?

5. What is the smallest prime number which can be expressed as a sum of 2 composite numbers and what are these composite numbers?

6. This year, a man's age is a multiple of 3. Next year, his age will be a multiple of 5. The year after next, his age will be a multiple of 13. Find his age.

7. In a certain year, Henry's age was a multiple of 3. The following year, his age was a multiple of 8. Find his age
   (a) if he was a boy,
   (b) if he was a father,
   (c) if he was a grandfather,
   (d) if he was a great grandfather.

8. Peter's age at present is a multiple of 2. The following year, his age will be a multiple of 3 and the year after next, his age will be a multiple of 5. Find his age
   (a) if he is a school boy,
   (b) if he is a school teacher,
   (c) if he is a retired man.

9. The total number of pupils in class *A* and class *B* is 76. There are 4 more pupils in class *A* than in class *B*.

   Class *A* has $1\frac{1}{2}$ times as many boys as class *B* and class *B* has twice as many girls as class *A*. Find the number of boys in class *B*.

10. The length of a stick is 32.4 cm, correct to 1 decimal place. State whether each of the following statements is true or false.
    (a) The actual length cannot be 32.35 cm.
    (b) The actual length cannot be 32.36 cm.
    (c) The actual length cannot be 32.45 cm.
    (d) The actual length cannot be 32.47 cm.
    (e) The actual length is greater than or equal to 32.35 cm.
    (f) The actual length is less than 32.45 cm.

11. A jug contains 365 m*l* of water, correct to the nearest m*l*. If a glass containing 245 m*l* of water, correct to the nearest m*l*, is poured into the jug, state whether each of the following statements is true or false.
    (a) The actual volume of water in the jug now cannot be 610.6 m*l*.
    (b) The actual volume of water in the jug now cannot be 610 m*l*.
    (c) The actual volume of water in the jug now cannot be 609.4 m*l*.
    (d) The actual volume of water in the jug now cannot be 609 m*l*.
    (e) The actual volume of water in the jug now is greater than or equal to 609 m*l*.
    (f) The actual volume of water in the jug now is less than 611 m*l*.

12. A jug contains 610 m*l*, correct to the nearest m*l*. If 245 m*l* of water, correct to the nearest m*l*, is poured out from the jug, state whether each of the following statements is true or false.
    (a) The volume of water left in the jug cannot be 364.4 m*l*.
    (b) The volume of water left in the jug cannot be 365 m*l*.
    (c) The volume of water left in the jug cannot be 365.6 m*l*.
    (d) The volume of water left in the jug cannot be 365.9 m*l*.
    (e) The volume of water left in the jug is less than 366 m*l*.
    (f) The volume of water left in the jug is greater than 364 m*l*.

13. Complete each of the following sentences using all the numbers 1, 3, 5, 7 and 9.
    (a) $\square \times \square \div \square + \square - \square = 1$
    (b) $(\square \times \square + \square) \div \square - \square = 3$
    (c) $\square \div \square \times \square + \square - \square = 5$
    (d) $\square - (\square + \square) \div \square \times \square = 7$
    (e) $\square \times \square \div \square + \square - \square = 9$

14. Complete each of the following sentences using all the numbers 2, 4, 6, 8 and 10.
    (a) $(\square + \square) \div \square \times \square - \square = 2$
    (b) $\square - (\square + \square \times \square) \div \square = 4$
    (c) $(\square + \square) \times \square \div \square - \square = 6$

(d) $\square \times \square \div \square + \square - \square = 8$

(e) $(\square - \square) \times \square \div \square + \square = 10$

15. Complete the following division by finding a digit for each *.

```
                    * * * * * *
          * * * ) 5 * * * * * * * *
                  * * *
                  ─────
                    * * * *
                    * * *
                    ─────
                      5 * *
                      * * *
                      ─────
                        * 5 * *
                        * * * *
                        ─────
                            0
```

INVESTIGATION 1

1.

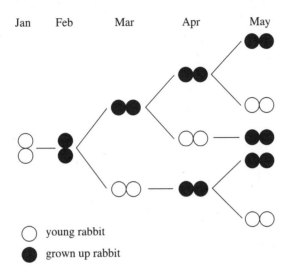

Jan   Feb   Mar   Apr   May

○ young rabbit
● grown up rabbit

Alice bought a pair of young rabbits (a male and a female) in January. By February, she had a pair of grown up rabbits. By March, she had 2 pairs of rabbits, the original pair plus a pair of young rabbits (a male and a female). By April, she had another pair of young rabbits (a male and a female), making a total of 3 pairs of rabbits and so on.

(a) Complete the sequence showing 12 terms.

$$1, 1, 2, 3, 5, \ldots$$

(b) How many pairs of rabbits will Alice have by the end of next year?
State the assumptions you have made.

2. **(a)** Verify

(i) $5\dfrac{1}{3} \div 3\dfrac{1}{5} = 5 \div 3,$

(ii) $7\dfrac{3}{5} \div 5\dfrac{3}{7} = 7 \div 5,$

(iii) $12\dfrac{7}{8} \div 8\dfrac{7}{12} = 12 \div 8.$

(b) Is there a rule for finding examples such as those given in (a)? Investigate.

3.

$$\begin{array}{ll} 4 = 2 + 2 & 10 = 3 + 7 \\ 6 = 3 + 3 & 12 = 5 + 7 \\ 8 = 3 + 5 & 14 = 3 + 11 \end{array}$$

We can see from the above that all the even numbers greater than 2 and less than or equal to 14 can be written as the sum of two prime numbers. Extend this list to include all even numbers less than or equal to 50. Do you think that every even number greater than 2 can be expressed as a sum of two prime numbers? Investigate.

4. **(a)** If $a = 36$ and $b = 24$, the LCM of a and b is $2 \times 2 \times 3 \times 3 \times 2 = 72$.

```
2 | 36, 24
2 | 18, 12
3 |  9,  6
     3,  2
```

If $a = 36$, $b = 24$ and $x = 12$, the LCM of a, b and x is
$2 \times 2 \times 3 \times 3 \times 2 = 72$.

```
2 | 36, 24, 12
2 | 18, 12,  6
3 |  9,  6,  3
     3,  2,  1
```

Find all the possible values of x other than 1, 24 and 36 so that the LCM of a, b and x is 72.

(b) Ali's method   John's method

```
2 | 72, 168            4 | 72, 168
2 | 36,  84            6 | 18,  42
2 | 18,  42                 3,   7
3 |  9,  21
     3,   7
```

LCM = $2 \times 2 \times 2 \times 3 \times 3 \times 7$ LCM = $4 \times 6 \times 3 \times 7$
      = 504   = 504

Notice that Ali uses prime numbers as divisors to find the LCM whereas John uses composite numbers to find LCM. Does John's method always work? Which method (Ali's or John's) would you use to find the LCM of 72, 168, 36. Investigate and describe your findings.

5.

1	2	3	4	5	6	7	8	9	10
11	12	13	14	15	16	17	18	19	20
21	22	23	24	25	26	27	28	29	30
31	32	33	34	35	36	37	38	39	40
41	42	43	44	45	46	47	48	49	50

Sundaram discovered a method to find prime numbers as follows:

Step 1
Cross out the numbers in the table, in steps of three, starting from the number 4 (i.e. crossing out 4, 7, 10, . . .).

Step 2
Cross out the numbers in the table, in steps of five, starting from the number 7 (i.e. crossing out 7, 12, 17, . . .).

Step 3

Cross out the numbers in the table, in step of seven, starting from the number 10 (i.e. crossing out 10, 17, 24, . . .).

Final step

Double each of the numbers that are not crossed out and add one to each of them. The numbers obtained are all the prime numbers less than 102, except 2.

(a) Use the 'Sundaram's sieve' to find all the prime numbers less than 102, except 2.

(b) Extend the table to 100 and use the same method to find the prime numbers between 102 and 200.

(c) Can you use this same method to find prime numbers beyond 200? Investigate.

Chapter 5

Simple Algebraic Expressions

Chapter Highlights

- Writing and evaluating algebraic expressions.
- Manipulating simple algebraic expressions including collecting like terms.

5.1 ALGEBRAIC EXPRESSIONS

Algebraic Notation

MATHSTORY

When writing products in algebra, the multiplication signs may be omitted. For example, we write $a \times b$ as ab, $3 \times k$ as $3k$, 3×5 as $3(5)$, $a \times (b + c)$ as $a(b + c)$ and $a \times a \times a$ as a^3. Division is often written in the form of a fraction. For example, we write $a \div b$ as $\dfrac{a}{b}$, $a \div b + c \div d$ as $\dfrac{a}{b} + \dfrac{c}{d}$ and $a \div b \times c$ as $\dfrac{ac}{b}$.

Note: $k \times 3$ can also be written as $3k$ since $k \times 3$ is equal to $3 \times k$.

$a \div \dfrac{b}{c}$ can be written in the form of a fraction as $\dfrac{a}{\frac{b}{c}}$ and $\dfrac{a}{b} \div c$ as $\dfrac{\frac{a}{b}}{c}$.

The study of algebra can be traced back as far as the Babylonians and Eygptians. However, in about the sixth century the Hindus developed problem-solving methods that were later expanded by the Arabs. The term 'algebra' is derived from the second word in the title of a book; Hisab al-jabr wal-mugabalah, written by a famous mathematician of the eighth century, Mohammed ibn Musa al-Khow-arizmi. In the centuries that followed, one of the primary interests of mathematicians involved solving algebraic equations.

Writing Algebraic Expressions

Suppose Samy is 12 years old now.

After 1 year, he will be $(12 + 1)$ years old.
After 2 years, he will be $(12 + 2)$ years old.
After 3 years, he will be $(12 + 3)$ years old.
After x years, he will be $(12 + x)$ years old.

Here, x may represent any number.

The algebraic expression $(12 + x)$ years old represents Samy's age in x year's time.

Note that the expression $(12 + x)$ should be thought of as a single symbol for a number.

If the value of the variable x is 10, then the value of the algebraic expression is $(12 + 10)$, i.e. 22.

Examples

(a) John is 3 cm taller than Hassan. If Hassan is x cm tall, then John is $(x + 3)$ cm tall.

(b) Mr Gani is three times as tall as his son, Ali. If Ali is x m tall, then Mr Gani is $3x$ m tall.

(c) Lilan and Limei have \$42 altogether. If Lilan has \$$y$, then Limei has \$$(42 - y)$.

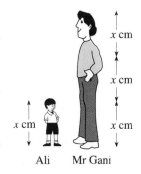

Ali   Mr Gani

Class Activity

1. Ali had $20. How much had he left if he spent **(a)** $9, **(b)** $*m*?

2. Paul had some money. He spent $30. How much money had he at first if he had **(a)** $16, **(b)** $*p* left?

3. The capacity of a mug is 1.2 *l*. A jug holds **(a)** 2.5 *l*, **(b)** *q l* more than the mug. Find the capacity of the jug in each case.

4. A pail has a capacity of 3.5 *l*. It holds **(a)** 1.5 *l*, **(b)** *w l* of water more than a vase. Find the capacity of the vase in each case.

5. Fresh milk cost $2.50 per *l*. How much will **(a)** 20 *l*, **(b)** *d l* cost?

6. Judy's mother is 3 years younger than Martha's mother. If Martha's mother is **(a)** 28, **(b)** *r* years old, how old is Judy's mother in each case?

7. There are only half as many pupils in Veloo's school as in Tom's school. If there are **(a)** 1 800, **(b)** *p* pupils in Tom's school, how many pupils are there in Veloo's school in each case?

8. The number of people in Dollah's family is 3 more than the number of people in Ramu's family. If there are **(a)** 4, **(b)** *m* people in Ramu's family, how many people are there in Dollah's family in each case?

9. 65 workers of a factory received the same monthly salary. If the factory paid out **(a)** $27 105, **(b)** $*k* as salaries to them, how much did each worker earn in each case?

10. The temperature of a liquid when heated increases by 3.5°C every second. What is the increase in temperature after the liquid is heated for **(a)** 20 s, **(b)** *t* s?

Exercise 5.1

answers on p. 426

1. The sum of two numbers is 100. If one of the numbers is *x*, write an expression for the other.

2. The difference between two numbers is 7. If the smaller number is *y*, write an expression for the other.

3. Jiaming and Abu have 30 bananas altogether. If Jiaming has *p* bananas, how many bananas has Abu?

4. Write an expression for each of the following.
   (a) The number of centimetres in s metres.
   (b) The number of metres in m kilometres.
   (c) The number of cents in q dollars.
   (d) The number of millimetres in d metres.
   (e) The number of grams in p kilograms.
   (f) The number of centimetres in s metres and t centimetres.
   (g) The number of grams in p kilograms and q grams.

5. Choose a number. Multiply it by 2 and subtract 5 from the product. Write an expression for the number obtained in terms of the chosen number.

6. A positive number is half of another number. Write an expression for the larger number in terms of the smaller number.

7. Given a number, add 10 to it, then multiply the sum by 3 and subtract the given number from the resulting number. Write an expression for the number obtained in terms of the given number.

8. **(a)** A number is 5 less than x. Write an expression for the number.
   (b) Use the expression to find the number which is 5 less than 3.

9. **(a)** A number is 2 greater than the number k. Write an expression for the number.
   (b) What number is 2 greater than (-14)?

10. **(a)** A number is greater than twice another number by 11. Write an expression for the larger number in terms of the smaller number.
   (b) What number is greater than twice the number $\left(-\dfrac{7}{16}\right)$ by 11?

11. Nanfa is 5 years older than Tim. Write an expression for Nanfa's age in terms of Tim's age.

12. A boy is 8 years younger than his sister. Write an expression for the boy's age in terms of his sister's age.

13. A boy's age is one-seventh the age of his father. Write an expression for the father's age in terms of his son's age.

14. In a certain community, there were two-thirds as many girls as boys. Write an expression for the number of girls in terms of the number of boys.

15. A man can paint a house in x days. Write an expression for the part of the house that he can paint in one day.

16. If a pipe fills $\dfrac{1}{6}$ of a swimming pool with water in one hour, write an expression for that part of the pool which is filled in y hours.

5.2 EVALUATION OF ALGEBRAIC EXPRESSIONS

Example

Mr Li ordered 5 tins of corned beef and 6 tins of sausages from his neighbourhood shop through the telephone. The owner was not in and his son, Zhihao, took the order. How much had Mr Li to pay?

Zhihao did not know the prices of the items, so he represented the amount by an algebraic expression $(5c + 6s)$, where c represented the cost of each tin of corned beef in dollars and s represented the cost of each tin of sausages in dollars. Later, he found from his father that $c = 4$ and $s = 3$. He evaluated the expression $(5c + 6s)$ like this:

$$
\begin{aligned}
5c + 6s &= 5 \times 4 + 6 \times 3 \\
&= 20 + 18 \\
&= 38
\end{aligned}
$$

Thus, Mr Li had to pay \$38.

Worked Example 1
Evaluate the following by taking $a = 2$, $b = 6$, $c = 4$ and $d = 5$.
(a) $(b - c) + a$ **(b)** $(ab + c)d$

Solution:

(a)
$$
\begin{aligned}
(b - c) + a &= (6 - 4) + 2 \\
&= 2 + 2 \\
&= 4
\end{aligned}
$$

(b)
$$
\begin{aligned}
(ab + c)d &= (2 \times 6 + 4)5 \\
&= (12 + 4)5 \\
&= 80
\end{aligned}
$$

Worked Example 2
Verify the following by taking $a = 2$, $b = -9$ and $c = 3$.
(a) $a(b + c) = ab + ac$ **(b)** $a(b - c) = ab - ac$

Solution:

(a) $a(b + c) = ab + ac$

$$
\begin{aligned}
\text{LHS} &= 2\,(-9 + 3) \\
&= 2(-6) \\
&= -12
\end{aligned}
$$

$$
\begin{aligned}
\text{RHS} &= 2 \times (-9) + 2 \times 3 \\
&= (-18) + 6 \\
&= -12
\end{aligned}
$$

$\therefore\ a(b + c) = ab + ac$ since LHS = RHS.

(b) $a(b - c) = ab - ac$

$\qquad$ LHS $= 2(-9 - 3)$

$\qquad\qquad = 2(-12)$

$\qquad\qquad = -24$

RHS $= 2 \times (-9) - 2 \times 3$

$\qquad = -18 - 6$

$\qquad = -24$

$\therefore\ a(b - c) = ab - ac$ since

LHS = RHS.

Exercise 5.2 ✐

answers on p. 426

1. Evaluate the following by taking $a = 2$, $b = 4$, $c = 3$, $d = 5$, $e = 7$ and $f = 6$.

    (a) $a(b + c)$

    (b) $e - (a + c)$

    (c) $e(f - c)$

    (d) $d(e - b)$

    (e) $c(f + b + a)$

    (f) $f(b + c + d)$

    (g) $a(e - a - b)$

    (h) $b(f - c - a)$

    (i) $a + b(c + d)$

    (j) $f + c(e - b)$

    (k) $b(c + d) + \dfrac{f}{e}$

    (l) $\dfrac{c}{d}(a + f)$

    (m) $\dfrac{\frac{a}{b}}{c}$

    (n) $\dfrac{a}{\frac{b}{c}}$

    (o) $\dfrac{\frac{d}{e}}{f}$

2. Evaluate the following by taking $a = -2$, $b = 6$, $c = -4$, $d = 7$, $e = -1$ and $f = 6$.

    (a) $\dfrac{a}{b}(b + e)$

    (b) $b\left(\dfrac{a}{b} + \dfrac{c}{d}\right)$

    (c) $a\left(bc + de + \dfrac{f}{c}\right)$

    (d) $d\left(df - bc + \dfrac{a}{d}\right)$

    (e) $a + \{[b + c(d + f) + cd] + ef\}$

    (f) $b\{a + e(a + b) + de] - cd\}$

    (g) $ef + b\{[b + e(a + b) - f] + ab\}$

    (h) $\dfrac{de}{a} - \left(\dfrac{a}{b} + \dfrac{c}{f}\right) + a^2$

3. Verify the following by taking $a = 2$, $b = \dfrac{1}{4}$ and $c = -6$.

    (a) $ab + ac = a(b + c)$

    (b) $ba + ca = (b + c)a$

    (c) $ab - ac = a(b - c)$

    (d) $ba - ca = (b - c)a$

4. Evaluate the following by taking $p = 3$, $q = \dfrac{1}{2}$, $x = -4$ and $y = -\dfrac{2}{3}$.

    (a) $2p + (x - y)$

    (b) $\dfrac{1}{2}(p - 2q) + \dfrac{x}{y}$

    (c) $5px^2 + 3qy^2$

    (d) $4\left(\dfrac{x}{p} - \dfrac{y}{q}\right)$

    (e) $pq\left(\dfrac{1}{x} - \dfrac{1}{y}\right)$

    (f) $\left(\dfrac{3x + y}{p - q}\right)^2$

    (g) $\dfrac{x + y}{p^2 + q^2}$

    (h) $\left(\dfrac{1}{q^2} - 3p\right)(x + y)$

5.3 ALGEBRAIC TERMS

Expressions such as $3 \times n$, $x \times 4$, $1 \times c$ and $a \times b$ can be written as $3n$, $4x$, c and ab. These are referred to as **algebraic terms**.

In the term $3n$, n is the variable and the number 3 attached to it is called the **coefficient** of the term $3n$. Likewise, the number 4 is the coefficient of the term $4x$. What is the coefficient of c? What about ab? Can you explain why?

A part of an algebraic expression which is a product of numbers and variables and is separated from the rest of the expression by plus or minus signs is called a term. The numbers and letters which are multiplied in a term are called factors of the term. The numerical factor is called the coefficient of the term.

Examples

(a) Find the sum of $3a$ and $4a$.

$3a$ means $3 \times a$, i.e. 3 groups of a.
$4a$ means $4 \times a$, i.e. 4 groups of a.
Adding 3 groups of a and 4 groups of a gives 7 groups of a.

We write

$$3a + 4a = 7a.$$

Notice that the terms $3a$ and $4a$ have the same variable. We call them **like terms**. When adding like terms, we simply add the coefficients.

(b) Find the sum of $3a$ and $4b$.

$3a$ and $4b$ are **unlike terms** because they have different variables. We do not add the coefficients of unlike terms. So, adding $3a$ and $4b$ gives $3a + 4b$.

Worked Example 3
Find the sum of
(a) $5a$ and $-7a$,   (b) $-3a$ and $-4ab$.

Solution:
(a) $5a + (-7a) = (5 - 7)a$ (b) $-3a + (-4ab) = -3a - 4ab$
$\qquad\qquad = -2a$

Note: The terms $-3a$ and $-4ab$ are unlike terms because their 'variable parts' are not exactly the same.

Worked Example 4
Find the product of
(a) $3a$ and $4b$,   (b) $-3a$ and $(-4ab)$.

Solution:

(a) $3a \times 4b = 3 \times a \times 4 \times b$

$\quad\quad\quad\quad\quad = 3 \times 4 \times a \times b$

$\quad\quad\quad\quad\quad = 12ab$

(b) $-3a \times (-4ab) = (-3) \times a \times (-4) \times a \times b$

$\quad\quad\quad\quad\quad\quad\quad = (-3) \times (-4) \times a \times a \times b$

$\quad\quad\quad\quad\quad\quad\quad = 12a^2b$

Note: You may omit the intermediate steps if you can do your calculations mentally.

Worked Example 5

Find the quotient **(a)** when $18a$ is divided by $3b$,

$\quad\quad\quad\quad\quad\quad$ **(b)** when $-6ab$ is divided by $14a$.

Solution:

(a) $18a \div 3b = \dfrac{18a}{3b}$

$\quad\quad\quad\quad = \dfrac{6a}{b}$

(b) $-6ab \div 14a = \dfrac{-6ab}{14a}$

$\quad\quad\quad\quad\quad\quad = -\dfrac{3b}{7}$

Exercise 5.3 ✍

answers on p. 427

1. Find the sum of the following.

(a) $3a$ and $5a$	**(b)** $6b$ and $6b$	**(c)** $5c$ and $-8c$
(d) $-5c$ and $8c$	**(e)** $-9m$ and $-3m$	**(f)** $4x$ and x
(g) $4a$ and $3b$	**(h)** $5a$ and $5b$	**(i)** $-9ab$ and $14ba$
(j) $12a^2b$ and $17ab^2$	**(k)** $-31ab^2$ and $52b^2a$	**(l)** $32ab^2$ and $-32cb^2$

2. Find the product of the following.

(a) $2a$ and $6b$	**(b)** $3a$ and $-5c$	**(c)** $6x$ and $2y$
(d) $6x$ and $-3z$	**(e)** $3n$ and $5m$	**(f)** $3n$ and $6p$
(g) $-4p$ and $3q$	**(h)** $-4p$ and $-7r$	**(i)** $3a^2$ and $-4ab$
(j) $31ab^2$ and $-12a^2b$	**(k)** $23xy$ and $-23x^2$	**(l)** $-17xy$ and $14y^2$

3. Find the quotient

(a) when $128a$ is divided by $16a$,

(b) when $-28ab$ is divided by $49b$,

(c) when $33m$ is divided by $44mn$,

(d) when $17pq$ is divided by $-34qp$,

(e) when $-32xy$ is divided by $-12yz$,

(f) when $22x(-y)$ is divided by $55y(-z)$.

4. Simplify the following.

(a) $3a + 7a$ (b) $3a \times 7a$ (c) $3b + (-7b)$

(d) $3b \times (-7b)$ (e) $3a + 5a + (-7b)$ (f) $3a \times 5a \times (-7b)$

(g) $-5c + (-6c) + 2c^2$ (h) $-5c \times (-6c) \times 2c^2$ (i) $4d + 5de + 3de$

(j) $4d \times 5de \times 3de$ (k) $4f + 4fg + 9f$ (l) $4f \times 4fg \times 9f$

(m) $4b - 3b - 7b$ (n) $-3ab \times 7a \div 42b$ (o) $-5x \div 15y \div 4xy$

(p) $-7a^2 + 7ab - 14a^2$ (q) $-32x \div 4y \times 5yz$ (r) $72xy \div 8yz \div 4zx$

5.4 USE OF BRACKETS

Let us look at the distributive law below.

$$a(b + c) = ab + ac$$

The LHS is in the form of a product: $\boxed{a}$ $\times$ $\boxed{(b + c)}$

The RHS is in the form of a sum: $\boxed{ab}$ $+$ $\boxed{ac}$

There are other forms of the distributive law, for example,

$$a(b - c) = ab - ac.$$

The LHS is a 'product': $\boxed{a}$ $\times$ $\boxed{(b - c)}$

The RHS is a 'sum': $\boxed{ab}$ $+$ $\boxed{(-ac)}$

Note that we view 'subtracting ac' as 'adding $(-ac)$'.

Using the distributive law, we can convert an expression from one form to another.

Examples

(a) Let us study these conversions.

Product		Sum
$a(3b + 5c)$	$\longrightarrow$	$3ab + 5ac$
$2x(3y + z)$	$\longrightarrow$	$6xy + 2xz$

Notice that we expand the 'product' to get the 'sum'. In this process, we have **removed the brackets**.

Conversely, we have

Sum		Product
$3ab + 5ac$	$\longrightarrow$	$a(3b + 5c)$
$6xy + 2xz$	$\longrightarrow$	$2x(3y + z)$

Notice that we factorise the 'sum' to get the 'product'. In this process, we have **inserted the brackets**. This process is also known as '**extracting common factors**'.

(b) The distributive law can be used to remove the brackets of expressions such as $x - (a - b)$. This expression can be interpreted as

$$x + (-1)(a - b).$$

So,
$$\begin{aligned}
x - (a - b) &= x + (-1)(a - b) \\
&= x + (-a) + b \\
&= x - a + b
\end{aligned}$$

Worked Example 6
Remove the brackets of the following.
(a) $-a(b + c)$ **(b)** $-a - (-b - c)$

Solution:
(a) $-a(b + c) = -ab - ac$ **(b)** $-a - (-b - c) = -a + b + c$

Worked Example 7
Remove the brackets of the following.
(a) $-(x + 3y)$ **(b)** $5z - (9y - 4w)$

Solution:
(a) $-(x + 3y) = -x - 3y$ **(b)** $5z - (9y - 4w) = 5z - 9y + 4w$

Worked Example 8
Remove the brackets of the following.
(a) $5p(2a + 3b)$ **(b)** $-2a(3b - 5c)$

Solution:
(a) $5p(2a + 3b) = 10pa + 15pb$ **(b)** $-2a(3b - 5c) = -6ab + 10ac$

Worked Example 9
Extract the common factors for the following.
(a) $3ab + 4ac$ **(b)** $3a + 3ab - 2a$

Solution:
(a) $3ab + 4ac = a(3b + 4c)$ **(b)** $\begin{aligned} 3a + 3ab - 2a &= a(3 + 3b - 2) \\ &= a(1 + 3b) \end{aligned}$

Note: For (b), you may simplify the expression first.

1. Remove the brackets of the following.
    (a) $a(b - c)$
    (b) $a(-b + c)$
    (c) $a(b + c)$
    (d) $a(-b - c)$
    (e) $-a(-b + c)$
    (f) $-a(-b - c)$
    (g) $a + (b - c)$
    (h) $a - (b + c)$
    (i) $a + (-b + c)$
    (j) $a + (-b - c)$
    (k) $a - (-b + c)$
    (l) $a - (-b - c)$

2. Remove the brackets of the following.
    (a) $x + (2b - c)$
    (b) $2x + (4a - 2b)$
    (c) $3a + (-2b + 3c)$
    (d) $2y + (-3x + 2w)$
    (e) $g + (-4b - 3c)$
    (f) $4m + (-3n - 4p)$
    (g) $2n - (-5t + 3u)$
    (h) $6p - (-2q + 5r)$
    (i) $-(2x + 7y)$
    (j) $-(10r + 35)$
    (k) $-(2m - 3n)$
    (l) $-(6p - 7q)$
    (m) $3x - (3t + 8u)$
    (n) $4r - (10s + 7t)$
    (o) $6z - (3y - 5w)$
    (p) $2w - (4x - 9y)$
    (q) $-x - (-3y - 4z)$
    (r) $-a - (-3b - 5c)$

3. Remove the brackets of the following.
    (a) $3a(4b - 5c)$
    (b) $6x(2y - 3z)$
    (c) $3n(5m + 6p)$
    (d) $-4p(3q - 7r)$
    (e) $(5x + 7y)4z$
    (f) $(9t + 8u)4v$
    (g) $(7m - 3n)5p$
    (h) $(6p - q)7r$

4. Extract the common factors of the following.
    (a) $4x + 3xy$
    (b) $15m + 6n + 9mn$
    (c) $7p + 8pq - 5p$
    (d) $4a + 8ab$
    (e) $3x + 6xy + 9yx$
    (f) $2ab + 3abc + 5cba$
    (g) $5rst + 3st - 2rt$
    (h) $6ab + 3bc - ba + b$

5.5 COLLECTING LIKE TERMS

Example

Consider $5a - b - 2b + 2c^2 - 8a - c + 4b$.

We can collect and simplify the like terms $5a$ and $-8a$ as follows:

$$5a - 8a = (5 - 8)a$$
$$= -3a$$

The terms $-b$, $-2b$ and $4b$ are also like terms. We can collect and simplify them in the same way:

$$-b - 2b + 4b = (-1 - 2 + 4)b$$
$$= b$$

The given expression which has seven terms can be simplified to four terms. Thus, we have

$$5a - b - 2b + 2c^2 - 8a - c + 4b = -3a + b + 2c^2 - c.$$

Note that the unlike terms $2c^2$ and $-c$ cannot be expressed as a single term.

Worked Example 10
Simplify the following.
(a) $2a + b + 6c + c + 5b + 3a - 3b - 4c + 2c$
(b) $a - 2b - [b - c + 2(c - a)]$
(c) $\frac{1}{4}(x - 1) + \frac{5}{6}(x + 7)$

Solution:
(a) $2a + b + 6c + c + 5b + 3a - 3b - 4c + 2c$
$= (2 + 3)a + (1 + 5 - 3)b + (6 + 1 - 4 + 2)c$
$= 5a + 3b + 5c$

Note: You may skip the intermediate step by computing the coefficients of the like terms mentally.

(b) $a - 2b - [b - c + 2(c - a)] = a - 2b - [b - c + 2c - 2a]$
$= a - 2b - b + c - 2c + 2a$
$= 3a - 3b - c$

(c) $\frac{1}{4}(x - 1) + \frac{5}{6}(x + 7) = \frac{1}{4}x - \frac{1}{4} + \frac{5}{6}x + \frac{35}{6}$
$= \left(\frac{1}{4} + \frac{5}{6}\right)x + \frac{35}{6} - \frac{1}{4}$
$= \frac{13}{12}x + \frac{67}{12}$

Exercise 5.5 ✍ *answers on p. 427*

Simplify the following expressions.
1. (a) $2a + 3b - 2b + a$
(b) $2a - 3b + c - b + 2a$
(c) $3d + e - f + 4e - 3f + d$
(d) $4a^2 + b - c + a + 2c + 2b$
(e) $5a + c - b - a - b - c^2 - 4a$
(f) $2a + b^2 + a - 7b + 3b^2$
(g) $b - 7a + 3b + 8a + 3c - a^2$
(h) $-7b - 7a - 6b - 6a + c^2 - 2b + c$

2. (a) $(a - b) + (b - a)$
(b) $(-a + b) + (b - a)$
(c) $(-a - b) - (-b - a)$
(d) $(a - b) - (b - c) - (c - a)$
(e) $(a - b) + (b - c) + (c - a)$
(f) $3(6b - 9a) + 7(6a - 5b)$
(g) $3(a - b) + 7(2a + 2b)$
(h) $17(1 - 3c) + 3(c + c^2)$

3. **(a)** $a(a - b) + b(b - c) + c(c - a)$ **(b)** $a(a - b) + b(b - a) + c(a - b)$
   — **(c)** $a(a - b) + [3(c + a^2) - ab]$ **(d)** $[(2a + 2b)c + d]c - 4ac^2 + bc^2$
   — **(e)** $c[a + b(a^2 + 2bc) - 3a^3] - a^2bc + b^2c^2 - ac$
   (f) $a(b^2 + 3c) - [b^2(a - 2c) - b(2ab + 1)]$
   — **(g)** $x(y - 3z) - y(z - 3x) - z(x - 3y)$
   (h) $3xy + [x(3z - 2y) - xy] - y(x - 2z)$

4. **(a)** $\dfrac{1}{4}(8x + 4) - 3$ **(b)** $\dfrac{1}{3}(3x + 9) - 2x$

   (c) $\dfrac{y}{2} - \dfrac{4y}{5} - 3$ **(d)** $\dfrac{1}{3}(x + 3) + \dfrac{5}{6}(x - 1)$

   (e) $\dfrac{5}{6}(x + 1) + \dfrac{1}{4}(x - 3)$ **(f)** $\dfrac{7}{8}(x - 1) - \dfrac{1}{6}(2x + 1)$

   (g) $\dfrac{7x - 6}{8} + \dfrac{5x + 3}{4}$ **(h)** $\dfrac{3(5x - 1)}{4} - \dfrac{3x + 7}{6}$

Chapter Review

1. **Evaluation of Algebraic Expressions**
   To evaluate an algebraic expression, we simply substitute the given values of the variables in the expression and simplify.
   Example: Evaluate $(ab + c)d$ given $a = 1$, $b = -2$, $c = 3$ and $d = 4$.
   So, $(ab + c)d = [1 \times (-2) + 3] \times 4 = 4$

2. **Collecting Like Terms**
   - Algebraic terms which are different only in the coefficients are called like terms.
   - To collect like terms, we simply do addition and subtraction of the coefficients to simplify several like terms to a single term.
   - When brackets are involved, we remove the brackets before collecting the like terms.

   Example: Simplify $3(2x - 1) - 4(3 - 2x)$.
   So, $3(2x - 1) - 4(3 - 2x) = 6x - 3 - 12 + 8x$
   $= 14x - 15$

CHALLENGER 5

1. Simplify the following.
   (a) $4(x^2 - 11xy - 3y^2) - 2(3xy - 4x^2 + y^2)$
   (b) $(x - 2x^2) \div (-x) - 3x$
   (c) $\dfrac{1 + a}{5} - \dfrac{1 + a}{3} + \dfrac{3 - a}{6}$

2. If $x = \dfrac{a + b}{a - b}$, find the following in terms of a and b simplifying your answers.

   (a) $ax - b$ **(b)** $bx + a$ **(c)** $\dfrac{ax - b}{bx + a}$

3. If $2a + b = 1$, find the value of
   (a) $2a + b - 2$,   **(b)** $4a + 2b + 4$.

4. If $a^2 + 6a = 6$, find the value of
   (a) $a(a^2 + 6a) + a^2$,   **(b)** $a^3 + 7a^2$.

5. If m dollars are shared between John and Paul so that John's share is n times Paul's share, write an expression for John's share.

6. The average age of m boys and n girls is p. If the average age of the boys is q, find an expression for the average age of the girls.

Problem Solving 5

Paper Folding

If a long piece of rectangular paper is folded 8 times, what is the greatest number of parallel creases you can get?

To solve this problem, we can get a piece of ordinary paper and make a few folds to find out whether there is a pattern.

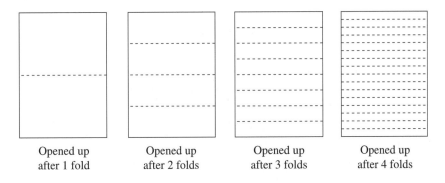

| Opened up after 1 fold | Opened up after 2 folds | Opened up after 3 folds | Opened up after 4 folds |

We then use tabulation to look for pattern.

Number of folds	1	2	3	4
Number of creases	1	3	7	15

If the additional number of creases for each additional fold is noted, we will discover the following pattern.

Thus, the maximum number of creases obtained
$= 1 + 2 + 4 + 8 + 16 + 32 + 64 + 128 = 225$.

The strategies used here are **simplify the problem, act it out, use tabulation** and **look for pattern**.

Alternatively, the strategy **think of a related problem** may be used. The related problem is usually a simpler problem, a familar problem or a more accessible problem.

Let us think of a related problem which asks for the greatest number of parts divided up by parallel creases.

It is easy to discover that

> 1 fold gives 2 parts, and for each additional fold, the number of parts is doubled.

Number of folds: 1, 2, 3, . . .
Number of parts: $2, 2^2, 2^3, \ldots$
So, 8 folds give 2^8, i.e. 256, parts.
Therefore, number of creases $= 256 - 1 = 255$.

1. **Manipulate with Coins**   20 $1 coins are laid on a table in a straight line. Replace each dollar coin at the *n*th position, where *n* is a multiple of 2 (i.e. at all the even positions) by a 50¢ coin.
    Next, replace each coin ($1 or 50¢) at the *m*th position, where *m* is a multiple of 3, by a 20¢ coin.
    Then, replace each coin ($1, 50¢ or 20¢) at the *r*th position, where *r* is a multiple of 5, by a 10¢ coin.
    Find the amount of money finally left on the table.

2. **Make a Square**   The figure is made of two squares. Explain how you would divide a cut-out of the figure into 3 pieces and then use the pieces to form a square.

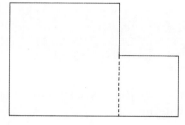

3. **Arrow of Message**   In this question, an arrow means 'is a factor of' (or 'divides exactly into'). The diagram on the right shows that 3 is a factor of 6, 15 and 18, and that 6 is a factor of 18. There is no line with an arrow connecting 6 to 15 and this means that 6 is not a factor of 15.

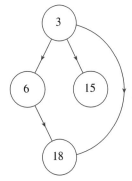

In the empty circles below, insert the five whole numbers (all different and all greater than 1) that are needed to complete this diagram correctly.

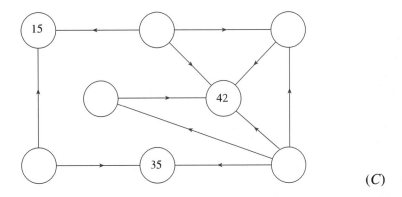

(C)

4. **More than One Right Order**   By inserting the operation signs +, −, ×, ÷ and brackets, we can make the following a 'true' sentence.

$$0.1 \quad 0.2 \quad 0.3 \quad 0.4 \quad 0.5 = 1$$

For example, $(0.1 ÷ 0.2 − 0.3) ÷ 0.4 ÷ 0.5 = 1$
   (a)   Can you do this in another way?
   (b)   Give another solution without using brackets.

Chapter 6

Open Sentences and Equations

Chapter Highlights

- Understanding the concept of open sentences.
- Solving linear equations for unknown terms.
- Evaluating formulae.
- Solving algebraic problems involving linear equations.

6.1 OPEN SENTENCES

Consider the sentences $9 + 5 = 14$ and $9 + 6 = 14$. The first sentence is true. The second is false. Here is another sentence: $\square + 5 = 3$. This sentence is neither true nor false, because we do not know what number the symbol $\square$ represents. This is called an **open sentence**. If $\square$ represents -1, the sentence is false and if it represents -2, then the sentence is true. A symbol such as $\square$ is a **variable**. Various symbols or letters such as $\diamond$, $\bigcirc$, a, b and c are used as variables.

Variables are letters used to represent numbers.

The number -2 which makes $\square + 5 = 3$ a true sentence is called a **solution** of the open sentence.

Open sentences which use the symbol '$=$' are called **equations**. Those involving the symbols '$>$', '$<$', '$\geq$', '$\leq$' or '$\neq$' are called **inequalities** or **inequations**.

An equation is a statement that two quantities are equal.

Note: '$\geq$' means 'greater than or equal to', '$\leq$' means 'less than or equal to' and '$\neq$' means 'not equal to'.

Worked Example 1
Find the solutions of the following by inspection.
(a) $x - 5 = 1$ **(b)** $5x = 12$

Solution:
By inspection,

(a) $x = 6$,   **(b)** $x = \dfrac{12}{5}$ or $2\dfrac{2}{5}$.

Worked Example 2
If x represents a natural number, find the solutions of
(a) $x < 6$ and $x > 3$,   **(b)** $x \leq 6$ and $x \geq 3$.

Solution:
By the trial and error method, the solutions are
(a) $x = 4$, $x = 5$;   **(b)** $x = 3$, $x = 4$; $x = 5$, $x = 6$.

Exercise 6.1

answer in p. 427

1. In each of the following sentences, decide whether the sentence is true if the variable has the suggested value.

    (a) $7 + \square = 12$; let $\square$ be 5   **(b)** $-2 + x = -2$; let x be 4

    (c) $y + (-3) = 2$; let y be 1   **(d)** $t + 9 = 11$; let t be -2

    (e) $5 + \triangle = -3$; let $\triangle$ be -2 **(f)** $\triangle - \dfrac{2}{3} = 0$; let $\triangle$ be $1\dfrac{2}{3}$

2. Find the solution of each of the following open sentences by inspection.

    (a) $\square + 4 = 9$ **(b)** $\square - 5 = 10$ **(c)** $x + \dfrac{1}{4} = \dfrac{7}{4}$

    (d) $x - \dfrac{4}{5} = \dfrac{1}{5}$ **(e)** $3 - x = 10$ **(f)** $3 - x = 0$

3. If x represents a natural number, find the solutions of the following by inspection.

    (a) $x < 3$ **(b)** $x \le 3$ **(c)** $x + 2 < 4$

    (d) $4 > x$ **(e)** $4 \ge x$ **(f)** $4 > x - 1$

4. If x represents a natural number, find the solutions of the following by inspection.

    (a) $x < 7$ and $x > 2$ **(b)** $x < 20$ and $x > 15$ **(c)** $x \le 15$ and $x \ge 9$

    (d) $x \le 20$ and $x \ge 15$ **(e)** $x - 7 \ne 14$ **(f)** $x + 3 \ne 10$

    (g) $x - 15 < 20$ **(h)** $x + 3 \le 15$ **(i)** $10 - x > 2$

    (j) $7 - x \ge 2$ **(k)** $\dfrac{x}{3} < 3$ **(l)** $3 - \dfrac{x}{3} > 1$

5. If x represents a natural number, state whether each of the following statements is true or false.

    (a) $x > 0$ **(b)** $x > -4$ **(c)** $x \ne 0$

    (d) $x \ne -1$ **(e)** $x \ne 4$ **(f)** $x \ge 1$

6. If x is an integer, find the solutions, if any, of the following by inspection.

    (a) $x^2 = 9$ **(b)** $4 - x^2 = 0$ **(c)** $x^2 + 1 = 0$

    (d) $\dfrac{1}{x^2} = \dfrac{1}{25}$ **(e)** $\dfrac{1}{2}x^2 = 2$ **(f)** $x^2 = \dfrac{4}{9}$

6.2 EQUATIONS

You have used the 'inspection' method to solve equations. The following activities will help you discover a better method.

Class Activity

Study the diagrams carefully before answering the questions.

1. If the mass on the left scale balances the mass on the right scale, is $2x + 2 = 8$?

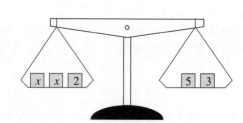

2. If a mass of 3 units is added to each scale in question 1, is $2x + 5 = 11$?

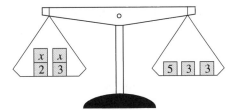

3. If a mass of 5 units is taken away from each scale in question 2, is $2x = 6$?

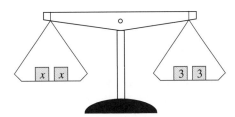

4. If we multiply the mass on each scale in question 3 by 3, is $6x = 18$?

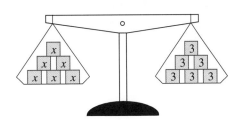

5. If we divide the mass on each scale in question 4 by 2, is $3x = 9$?

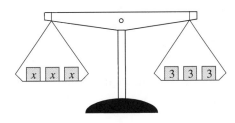

6. What do you think will happen to the scales in question 5 if
(a) a mass of the same unit is added to each scale,
(b) a mass of the same unit is taken away from each scale,
(c) the mass on each scale is multiplied by the same number,
(d) the mass on each scale is divided by the same number?

7. Do you agree that an equation can be thought of as an 'algebraic balance'?

Equivalent Equations

Study the following equations.

$$2x + 2 = 8 \quad \text{................................(1)}$$
$$2x + 5 = 11 \quad \text{................................(2)}$$
$$2x = 6 \quad \text{................................(3)}$$
$$6x = 18 \quad \text{................................(4)}$$
$$3x = 9 \quad \text{................................(5)}$$

MATHSTORY

Mathematicians chose the symbol '=' to represent equality because it was thought that nothing could be more equal than two line segments.

The above five equations have the same solution, i.e. $x = 3$. Equations with the same solution are called **equivalent equations**

When two equations have exactly the same solutions, they are called equivalent equations.

Notice that the preceding five equations are related as follows:
- If we add 3 to both sides of equation (1), we obtain equation (2).
- If we subtract 5 from both sides of equation (2), we obtain equation (3).
- If we multiply both sides of equation (3) by 3, we obtain equation (4).
- If we divide both sides of equation (4) by 2, we obtain equation (5).

Thus, we can sum up our observations briefly as follows:

> **If we add the same number to or subtract the same number from both sides of an equation or multiply or divide both sides of the equation by the same number, the new equation is equivalent to the original equation.**

Note: In practice, 'multiply or divide both sides by' is the same as 'multiply or divide each term by'.

Solving Equations

'To find the solutions of the equation', 'to solve the equation' and 'to find the roots of the equation' mean the same thing. The value of each root is said to **satisfy** the equation.

In an equation, we refer to the variable as the **unknown**, all the terms involving the unknown as the **unknown terms** and all numerical terms as the **constant terms**.

For example, in $2x + 3 = 33 - x$,

x is the unknown,
$2x$ and $-x$ are the unknown terms,
and 3 and 33 are the constant terms.

Worked Example 3
Find the value of x in $5x - 6 = 34$.

Solution:
$$5x - 6 = 34$$
$$5x - 6 + 6 = 34 + 6 \quad \text{(Add 6 to both sides.)}$$
$$5x = 40$$
$$\frac{5x}{5} = \frac{40}{5} \quad \text{(Divide both sides by 5.)}$$
$$x = 8$$

Therefore, the value of x is 8.

Note: 1. To eliminate −6 on the LHS of the given equation, we add 6 to both sides. To eliminate the coefficient of x in the step $5x = 40$, we divide both sides by the coefficient, i.e. 5.

2. Checking of answer is always beneficial even though it is not required to be written down as part of your answer.

Worked Example 4

Find the solution of $5x + 8 = 13 - 2x$.

Solution:

$$5x + 8 = 13 - 2x$$
$$5x + 8 + 2x = 13 - 2x + 2x \quad \text{(Add } 2x \text{ to both sides.)}$$
$$7x + 8 = 13$$
$$7x + 8 - 8 = 13 - 8 \quad \text{(Subtract 8 from both sides.)}$$
$$7x = 5$$
$$\frac{7x}{7} = \frac{5}{7} \quad \text{(Divide both sides by 7.)}$$
$$x = \frac{5}{7}$$

Therefore, the solution is $\frac{5}{7}$.

Note: To eliminate the term $-2x$ on the RHS of the given equation, we add $2x$ to both sides. To eliminate the coefficient of x in the step $7x = 5$, we divide both sides by the coefficient, i.e. 7.

Worked Example 5

Solve $3(3 - 2x) - (1 + x) = 10 - 13x$.

Solution:

$$3(3 - 2x) - (1 + x) = 10 - 13x$$
$$9 - 6x - 1 - x = 10 - 13x$$
$$8 - 7x = 10 - 13x$$
$$8 - 7x + 13x = 10 - 13x + 13x \quad \text{(Add } 13x \text{ to both sides.)}$$
$$8 + 6x = 10$$
$$8 + 6x - 8 = 10 - 8 \quad \text{(Subtract 8 from both sides.)}$$
$$6x = 2$$
$$\frac{6x}{6} = \frac{2}{6} \quad \text{(Divide both sides by 6.)}$$
$$x = \frac{1}{3}$$

Therefore, the solution is $\frac{1}{3}$.

Note: After you have had some practice, you may be able to solve equations in fewer steps. At this stage, it is advisable to solve the equations step by step.

Generally, solving an equation involves four tasks:

Task 1 Remove all brackets and simplify.

Task 2 Eliminate the unknown term on the RHS by adding the appropriate term to or subtracting the appropriate term from both sides of the equation, and then simplify.

Task 3 Eliminate the constant term on the LHS by adding the appropriate term to or subtracting the appropriate term from both sides of the equation, and then simplify.

Task 4 Eliminate the coefficient of the unknown on the LHS by dividing both sides of the equation by the coefficient, and then simplify.

Exercise 6.2

answers on p. 428

1. The following are four groups of equivalent equations. State, in each group, how the first equation can be converted to the second and the second to the third.

   (a) $6x + 3 = 5 + x$
   $5x + 3 = 5$
   $5x = 2$

   (b) $3x - 4 = 14 - 3x$
   $6x - 4 = 14$
   $6x = 18$

   (c) $3(2x - 5) = 12$
   $2x - 5 = 4$
   $2x = 9$

   (d) $3[(x - 5) + 2x] = 0$
   $x - 5 + 2x = 0$
   $x + 2x = 5$

2. Find the solution of each of the following equations.
   (a) $3x - 13 = 26$
   (b) $3x - 7 = 32$
   (c) $4y - 9 = -5$
   (d) $8 + 3a = 11$
   (e) $8 + 2x = 14$
   (f) $y + 6 = 18$
   (g) $8x + 4 = 12$
   (h) $2x - 10 = 8$
   (i) $3x + 6 = 1$
   (j) $x + 4 = 60$
   (k) $2a + 45 = 0$
   (l) $7y + 3 = y + 18$
   (m) $x + 3 = 18 - 3x$
   (n) $2y - 2 = 4 - y$
   (o) $5x - 4 = 2x + 11$
   (p) $4x = 7 + 3x$

3. Solve the following equations.
   (a) $3(x + 2) + 7(x - 1) = 12$
   (b) $5(x + 1) + 3(x - 1) = 5$
   (c) $4(x - 1) - (x + 3) = 0$
   (d) $3(1 - x) + 4(x - 5) = 10$
   (e) $28(x - 3) - (x - 3) = 0$
   (f) $9(x - 4) + (2 + 8x) = 0$
   (g) $3x + 3(x - 3) - (4 - 4x) = 0$
   (h) $3(2x - 3) - (2x + 2) = x - 3$
   (i) $3y + 6(y + 3) - (8y - 16) = 60$
   (j) $3 + (4 + 4p) = 6(4 - p)$
   (k) $3(u - 3) - 3(4 + u) = 5 + u$
   (l) $5 - 3(q - 7) = 2(2 - q) - 8$

    (m) $5(3 - s) - 4(s - 3) = 5 - 4s$ **(n)** $x(3 + x) - 3(1 + 2x) = 3 + x^2$

    (o) $n(3n - 3) - 5(3 + n) = 3n^2 + 2n + 3$

    (p) $w^2 - w(w - 3) = 12(1 + w)$

4. Solve these equations.

    (a) $x^2 - 3 = 1$ **(b)** $2x^2 + 5 = 23$ **(c)** $2x^2 + 7 = 55 - x^2$

    (d) $2(x^2 + 1) = 52$ **(e)** $2(x^2 - 9) = 90 - x^2$ **(f)** $(x - 1)^2 = 4$

6.3 EQUATIONS WITH FRACTIONAL AND DECIMAL COEFFICIENTS

Worked Example 6

Solve $\dfrac{1}{2}x - 1 = 3$.

Solution:

$$\frac{1}{2}x - 1 = 3$$

$$\frac{1}{2}x - 1 + 1 = 3 + 1 \qquad \text{(Add 1 to both sides.)}$$

$$\frac{1}{2}x = 4$$

$$2\left(\frac{1}{2}x\right) = 2(4) \qquad \text{(Multiply both sides by 2.)}$$

$$\therefore \ x = 8$$

Worked Example 7

Solve $\dfrac{3}{4}(2x - 1) = 4$.

Solution:

$$\frac{3}{4}(2x - 1) = 4$$

$$\frac{6}{4}x - \frac{3}{4} = 4$$

$$\frac{3}{2}x - \frac{3}{4} + \frac{3}{4} = 4 + \frac{3}{4} \qquad \text{(Add } \frac{3}{4} \text{ to both sides.)}$$

$$\frac{3}{2}x = 4\frac{3}{4}$$

$$\frac{2}{3}\left(\frac{3}{2}x\right) = \frac{2}{3}\left(\frac{19}{4}\right) \qquad \text{(Divide both sides by } \frac{3}{2} \text{.)}$$

$$\therefore \ x = \frac{19}{6}$$

Note: Dividing by $\dfrac{3}{2}$ is the same as multiplying by $\dfrac{2}{3}$.

Alternative solution:

$$\frac{3}{4}(2x - 1) = 4$$

$$3(2x - 1) = 16 \qquad \text{(Multiply both sides by 4.)}$$

$$6x - 3 = 16$$

$$6x - 3 + 3 = 16 + 3 \qquad \text{(Add 3 to both sides.)}$$

$$6x = 19$$

$$\frac{6x}{6} = \frac{19}{6} \qquad \text{(Divide both sides by 6.)}$$

$$\therefore \ x = \frac{19}{6}$$

Worked Example 8

Solve $3x - \dfrac{5}{4} = 8 + \dfrac{5}{3}x + \dfrac{1}{6}$.

Solution:

$$3x - \frac{5}{4} = 8 + \frac{5}{3}x + \frac{1}{6}$$

$$3x - \frac{5}{3}x - \frac{5}{4} = 8 + \frac{5}{3}x - \frac{5}{3}x + \frac{1}{6} \qquad \text{(Subtract } \frac{5}{3}x \text{ from both sides.)}$$

$$\frac{4}{3}x - \frac{5}{4} = \frac{49}{6}$$

$$\frac{4}{3}x - \frac{5}{4} + \frac{5}{4} = \frac{49}{6} + \frac{5}{4} \qquad \text{(Add } \frac{5}{4} \text{ to both sides.)}$$

$$\frac{4}{3}x = \frac{98 + 15}{12}$$

$$\frac{3}{4}\left(\frac{4}{3}x\right) = \left(\frac{113}{12}\right)\frac{3}{4} \qquad \text{(Divide both sides by } \frac{4}{3}.\text{)}$$

$$\therefore \ x = \frac{113}{16}$$

Alternative solution:

$$3x - \frac{5}{4} = 8 + \frac{5}{3}x + \frac{1}{6}$$

$$36x - 15 = 96 + 20x + 2 \qquad \text{(Multiply every term by 12, the LCM of 4, 3 and 6.)}$$

$$36x - 20x = 96 + 2 + 15 \qquad \text{(Subtract } 20x \text{ from and add 15 to both sides.)}$$

$$16x = 113$$

$$\therefore \ x = \frac{113}{16} \qquad \text{(Divide both sides by 16.)}$$

Worked Example 9

Solve $4(1.2x - 3) = 2.7x$.

Solution:

$$4(1.2x - 3) = 2.7x$$
$$4.8x - 12 = 2.7x$$
$$4.8x - 12 - 2.7x = 2.7x - 2.7x \quad \text{(Subtract } 2.7x \text{ from both sides.)}$$
$$(4.8 - 2.7)x - 12 = 0$$
$$(4.8 - 2.7)x - 12 + 12 = 0 + 12 \quad \text{(Add 12 to both sides.)}$$
$$2.1x = 12$$
$$\therefore \ x = 12 \div 2.1 \quad \text{(Divide both sides by 2.1.)}$$
$$= 5.71 \quad \text{(3 significant figures)}$$

Note: When rounding off is necessary, we shall give answers rounded off to 3 significant figures, unless otherwise stated.

Exercise 6.3 ✍

answers on p. 428

Solve the following equations.

1. $\dfrac{1}{2}y + 3 = 9$

2. $\dfrac{1}{4}(8x + 4) = 3$

3. $\dfrac{1}{3}(3x + 9) = 2x + 3$

4. $\dfrac{2}{5}(2x + 3) = x + 1$

5. $\dfrac{1}{3}(x + 4) = 20$

6. $\dfrac{2}{5}a + 9 = 0$

7. $\dfrac{3}{5}y - \dfrac{2}{5} = \dfrac{4}{5}$

8. $\dfrac{1}{2}(5x - 4) = x + \dfrac{11}{2}$

9. $\dfrac{4}{3}x = \dfrac{7}{3} + x$

10. $\dfrac{y}{2} - \dfrac{4y}{5} = 3$

11. $\dfrac{9}{10}a + 7 = \dfrac{4}{5}a$

12. $\dfrac{m}{6} - \dfrac{m}{4} + \dfrac{m}{5} = 2$

13. $\dfrac{1}{2}(x - 1) + \dfrac{3}{4}(x + 3) = 0$

14. $\dfrac{2}{3}(7 - x) + \dfrac{1}{4}(x + 2) = 0$

15. $\dfrac{3}{4}(x + 4) - \dfrac{5}{6}\left(\dfrac{1}{4} - x\right) = 0$

16. $\dfrac{1}{6}(4 - p) - \dfrac{3}{4}(1 + p) = \dfrac{1}{4}$

17. $6.2x - 1.3 = 5.2$

18. $4.7y - 3 = 0.2$

19. $1.41 - 1.2x = 1.02$

20. $1.12x - 4.1 = 0.12$

21. $6.4z - 3 = z + 1.2$

22. $6.1x = 6 + 1.3x$

23. $3(1.4x - 1) = 3.3x + 1.2$

24. $1.2(1 - x) = 8.1 + 3.5x$

25. $\dfrac{3x - 1}{4} + \dfrac{x + 3}{8} = 0$

26. $\dfrac{x + 2}{6} - \dfrac{3x - 5}{4} = 0$

27. $\dfrac{2 - y}{8} - \dfrac{3(2 + y)}{4} = 0$

28. $\dfrac{3(x + 2)}{4} - \dfrac{5(1 - x)}{6} = 1$

*29. $\dfrac{1}{x} - 1 = \dfrac{1}{3}$

*30. $\dfrac{1}{x} + 1 = \dfrac{3}{x} + \dfrac{1}{2}$

6.4 EVALUATION OF FORMULAE

$P = 2(L + B)$ is a formula for finding the perimeter (P) of a rectangle when the length (L) and the breadth (B) are given. We can also find L when P and B are given. Suppose $P = 38$ and $B = 7$. Then,

$$
\begin{aligned}
38 &= 2(L + 7) \\
38 &= 2L + 14 \\
38 - 14 &= 2L \\
24 &= 2L \\
\therefore \quad L &= 12
\end{aligned}
$$

Worked Example 10

If $s = \dfrac{1}{2}(u + v)t$, find v when $u = 4$, $t = 13$ and $s = 42$.

Solution:

$$
\begin{aligned}
42 &= \frac{1}{2}(4 + v)(13) \\
2(42) &= (4 + v)(13) \\
84 &= 52 + 13v \\
32 &= 13v \\
\therefore \quad v &= \frac{32}{13} \\
&= 2\frac{6}{13}
\end{aligned}
$$

Worked Example 11

If $s = 2\pi r(r + h)$, find h when $s = 440$ and $r = 7$.

$\left(\text{Take } \pi = \dfrac{22}{7}.\right)$

Solution:

$$
\begin{aligned}
s &= 2\pi r(r + h) \\
440 &= 2 \times \frac{22}{7} \times 7(7 + h) \\
440 &= 44(7 + h) \\
10 &= 7 + h \\
\therefore \quad h &= 3
\end{aligned}
$$

Exercise 6.4 ✍

answers on p. 428

1. If $a = \dfrac{t - q}{qr}$, find a when $t = 120$, $q = 20$ and $r = 10$.

2. If $A = h(R^2 - r^2)$, find A when $R = 13$, $r = 5$ and $h = 2$.

3. If $s = ut + \dfrac{1}{2}ft^2$, find s when $u = 20$, $t = 10$ and $f = 15$.

4. If $A = LB$, find L when $A = 450$ and $B = 18$.

5. If $A = 2\pi rh$, find h when $A = 33$ and $r = \dfrac{7}{4}$. $\left(\text{Take } \pi = \dfrac{22}{7}.\right)$

6. If $E = \dfrac{1}{2}mV^2$, find V when $E = 180$ and $m = 10$.

7. If $v = u + ft$, find f when $v = 80$, $u = 14$ and $t = 16$.

8. If $v^2 = u^2 + 2fs$, find s when $f = 64$, $u = 10$ and $v = 120$.

9. If $\dfrac{t}{100} = \dfrac{w - v}{u - v}$, find t if $w = 5$, $v = 4$ and $u = 10$.

10. If $\dfrac{a^2 - b^2}{c^2 - b^2} = \dfrac{p}{q}$, find p if $a = 2$, $b = 3$, $c = 4$ and $q = 5$.

11. If $\dfrac{b}{h} = r\left(1 + \dfrac{k}{h}\right)$, find r if $b = 3$, $h = 4$ and $k = 12$.

12. If $A = \dfrac{1}{2}(a + b)h$, find a when $b = 12$, $h = 10$ and $A = 225$.

13. If $v = \dfrac{1}{3}\pi r^2 h$, find r when $h = 70$ and $v = 660$. $\left(\text{Take } \pi = \dfrac{22}{7}.\right)$

14. If $\dfrac{1}{t} = (u - 1)\left(\dfrac{1}{r_1} + \dfrac{1}{r_2}\right)$, find t when $u = \dfrac{3}{2}$, $r_1 = 20$ and $r_2 = 10$.

6.5 ALGEBRAIC PROBLEMS

Worked Example 12

The total cost of 5 pens and 15 pencils is $33. If the pencils cost 20 cents each, find the cost of each pen.

Solution:

Let the price of each pen be $x. Then, 5 pens cost $(5x).

15 pencils cost $15 \times 20¢$, i.e. $3.

The total cost of the pens and pencils is $(5x + 3)$. This cost is given as $33.

Thus,
$$5x + 3 = 33$$
$$5x = 30$$
$$x = \frac{30}{5}$$
$$= 6$$

Therefore, the price of 1 pen is $6.

Note: Checking of answers is always beneficial even though it is not required to be written down as part of your answer.

Worked Example 13

The sum of two numbers is 24. Twice the first plus the second is 26. Find the numbers.

Solution:

Let x be the first number. Then, $(24 - x)$ is the second number.

But twice the first plus the second is 26.

Thus,
$$2x + (24 - x) = 26$$
$$2x + 24 - x = 26$$
$$2x - x = 26 - 24$$
$$x = 2$$

Also,
$$24 - x = 24 - 2$$
$$= 22$$

Therefore, the numbers are 2 and 22.

Worked Example 14

A boy is 24 years younger than his father. In 2 years' time, the sum of their ages will be 40. How old is the father and how old is the son now?

Solution:

Let the father's age now be x years. Then, the son's age is $(x - 24)$ years.

In two years' time, their ages will be $(x + 2)$ and $(x - 24 + 2)$ years respectively.

Since the sum of their ages will then be 40 years, we have

$$
\begin{aligned}
(x + 2) + (x - 24 + 2) &= 40 \\
x + 2 + x - 24 + 2 &= 40 \\
2x - 20 &= 40 \\
2x &= 60 \\
x &= 30
\end{aligned}
$$

Therefore, the father is 30 years old now and the son is $(30 - 24)$, i.e. 6 years old.

Worked Example 15

A man mixes 5 kg of grade B coffee powder with 4 kg of grade A coffee powder. The grade A coffee powder costs $4.50 per kg more than the grade B coffee powder. If the cost of the mixture is $16 per kg, find the price of 1 kg of grade B coffee powder.

Solution:

Let x be the cost of 1 kg of grade B coffee powder. Then, $\$\left(x + 4\dfrac{1}{2} \right)$ is the cost of 1 kg of grade A coffee powder. We have

$$
\begin{aligned}
5x + 4\left(x + 4\tfrac{1}{2} \right) &= 16 \times 9 \\
5x + 4x + 18 &= 144 \\
9x &= 126 \\
x &= 14
\end{aligned}
$$

Therefore, the price of 1 kg of grade B coffee powder is $14.

Here are some points to remember when solving word problems:

1. Try to understand the problem clearly.

2. Look for the unknown quantities.

3. State clearly what your variable represents and the units used.

4. If necessary, write expressions for other unknown quantities in terms of the variable.

5. Write an equation which states the fact of the problem.

6. Use a sequence of equivalent equations to solve that equation.

7. Check the answers by testing them with the conditions as stated in the problem.

Exercise 6.5 ✍

answers on p. 428

1. Arthur has 12 more mangoes than Margaret. If they have 28 mangoes altogether, find the number of mangoes Arthur has.

2. Michael and Hassan together have 19 pineapples. If Hassan has 3 pineapples less than Michael, find the number of pineapples Michael has.

3. A number is only one third another. If their difference is 38, find the numbers.

4. A certain number is less than another by $\frac{3}{4}$. If their sum is $9\frac{1}{4}$, find the numbers.

5. One number is greater than half of another by 15. If their sum is 48, find the numbers.

6. A father is four times as old as his son now. If the father was 46 years old two years ago, find the son's age now.

7. A plant grows 3.5 cm per week. It is now 10 cm tall. How many weeks from now will the plant grow to a height of 27.5 cm?

8. The sum of two consecutive even numbers is 54. Find the numbers.

9. If the sum of two consecutive odd numbers is 208, what are the numbers?

10. If m is an odd number, write an expression for the next three consecutive odd numbers. If the sum of these four numbers is 32, find m.

11. The sum of a number, $\frac{3}{8}$ of the number and $\frac{5}{16}$ of the number is $7\frac{1}{2}$. Find the number.

12. I think of a certain number. If I multiply it by 6, add -18 to the product and take away one-third of the sum, I will get -2. What is the number?

13. The sum of two numbers is 2 and their difference is 10. Find the numbers.

14. There are twice as many 50-cent coins as there are one dollar coins in a box. If the total value of the money in the box is 154 dollars, how many 50-cent coins are there in the box?

15. Divide 102 dollars among three boys, A, B and C, so that A gets twice as much as B and C gets $1\frac{1}{2}$ times as much as A. How much does each boy get?

16. Abdul bought three plates and three mugs. If each plate cost him 30 cents more than each mug and if he paid $2.40 altogether, find the cost of each mug.

17. A father is now four times as old as his son. If the sum of their ages ten years ago was sixty, find their present ages.

18. A man bought 20 books. Some cost 18 dollars each and the others cost 3 dollars each. If he spent 210 dollars in all, how many of the 3-dollar books did he buy?

19. A boy is three years younger than his sister. If his age three years ago was two-thirds her age at that time, what are their present ages?

*20. John bought a certain number of apples at 30¢ each and he had $3 left. If he bought the same number of pears at 40¢ each instead of the apples, he would be short of $1. How many apples did he buy?

*21. There were 50 more pupils who took the mathematics test than the geography test. $\frac{1}{5}$ of those who took the mathematics test were girls and $\frac{1}{4}$ of those who took the geography test were girls. If the number of girls who took the mathematics test was 6 more than the number of girls who took the geography test, find the number of pupils who took the mathematics test.

*22. Meatballs and fishballs were sold in packets, each packet containing the same number of meatballs or fishballs. Meatballs were priced at 4 pieces for $1 and fishballs at 6 pieces for $1. A man had just enough money to buy 2 packets of meatballs and 1 packet of fishballs. He needed one more dollar if he were to buy 3 packets of meatballs instead. Find the number of meatballs or fishballs in a packet.

*23. A man has just enough money to buy 20 mangoes or 30 oranges If he wants to buy equal numbers of mangoes and oranges, how many of each type can he buy with the money?

Chapter Review

Equations

Solving an equation involves four tasks:

1. Remove all brackets and simplify.

2. Eliminate the unknown term on the RHS (right-hand side of the equation) by adding the appropriate term to both sides of the equation, and then simplify.

3. Eliminate the constant term on the LHS (left-hand side of the equation) by adding the appropriate term to both sides of the equation, and then simplify.

4. Eliminate the coefficient of the unknown on the LHS by multiplying both sides by the reciprocal of the coefficient, and then simplify.

CHALLENGER 6

1. Solve the following.

    (a) $\dfrac{x}{3} + \dfrac{2x}{4} - \dfrac{3x}{5} = 1$

    (b) $\dfrac{3x - 7}{3} - \dfrac{x - 3}{2} = 1$

    (c) $\dfrac{x + 1}{2} - \dfrac{x - 3}{5} = \dfrac{x + 2}{4}$

    (d) $\dfrac{3 - 7y}{3y} - \dfrac{1 - 3y}{2y} = 1$

2. Samy wanted to save money to buy a bicycle. In the first week, his savings were \$6 less than $\dfrac{1}{8}$ the price of the bicycle. In the second week, he saved another \$20.75. In the third week, his savings were 50 cents more than his total savings for the first and second weeks. He was still short of \$12. Find the price of the bicycle.

3. A certain amount of water is poured from a jug into an empty mug so that the amount of water in the mug is $\dfrac{1}{6}$ the amount of water left in the jug. If 50 ml of water is further poured from the jug to the mug, the amount of water in the mug will be $\dfrac{1}{5}$ of that left in the jug. Find the original amount of water in the jug.

4. Mr Lin wrote two numbers on the blackboard for his pupils to calculate the product of these two numbers. The last digit 8 (i.e. at the 'ones' place) of one of these numbers was not written clearly and John mistook it for 6. As a result, he obtained 4 740 as the answer which was wrong. Mary mistook the digit 8 for 3 and obtained 4 695 as the answer which was also incorrect. What should be the correct answer?

5. Mrs Wong bought two types of soft drinks. She bought the same number of cans for each type and paid 55 cents per can for one type and 65 cents per

can for the other type. If she had spent the same amount of money for each type, she would have bought 2 more cans of drinks. Find the total amount of money she spent on the drinks.

6. At a musical concert, class *A* tickets were sold at \$4 each, class *B* tickets at \$2 each and souvenir programmes at \$1 each. $\frac{3}{4}$ of the audience who bought class *A* tickets and $\frac{2}{3}$ of the audience who bought class *B* tickets also bought the programmes. The total amount of money collected from both types of tickets was \$1 400 and the amount of money collected from the programmes was \$350. Find the total number of people who attended the concert.

Problem Solving 6

Unfair Sharing

11 boys sat round a table. A plate of 52 biscuits was passed round. Each boy took 1 biscuit each time the plate came to him and then passed it round again until the plate was empty. How many of them received more biscuits than the others?

The strategy to use is **restate a problem in another way**.

Ask yourself: If the biscuits were shared equally, would there be some biscuits left over?

You may restate the problem as follows:
11 boys shared 52 biscuits equally. How many boys would get 1 more biscuit if the remaining biscuits were given away?

Now, you can easily solve the original problem.

$$11 \overline{)52} \\ \quad \underline{44} \\ \quad \ 8 \qquad 4$$

From the remainder, we see that 8 boys received more biscuits than the others. Check your answer.

Ask yourself: What do I like most about the given problem? About the strategy?

Problems...

1. **Sharing Flowers**   A group of girls shared 135 flowers. Some girls received 9 flowers each and the rest received 8 flowers each. How many girls received 8 flowers?

2. **Round Table**   A group of children sat round a table. A plate of 48 biscuits was passed round and round and each child took 1 biscuit until the plate was empty. If 3 children received 6 biscuits and the rest received less, how many children were there?

3. **Greatest Value**   Form proper fractions by putting different single-digit numbers in the boxes so that the expression obtained has the greatest possible value.

4. **Smallest Value**   Put 4 different single-digit numbers (except zero) in the boxes so that the expression obtained has the smallest possible value.

$$\frac{\square}{\square} + \frac{\square}{\square}$$

Rate, Ratio and Percentage

Chapter Highlights

- Solving problems involving rate and speed.
- Finding the ratio of two or more quantities.
- Solving problems involving ratio and direct and inverse proportions.
- Expressing one quantity as a percentage of another.
- Solving problems involving percentage.

7.1 RATE AND SPEED

Rate

Examples

(a) If a typist can type 250 words in 5 minutes, how many words can she type in 1 minute?

In 5 minutes, she can type 250 words.

In 1 minute, she can type $\dfrac{250}{5}$ words.

We say that she can type at the rate of $\dfrac{250}{5}$ words per minute or 50 words/min.

(b) If a man earns $36 for 3 hours of work, at what rate is he paid?

He is paid at the rate of $\dfrac{\$36}{6}$ per hour or $12/h.

In the above examples, the term '**rate**' is used to describe how a quantity is changing with time. We can also use the term 'rate' in other ways. For example, if a man buys 3 kg of fish for $12, he pays at the rate of $4 per kg for the fish.

When a ratio is used to compare two quantities that involve different units, the result is called a rate.

Speed

Examples

(a) If a man walks 7 kilometres in 2 hours, how many kilometres does he walk in 1 hour?

He walks at the rate of $\dfrac{7}{2}$ kilometres per hour or $3\dfrac{1}{2}$ km/h. We can also say that he walks at a speed of $3\dfrac{1}{2}$ km/h. The term '**speed**' is used for the rate of distance travelled per unit of time.

$$\text{Speed} = \frac{\text{Distance travelled}}{\text{Time taken}}$$

(b) When the indicator in the speedometer of a car points at 60 on a scale labelled in km/h, it means that the speed of the car is 60 km per hour at that instant. If the needle points at 60 all the time, the car is said to be travelling at a **constant** or **uniform speed**. But it is very seldom that the indicator remains at 60 all the time. Suppose that the car has covered 300 km in 5 hours. Its speed is unlikely to be $\dfrac{300}{5}$ km per hour at every instant. We can, however, say that the **average speed** is $\dfrac{300}{5}$ km/h or 60 km/h.

Worked Example 1

If 36 kg of insecticide is required to dress a field of area 3 000 m², calculate the rate

(a) in g/m²,

(b) kg/m².

Solution:

(a) For 3 000 m² of a field, 36 kg (i.e. 36 000 g) of insecticide is needed.

For 1 m² of the field, the required amount of insecticide is $\dfrac{36\ 000}{3\ 000}$ g/m² or 12 g/m².

(b)
$$1\ \text{kg} = 1\ 000\ \text{g}$$
$$1\ \text{g} = \dfrac{1}{1\ 000}\ \text{kg or } 0.001\ \text{kg}$$

Therefore, 12 g/m² = 12 × 0.001 kg/m²
$$= 0.012\ \text{kg/m}^2.$$

Worked Example 2

A motorist took $2\dfrac{1}{2}$ hours to travel from town X to town Y. His average speed for the whole journey was 80 km/h. For the first $\dfrac{1}{4}$ of the journey, he travelled at an average speed of 60 km/h. Find his average speed for the second part of the journey.

Solution:

Journey	Distance in km	Time in h	Speed in km/h
X to Y (whole journey)	(a)	$2\dfrac{1}{2}$	80
First $\dfrac{1}{4}$ of journey	(b)	(d)	60
Second part of journey	(c)	(e)	?

(a) Distance from X to Y = $\left(2\dfrac{1}{2} \times 80\right)$ km = 200 km

(b) Distance of first $\dfrac{1}{4}$ of journey = $\left(200 \times \dfrac{1}{4}\right)$ km = 50 km

(c) Distance of second part of journey = (200 − 50) km = 150 km

(d) Time taken for first $\dfrac{1}{4}$ of journey = $\dfrac{50}{60}$ h = $\dfrac{5}{6}$ h

(e) Time taken for second part of journey = $\left(2\dfrac{1}{2} - \dfrac{5}{6}\right)$ h = $1\dfrac{2}{3}$ h

Therefore, average speed for the second part of the journey $= \left(150 \div 1\frac{2}{3}\right)$ km/h

$$= 90 \text{ km/h.}$$

Exercise 7.1 ✍

answers on p. 428

1. Copy and complete the following.
   (a) If a car travels 100 km in 4 hours, the rate of travel is _____ km/h.
   (b) If one dozen eggs is sold for $2.40, the rate is _____ cents per egg.
   (c) If a tap fills a 450-litre tank with water in 1 hour, the water flows at the rate of _____ litres per minute.
   (d) If $24.00 is charged for 120 kWh of electricity consumed, the rate is _____ cents/kWh.

2. From 10 00 to 12 00, the rise in temperature is 4°C and from 15 00 to 17 00, the fall in temperature is 6°C. What is the average rate of
   (a) the rise in temperature per hour,
   (b) the fall in temperature per hour?

3. If a car travels 150 km on 15 l of petrol, what is the rate of petrol consumption in km/l? What is this rate in l/100 km?

4. If 150 g of fertiliser is needed to dress an area of 6 m², express this rate in
   (a) g/m²,
   (b) kg/m².

5. If an aeroplane travels at a speed of 450 km/h, how many metres does it travel in 10 s?

6. A clock is slow by 300 s in 1 week. How many seconds will it lose in 14 days?

7. Copy and complete the following.
   (a) 30 km/h = _____ cm/s
   (b) $100 per km = _____ cents per m
   (c) $2.50 per litre = _____ cents per ml

8. A motor cyclist took $1\frac{1}{2}$ h to travel 143 km from town P to town Q. He then took another $1\frac{1}{2}$ h to reach his destination, town R, which was 97 km from town Q. Find his average speed for the whole journey.

9. (a) If the average speed of a current is 1.5 m/s, find its speed in km/h.
   (b) A train passes a station at 30 km/h. Find its speed in m/s.
   (c) If water flows from a pipe at 200 cm/s, express the rate of flow in m/min.

10. A motorist travelled from town X to town Y at an average speed of 90 km/h. After travelling $\frac{1}{3}$ of the journey in 45 min, he continued to travel another 120 km to reach town Y. Find his average speed for the second part of the journey.

11. A car and a bus were travelling towards each other at uniform speeds. They were 250 km apart at noon and passed each other at 14 00. If the speed of the car was 80 km/h, find the speed of the bus.

12. A space capsule completes 1 orbit around the earth (about 42 000 km) in $1\frac{1}{2}$ h. At what speed, in km/h, is the capsule travelling? What distance would the capsule have travelled in 1 day?

*13. A motorist left town A at 08 30 and reached town B at 13 00. The distance travelled was 243 km. If he took a short-cut to save 13 km but drove at a slower speed by 4 km/h, at what time would he arrive at town B?

*14. A cyclist, riding steadily from his hometown, reached his destination in $4\frac{1}{2}$ h. He would have taken 45 min less time if he had ridden his bicycle at a speed faster by 3 km/h. Find the distance from his hometown to his destination.

*15. A car travelled along a straight road from town X to town Y at 65 km/h. A motorcycle travelled from town Y to town X at 50 km/h. Both started their journeys at the same time and travelled on the same road. If the two vehicles passed each other after travelling for 1 h 45 min, find the distance between the two towns.

*16. At 09 30, car A started its journey and travelled at 65 km/h. At 11 00, car B started its journey from the same place and travelled on the same road as car A. If car B, travelling at a constant speed, took five hours to catch up with car A, find the speed of car B.

7.2 RATIO

Examples

(a) The label on a bottle of detergent reads 'Before use, mix 3 parts of detergent with 5 parts of water'.

   A ratio is a way to compare two numbers.

   We say that the **ratio** of the amount of detergent to the amount of water is 3 to 5. We write

   amount of detergent : amount of water = 3 : 5.

Reversing the order, we say that the ratio of the amount of water to the amount of detergent is 5 to 3. We write

amount of water : amount of detergent = 5 : 3.

How much detergent is needed to mix with 1 250 ml of water?

Let us draw a diagram to illustrate this.

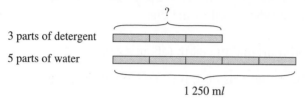

3 parts of detergent

5 parts of water

1 250 ml

Fig. 7.1

Suppose each part is p ml.
Then,
$$5p = 1\ 250$$
$$p = 250$$
$$3p = 3 \times 250$$
$$= 750$$

Therefore, 750 ml of detergent is needed.

Alternatively, we can also find the amount of detergent by using division.

$$\frac{\text{Amount of detergent}}{\text{Amount of water}} = \frac{3p}{5p} = \frac{3}{5}$$

$$\text{Amount of detergent} = \frac{3}{5} \times \text{Amount of water}$$

$$= \frac{3}{5} \times 1\ 250 \text{ ml}$$

$$= 750 \text{ ml}$$

Therefore, 750 ml of detergent is needed.

If we denote the amount of detergent by D and the amount of water by W, we have the following equivalent sentences.

$D : W = 3 : 5$	$W : D = 5 : 3$
$\dfrac{D}{W} = \dfrac{3}{5}$	$\dfrac{W}{D} = \dfrac{5}{3}$
$D = \dfrac{3}{5} \times W$	$W = \dfrac{5}{3} \times D$

Notice that a given ratio helps us to express one quantity as a fraction of the other.

MATHSTORY

The ratio $\frac{l}{w}$ (where l is the length and w the width of a rectangle) can be approximated by $\frac{8.1}{5.0} = 1.62$. This is called the golden ratio. This ratio has many occurrences in nature.

(b) If the price of a pen is raised from \$30 to \$40, we can compare the new price and the old price using ratio.

$$\frac{\text{New price of the pen}}{\text{Old price of the pen}} = \frac{\$40}{\$30}$$

$$= \frac{4}{3}$$

Let us express the new price as a fraction of the old price.

Thus, the new price = $\frac{4}{3}$ × the old price.

Since the new price is $\frac{4}{3}$ as much as the old price, we say that the price of the pen has **increased in the ratio** 4 : 3.

If the price of a pen is reduced from \$40 to \$35, comparing the new and old prices, we have the following ratio.

$$\frac{\text{New price of the pen}}{\text{Old price of the pen}} = \frac{\$35}{\$40}$$

$$= \frac{7}{8}$$

Then, the new price = $\frac{7}{8}$ × the old price.

Since the new price is $\frac{7}{8}$ as much as the old price, we say that the price of the pen has **decreased in the ratio** 7 : 8.

(c) Mrs Li used the following formula to make a drink.

Pineapple juice : 2 parts
Mango juice   : 3 parts
Apple juice   : 5 parts

We say that the pineapple juice, mango juice and apple juice are mixed in the ratio 2 : 3 : 5.

If she wants to make 5 *l* of drink, how much of each type of juice is needed?

Let us illustrate this with a diagram.

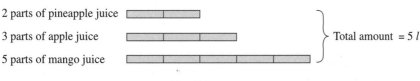

2 parts of pineapple juice

3 parts of apple juice

5 parts of mango juice

Total amount = 5 *l*

Fig. 7.2

Let each part be p l.

Then,
$$2p + 3p + 5p = 5$$
$$10p = 5$$
$$p = \frac{1}{2}$$

Therefore, the amounts of fruit juice needed are as follows:

Amount of pineapple juice $= 2 \times \frac{1}{2}$ $l = 1$ l

Amount of mango juice $= 3 \times \frac{1}{2}$ $l = 1\frac{1}{2}$ l

Amount of apple juice $= 5 \times \frac{1}{2}$ $l = 2\frac{1}{2}$ l

(d) We have learnt that $\frac{3}{5}, \frac{6}{10}, \frac{9}{15}, \ldots$ are equivalent fractions. The corresponding ratios $3 : 5, 6 : 10, 9 : 15, \ldots$ are referred to as **equivalent ratios**. Note that any ratio in the form $3m : 5m$ is equivalent to $3 : 5$.

For three-term ratio, $2 : 3 : 5, 4 : 6 : 10, 6 : 9 : 15, \ldots$ are known as equivalent ratios. In other words, any ratio in the form $2m : 3m : 5m$ is equivalent to $2 : 3 : 5$.

Worked Example 3

Express each of the following ratios as simply as possible in the form $a : b$.

(a) A mass of 2 kg to a mass of 850 g

(b) $0.4 : 1.2$

(c) A length of $\frac{3}{4}$ m to a length of $\frac{2}{3}$ m

Solution:

(a)
$$\frac{2 \text{ kg}}{850 \text{ g}} = \frac{2\,000}{850}$$
$$= \frac{40}{17}$$
$$2 \text{ kg} : 850 \text{ g} = 40 : 17$$

(b)
$$\frac{0.4}{1.2} = \frac{4}{12}$$
$$= \frac{1}{3}$$
$$0.4 : 1.2 = 1 : 3$$

(c)
$$\frac{\frac{3}{4}}{\frac{2}{3}} = \frac{3}{4} \times \frac{3}{2}$$
$$= \frac{9}{8}$$
$$\frac{3}{4} : \frac{2}{3} = 9 : 8$$

Worked Example 4

If $A : B = 5 : 6$ and $B : C = 4 : 5$, find $A : B : C$.

Solution:

$A : B = 5 : 6 = 10 : 12$

$B : C = 4 : 5 = 12 : 15$

$\therefore$ $A : B : C = 10 : 12 : 15$

2	6, 4
2	3, 2
3	3, 1
	1, 1

$\text{LCM} = 2^2 \times 3 = 12$

Alternative solution:

$$A : B : C$$
$$5 : 6 \qquad \dots\dots\dots\dots (1)$$
$$\qquad 4 : 5 \quad \dots\dots\dots\dots (2)$$

Thus,

$$\quad\quad\quad\quad\quad A \ : \ B \ : \ C$$

$(1) \times 2,$	$10 : 12$
$(2) \times 3,$	$\quad\ 12 : 15$

$$\therefore \quad A : B : C = 10 : 12 : 15$$

Worked Example 5

The monthly rent of a stall is decreased in the ratio 5 : 6. As a result, the stall holder saves $40 a month. Find the original rent.

Solution:

Let the original rent be x. Then, the new rent is $(x - 40)$.

$$\frac{\text{New rent}}{\text{Original rent}} = \frac{5}{6}$$
$$\frac{x - 40}{x} = \frac{5}{6}$$
$$6(x - 40) = 5x$$
$$6x - 240 = 5x$$
$$x = 240$$

Therefore, the original rent is $240.

Worked Example 6

A ribbon is cut into 3 pieces, A, B and C, in the ratio 1 : 2 : 4. If C is longer than B by 16 cm, find the length of the ribbon.

Solution:

Let the length of each part be p cm.

$$2p = 16$$
$$p = 16 \div 2$$
$$\ \ = 8$$
$$7p = 7 \times 8$$
$$\ \ \ = 56$$

Therefore, the length of the ribbon is 56 cm.

Alternative solution:
Let x cm be the length of the ribbon.

$$\frac{4}{7}x - \frac{2}{7}x = 16$$
$$4x - 2x = 112$$
$$2x = 112$$
$$x = 56$$

Therefore, the length of the ribbon is 56 cm.

Exercise 7.2

answers on p. 429

1. Express each of the following ratios as simply as possible in the form $a : b$.
   - **(a)** $10 : 6$
   - **(b)** $24 : 8$
   - **(c)** $3.5 : 2.1$
   - **(d)** $\frac{2}{3} : \frac{1}{4}$
   - **(e)** $2.4 : 3.6$
   - **(f)** $3\frac{1}{2} : 1\frac{1}{7}$

2. Find the ratio of each of the following.
   - **(a)** 20 cm to 1 m
   - **(b)** 1 kg to 70 g
   - **(c)** 80 m to 1 km
   - **(d)** 40 cm² to 1 m²
   - **(e)** 2 h to 45 min
   - **(f)** $\frac{1}{2}$ m³ to 20 000 cm³

3. Given $A = 24$ cm and $B = 64$ cm,
   - **(a)** find $A : B$,
   - **(b)** express A as a fraction of B.

4. If $A = \frac{3}{4}B$, find $A : B$.

5. There are 5 boys to every 6 girls in a class of 44 pupils. Find the number of boys in the class.

6. In a school there are 64 teachers, 1 024 girls and 1 536 boys.
   - **(a)** Find the ratio of the number of teachers to the number of pupils.
   - **(b)** Find the ratio of the number of girls to the total number of pupils.
   - **(c)** Express the number of teachers as a fraction to the number of boys.

7. If the ratio of the sides of 2 squares is 2 : 3, find the ratio of their areas.

8. If the ratio of the sides of 2 cubes is 1 : 3, what is the ratio of their volumes?

9. A man earns $3 500 a month.
   - **(a)** If the ratio of his expenditure to his income is 2 : 5, what is his expenditure?
   - **(b)** What is the ratio of his savings to his income?

10. **(a)** A sum of $24 000 is to be divided into three shares in the ratio of 3 : 5 : 7. Find the largest share.
    (b) The lengths of the sides of a triangle are in the ratio of 4 : 5 : 6. If the perimeter is 45 cm, find the sides.

11. Mr Chen earns $2 500 and spends $1 750 a month. Find the ratio of
    (a) his income to his expenditure,
    (b) his savings to his income,
    (c) his savings to his expenditure.

12. **(a)** If $A : B = 3 : 4$ and $B : C = 2 : 3$, find $A : B : C$.
    (b) If $X : Y = 5 : 4$ and $Y : Z = 6 : 1$, find $X : Y : Z$.

13. If the price of petrol is increased from $1.20 to $1.50 per litre, find the ratio in which the price increases.

14. The price of a book is increased in the ratio 6 : 5. Find the new price if the old price was $15.

15. In a sale, the prices of all stationery articles were reduced in the ratio 4 : 5. Find the sale price of
    (a) a pen whose original price was $25,
    (b) a pencil box whose original price was $1.50,
    (c) a clipboard whose original price was $3.75.

16. A picture measuring 8.5 cm by 5.5 cm is enlarged in the ratio 7 : 5. Find the dimensions of the new picture.

17. When the price of 1 *l* of petrol is reduced from $1.50 to $1.20, Mr Rajan increased his monthly petrol consumption from 200 *l* to 300 *l*. In what ratio does his petrol bill increase or decrease?

18. A school's computer club has 250 boys and 175 girls. If the number of girls is decreased in the ratio 4 : 5 while the number of boys is increased in the ratio 6 : 5, what is the new ratio of boys to girls?

19. David's expenditure in April has decreased in the ratio 4 : 5 and as a result he saves $120. Find his expenditure in March.

20. A piece of wood is cut into 3 pieces A, B and C, in the ratio 2 : 3 : 5. If C is longer than B by 8 cm, find the length of the stick.

*21. The ratio of the number of boys to the number of girls in a group of pupils is 2 : 3. If $\frac{1}{4}$ of the boys and $\frac{1}{3}$ of the girls wear glasses, find the ratio of the number of girls who wear glasses to the number of boys who wear glasses.

*22. A sum of money was shared between Mr and Mrs Lin in the ratio 2 : 5. If the sum was shared in the ratio 5 : 2 instead, Mr Lin would receive $600 more. Find the sum of money.

*23. The subscriptions to a club for men and women are in the ratio 4 : 3. Two men and five women pay a total sum of $460. What is the subscription fee for each man?

*24. A sum of money was shared between A, B and C so that A received $\frac{1}{4}$ of the sum, and the remainder was shared between B and C in the ratio 3 : 2. Find the ratio in which the sum was shared between A, B and C.

7.3 DIRECT AND INVERSE PROPORTIONS

Direct Proportion

Examples

(a) A man earns $30 a day working in a factory. Table 7.1 shows his earnings and the corresponding number of days he works.

A proportion is an equation stating that two ratios are equal.

Earnings in $	30	60	90	120
Days of work	1	2	3	4

Table 7.1

Let us study any two cases from the table.

Case (i) The man earns $60 for 2 days of work.
Case (ii) The man earns $120 for 4 days of work.

We have

$$\frac{\text{amount earned in case (i)}}{\text{amount earned in case (ii)}} = \frac{\$60}{\$120} = \frac{1}{2}.$$

Also, $$\frac{\text{number of days of work in case (i)}}{\text{number of days of work in case (ii)}} = \frac{2}{4} = \frac{1}{2}.$$

Notice that these two ratios are equal. We say that the earnings are **directly proportional** to the number of days of work.

Notice also that the quotient,

$$\frac{\text{amount earned}}{\text{number of days of work}},$$

has a constant value, i.e. 30.

(b)   Suppose a lorry is travelling at a constant speed.

We have

$$\frac{\text{distance travelled}}{\text{time taken}} = \text{speed (constant)}.$$

Thus, the distance travelled is directly proportional to the time taken if the speed is constant.

Worked Example 7

Salleh would have earned \$504 for working 42 hours a week but he was absent for 4 hours. How much was he paid then?

Solution:
The number of hours Salleh worked = (42 − 4) h
                                                      = 38 h
Let \$x be the amount Salleh received.

$$\frac{x}{504} = \frac{38}{42}$$

$$\therefore \quad x = \frac{38}{42} \times 504$$

$$= 456$$

Salleh was paid \$456.

Alternative solution:
Pay for 42 h work = \$504

Pay for 1 h work $= \dfrac{\$504}{42}$

Pay for 4 h work $= \$\left(\dfrac{504}{42} \times 4\right) = \$48$

Therefore, he was paid \$(504 − 48), i.e. \$456.

Inverse Proportion

Examples

(a)   The table below shows the number of men required to paint a house and the corresponding time they take to complete the job.

Number of men	1	2	3	4
Time in hours	12	6	4	3

Table 7.2

Let us study any two cases from the table.

Case (i)   2 men take 6 h to complete the job.
Case (ii)   4 men take 3 h to complete the job.

We have

$$\frac{\text{number of men required in case (i)}}{\text{number of men required in case (ii)}} = \frac{2}{4} = \frac{1}{2}.$$

Also, $$\frac{\text{number of hours required in case (i)}}{\text{number of hours required in case (ii)}} = \frac{6}{3} = \frac{2}{1}.$$

Notice that these two ratios are not equal. But one is the reciprocal of the other because $\frac{1}{2} \times \frac{2}{1} = 1$. We say that the number of men required is **inversely proportional** to the number of hours required.

Notice also that the product,

number of men required × number of hours required,

has a constant value, i.e. 12.

(b)   Suppose a journey of a fixed distance has to be made.

We have

speed × time taken = distance travelled (constant).

Thus, the speed is inversely proportional to the time taken if the distance travelled is constant.

Worked Example 8
A job can be completed in 15 days by 9 men. How long will it take 5 men to finish the same job if they work at the same rate?

Solution:
9 men can finish a job in 15 days.
1 man can finish the same job in (9 × 15) days.

Therefore, 5 men can finish this job in $\frac{9 \times 15}{5}$ or 27 days.

Note: 9 men take 15 days to do a job, 1 man takes 15 days to do $\frac{1}{9}$ of the job
or (9 × 15) days to do the whole job.

Alternative solution:

Let the number of days required by 5 men to complete the job be x.

$$9 \text{ men correspond to } 15 \text{ days.}$$
$$5 \text{ men correspond to } x \text{ days.}$$

For inverse proportion, we have

$$\frac{9}{5} = \frac{x}{15}$$
$$\therefore \quad x = \frac{15 \times 9}{5} = 27$$

It takes 27 days for 5 men to finish the job.

Note: For inverse proportion, the ratio of the number of men required in the two cases is equal to the reciprocal of the ratio of the corresponding number of days.

Worked Example 9

4 men can unload 300 kg of goods in 3 hours. How many men are needed to unload 450 kg of goods in 2 hours?

Solution:

In 3 h, 4 men are needed to unload 300 kg of goods.

In 2 h, $\left(\frac{3}{2} \times 4\right)$ or 6 men are needed to unload 300 kg of goods.

In 2 h, $\frac{450}{300} \times 6$ or 9 men are needed to unload 450 kg of goods.

Note: The solution may be presented using the idea of man-hour as follows:
Let x be the required number of men.
4×3, i.e. 12, man-hours are needed to unload 300 kg.
$x \times 2$, i.e. $2x$, man-hours are needed to unload 450 kg of goods.

So, $$\frac{2x}{12} = \frac{450}{300}$$
$$\therefore \quad x = 9$$

Alternative solution:

Number of men	Number of kg of goods	Number of hours
4	300	3
x	300	2
y	450	2

For inverse proportion,

$$\frac{x}{4} = \frac{3}{2}$$

$$\therefore \quad x = \frac{3}{2} \times 4$$

$$= 6$$

For direct proportion,

$$\frac{y}{x} = \frac{450}{300}$$

$$\therefore \quad y = \frac{450}{300}x$$

$$= \frac{3}{2} \times 6$$

$$= 9$$

Therefore, 9 men are needed.

Note: In the table, the 1st and 2nd rows show inverse proportion since more men take shorter time to unload the same 300 kg of goods, and the 2nd and 3rd rows show direct proportion since more men are needed to unload more goods in the same 2 hours.

Exercise 7.3

answers on p. 429

1. A car used 35.5 *l* of petrol for a journey of 426 km. How much petrol would it use for a journey of 600 km?

2. A car travelling at a uniform speed started at noon and covered the first 150 km of a journey by 3.00 p.m. Find the time when it had completed the whole journey of 600 km.

3. Samad's normal pay for working 42 hours a week is $630. He is paid at a double rate when he works overtime. Find his total earnings if he works 48 hours a week.

4. A carpet, measuring 4 m by 2.5 m, costs $86. Find the cost of a carpet of the same quality, measuring 5 m by 3 m.

5. If 3 men can load a lorry of goods in 2 h, how long will it take **(a)** 6 men, **(b)** 5 men, and **(c)** 2 men, to load the lorry of goods if they work at the same rate?

6. If 5 men can complete a job in 2 weeks, how long will it take 10 men to complete the same job if they work at the same rate?

7. A piece of work can be completed in 30 days by 10 men. If the work is to be completed 5 days earlier, how many more men are needed? (Assume that the men work at the same rate.)

8. If 9 men can complete a job in 4 days, how long will 8 men take to complete the same job, assuming that all the men are working at the same rate?

9. The wages of 6 men working for 5 hours amount to $480. Find the wages of 10 men working for 8 hours.

10. Working 8 hours a day, 48 men can complete a job in 1 week. How many men working 6 hours a day will complete the same job in 16 days?

11. If 125 kg of food is sufficient for 24 soldiers for 5 days, how long will the food last for 30 soldiers?

12. At noon, car *A* started to travel at a uniform speed from town *X* to town *Y* which was 60 km away from town *X*. One and a half hours later, car *B* started to travel at the same uniform speed as car *A* from town *Y* to town *X*. They passed each other at 3.00 p.m. What distance had they each travelled when they passed each other?

13. A cyclist took 45 min to cycle uphill. He then took 30 min to cycle the same distance downhill. The difference between their average speeds was 4 km/h. At what speed did he cycle uphill?

14. A car travelling at 60 km/h for 3 h uses 9 *l* of petrol. How much petrol will be needed when it travels for 4 h at 40 km/h?

15. 14 men took 6 h 40 min to complete a certain job.
    (a) How long will it take 8 men, working at the same rate, to complete the same job?
    (b) If 2 of the 8 men leave the job after working for 1 h, how long will it take the remaining 6 men working at the same rate to complete the job?

7.4 PERCENTAGE

When you sit for an examination, the teacher often reports your grades in **percentages**. The expression *per cent* comes from a Latin phrase *per centum* meaning 'for each hundred' or 'out of a hundred'. We write % as a short form for 'per cent'.

In an examination, there are ten questions, all carrying equal marks. If a boy has six of the questions correct, he then obtains $\frac{6}{10}$ of the marks. The fraction $\frac{6}{10}$ is equivalent to $\frac{60}{100}$. Therefore, we say that the student has 60 per cent or 60% of the questions correct. Thus, if a fraction is expressed with 100 as its denominator, it is said to be expressed as a percentage. Note that 60% can also be written as $60 \times \frac{1}{100}$. Thus, $60\% = 60 \times \frac{1}{100} = \frac{60}{100}$.

A percentage can be converted to a decimal or a fraction. For example, $35\% = \frac{35}{100} = 0.35$ or $35\% = \frac{35}{100} = \frac{7}{20}$. Thus, $35\% = 0.35 = \frac{7}{20}$. This shows that there is a link between percentages, decimals and fractions.

Worked Example 10

Express the following as percentages.

(a) $\dfrac{7}{8}$ (b) $1\dfrac{5}{8}$ (c) 0.12

Solution:

(a) $\dfrac{7}{8} = \dfrac{7}{8} \times 100\%$

$= \dfrac{700}{8}\%$

$= 87.5\%$

(b) $1\dfrac{5}{8} = \dfrac{13}{8} \times 100\%$

$= \dfrac{1\,300}{8}\%$

$= 162.5\%$

(c) $0.12 = \dfrac{12}{100} \times 100\%$

$= 12\%$

Note: Customarily we express percentage either in the form of a decimal or as a mixed number.

Thus, it is better to take the answer for (a) as 87.5% or $87\dfrac{1}{2}\%$ rather than $\dfrac{700}{8}\%$ or $\dfrac{175}{2}\%$.

Worked Example 11

Express $11\dfrac{3}{5}\%$ as **(a)** a fraction reduced to its lowest terms, and **(b)** a decimal.

Solution:

(a) $11\dfrac{3}{5}\% = \dfrac{58}{5} \times \dfrac{1}{100}$

$= \dfrac{29}{250}$

(b) $11\dfrac{3}{5}\% = 11.6\%$

$= 11.6 \times \dfrac{1}{100}$

$= 0.116$

Worked Example 12

Find the value of 25% of $124.16.

Solution:

$$25\% \text{ of } \$124.16 = 25\% \times \$124.16$$
$$= 25 \times \frac{1}{100} \times \$124.16$$
$$= \$\frac{124.16}{4}$$
$$= \$31.04$$

Worked Example 13

Express the first quantity as a percentage of the second quantity in each of the following.

(a) 15.4 m; 9.5 m

(b) 4 months; $1\frac{1}{2}$ years

Solution:

(a) Suppose 15.4 m = x% of 9.5 m.

Then,
$$15.4 = \frac{x}{100} \times 9.5$$
$$x = \frac{15.4 \times 100}{9.5}$$
$$= 162.1$$

Therefore, 15.4 m = 162.1% of 9.5 m.

(b) Suppose 4 months = x% of $1\frac{1}{2}$ years,

i.e. 4 months = x% of 18 months.

Then,
$$4 = \frac{x}{100} \times 18$$
$$x = \frac{4 \times 100}{18}$$
$$= 22.2$$

Therefore, 4 months = 22.2% of $1\frac{1}{2}$ years.

Note: Alternatively, we can express the first quantity as a fraction of the second quantity and then convert the answer to a percentage as shown below.

(a) Required percentage = $\frac{15.4}{9.5} \times 100$ %

$$= 162.1\%$$

Therefore, 15.4 m = 162.1% of 9.5 m.

(b) $1\frac{1}{2}$ years = 18 months

Required percentage = $\frac{4}{18} \times 100\%$

$$= 22.2\%$$

Therefore, 4 months = 22.2% of $1\frac{1}{2}$ years.

Exercise 7.4 ✍

answers on p. 429

1. Express the following as percentages.

    (a) $\dfrac{3}{4}$ **(b)** $\dfrac{4}{125}$ **(c)** $\dfrac{5}{5}$

    (d) $2\dfrac{1}{2}$ **(e)** $\dfrac{110}{100}$ **(f)** $\dfrac{1}{50}$

2. Express the following as percentages.
    (a) 0.325 **(b)** 0.05 **(c)** 2.3
    (d) 1.25 **(e)** 0.225 **(f)** 0.015

3. Express each of the following as a fraction reduced to its lowest terms.

    (a) 4% **(b)** 5% **(c)** $55\dfrac{1}{2}\%$

    (d) 0.2% **(e)** $7\dfrac{1}{3}\%$ **(f)** $7\dfrac{1}{5}\%$

4. Express the following as decimals.

    (a) 33% **(b)** $\dfrac{1}{2}\%$ **(c)** 1.5%

    (d) $12\dfrac{1}{2}\%$ **(e)** 250% **(f)** 75%

5. Find the values of the following.

    (a) $5\dfrac{1}{5}\%$ of \$74 **(b)** 10% of \$230 **(c)** 25% of \$750.28

    (d) 5% of \$130 **(e)** $7\dfrac{1}{2}\%$ of \$100 **(f)** 110% of \$220

6. Express the first quantity as a percentage of the second in each of the following.
    (a) 10 m; 1 km **(b)** 5 mm; 1 m **(c)** 120°; 360°
    (d) 20 min; 1 h **(e)** 3 months; 1 year **(f)** 33 cents; \$3

7.5 APPLICATION OF PERCENTAGES

Examples

(a) If the price of an article is increased by 35%, then the increased price is 100% + 35% or 135% of the original price.

(b) If the increased price of an article is 112% of the original price, then the increase in price is 112% – 100% or 12% of the original price.

(c) If the price of an article is decreased by 18%, then the decreased price is 100% – 18% or 82% of the original price.

(d) If the decreased price of an article is 76% of the original price, then the decrease in price is 100% – 76% or 24% of the original price.

Note: Customarily, when we say 'the price . . . increased by 35%', we mean 'the price . . . increased by 35% of the original price'. Thus, the original price is taken to correspond to 100%.

Worked Example 14

A man saved $80 in a certain month.

(a) In the following month, he saved $96. Find the percentage increase in his savings.

(b) In the third month, he saved $86.40. Find the percentage decrease in his savings.

Solution:

(a) The increase in his savings = $96 – $80
$$= \$16$$

$\therefore$ the percentage increase $= \dfrac{16}{80} \times 100\%$
$$= 20\%$$

(b) The decrease in his savings = $96 – $86.40
$$= \$9.60$$

$\therefore$ the percentage decrease $= \dfrac{9.60}{96} \times 100\%$
$$= 10\%$$

Note: When we talk about percentage increase, we first think of the word 'increase'. In this case, we think of the increase over the previous savings. Thus, the increase is $96 – $80. Then, consider the question 'find the percentage increase' which means 'find out how many per cent of the previous savings this increase is'.

Since the increase is $\dfrac{16}{80}$ of the previous savings, we can express the fraction $\dfrac{16}{80}$ in the form of a percentage, i.e. $\dfrac{16}{80} \times 100\% = 20\%$.

We follow the same argument for percentage decrease, bearing in mind that the previous savings in this case is $96 and not $80.

Worked Example 15

If the price of a watch is increased by 20% to $150, what was the original price?

Solution:

$$120\% \text{ of the original price} = \$150$$

$$1\% \text{ of the original price} = \$\frac{150}{120}$$

$$100\% \text{ of the original price} = \$\frac{150}{120} \times 100$$

$$= \$125$$

Thus, the original price was $125.

Alternative solution:

Let x be the original price.

Then, 20% of $x = \frac{20}{100}x$.

Now,

$$x + \frac{20}{100}x = 150$$

$$\frac{120}{100}x = 150$$

$$120x = 150 \times 100$$

$$x = \frac{150 \times 100}{120}$$

$$= 125$$

Thus, the original price was $125.

Worked Example 16

Two students, A and B, stood for election for the post of House Captain. A received 60% of the votes cast and secured a majority of 45 votes, that is, 45 votes more than B. How many students voted?

Solution:

A received 60% of the votes. Then, B received 40% of the votes. So, A received 60% − 40% or 20% of the votes more than B.

$$20\% \text{ of the votes} = 45$$

$$1\% \text{ of the votes} = \frac{45}{20}$$

$$100\% \text{ of the votes} = \frac{45}{20} \times 100$$

$$= 225$$

Therefore, 225 students voted.

Alternative solution:

Let the number of students who voted be x.

If A received 60% of the votes, then B received 40% of the votes.

Now,   60% of x – 40% of x = 45

$$\frac{60}{100}x - \frac{40}{100}x = 45$$
$$60x - 40x = 4\ 500$$
$$20x = 4\ 500$$
$$x = 225$$

Therefore, 225 students voted.

Exercise 7.5 ✍

answers on p. 429

1. Copy and complete the following.
   (a) If the price of a car is increased by 15%, then the increased price is ____% of the original price.
   (b) If the increased price of a bicycle is 105% of the original price, then the increase in price is ____ % of the original price.
   (c) If the price of a refrigerator is decreased by 16%, then the decreased price is ____ % of the original price.
   (d) If the decreased price of a TV set is 96% of the original price, then the decrease in price is ____ % of the original price.

2. In 1980, the population of a town was 72 000. In 1990, the population had risen to 81 000. Find the percentage increase of the population.

3. A primary school had an enrolment of 1 275 pupils in January 1980. In January 1990, the enrolment was 1 020. What was the percentage decrease for the enrolment?

4. In a certain month, a family spent $750 on food.
   (a) In the following month, the family spent $810 on food. What was the percentage increase in the money spent on food?
   (b) In the third month, the family spent $729 on food. What was the percentage decrease in the money spent on food?

5. The enrolment of a certain secondary school was 450 in 1989. By 1990, the enrolment had increased by 16%. What was the enrolment in 1990?

6. If the price of a bicycle is increased by 25% to $95, what was the original price?

7. If the price of a book is decreased by 5% to $19, what was the original price?

8. The increase in price of an article is 20% of the original price. If the new price is $150, what was the original price?

9. The decrease in price of an article is 5% of the original price. If the new price is $285, what was the original price?

10. In an examination, 70 problems were given and all the problems carried equal marks. A boy solved 55 problems correctly. What percentage was this? In order to pass the examination, it was necessary to answer at least 40% correctly. What was the least number of correct answers needed to pass?

11. A boy scored 90 marks for his mathematics test. This was 20% more than what he had scored for his geography test. What was his score in geography?

12. In an election, there were two candidates. One of them received 65% of the votes cast and secured a majority of 1 500 votes, that is, 1 500 votes more than his competitor. How many people voted?

13. A 40-litre barrel is full of a wine which contains 8% of alcohol. 10 litres of the wine is drawn off and replaced by water. What percentage of alcohol is the mixture?

*14. Peter is 8% heavier than Henry, and James is 10% lighter than Henry. By what percentage is Peter heavier than James?

*15. In the course of a year, $\frac{1}{3}$ of a company's capital increases by 4%, $\frac{1}{5}$ of it decreases by 5% and the rest increases by 10%. What is the percentage increase on the whole?

*16. 10 workers planned to produce 10 tonnes of soap powder in 10 weeks, working 10 hours every day. In the first 10 days, they produced 10 kg less than 10% of the total amount they planned to produce. In the next 10 days, they produced 10% more soap powder than in the first 10 days. They then decided to complete the job 10 days earlier. At what rate must they work in order to meet the new target? Give your answer correct to the nearest gram per hour per worker.

*17. Samy wanted to save money to buy a tennis racket. In the first week, he saved 40% of the money needed for the racket. In the second week, he saved $\frac{3}{4}$ of the remaining part of the money he needed. By then, there was a 5% increase in the price of the racket. As a result, he was still short of $12. What was the original price of the racket?

*18. How much water must be added to a bottle of 840 cm³ of acid which contains 10% of pure acid to obtain a solution containing 7% of pure acid?

*19. A solution is prepared by adding 30 g of sugar in 500 g of water. How much sugar must be added to the solution to obtain a new solution containing 40% of sugar?

*20. An alloy of copper and silver containing 60% of pure silver is mixed with another alloy, also of copper and silver containing 65% of pure silver. How much of each type is needed to produce 1 200 g of alloy containing 62% of pure silver?

Chapter Review

1. **Rate**

   Rate is used to describe how a quantity is changing with another quantity.
   Examples: 50 words in one minute or 50 words/min
   $12/h
   $4/kg

2. **Speed**

   Speed is the rate of distance travelled per unit of time.

   $$\text{Speed} = \frac{\text{Distance travelled}}{\text{Time taken}}$$

   Example: 45 kilometres in 1 hour or 45 km/h

3. **Ratio**

   A ratio indicates what fraction one quantity is of the other, or how many times one quantity is as much as the other. The following are equivalent statements.

   $$a : b = 3 : 5 \qquad\qquad b : a = 5 : 3$$
   $$\frac{a}{b} = \frac{3}{5} \qquad\qquad\qquad \frac{b}{a} = \frac{5}{3}$$
   $$a = \frac{3}{5} \times b \qquad\qquad b = \frac{5}{3} \times a$$

4. **Direct and Inverse Proportions**

   If $\dfrac{y}{x}$ is constant, we say that y is directly proportional to x.

   If $\dfrac{y}{\left(\frac{1}{x}\right)}$ (or yx) is constant, we say that y is inversely proportional to x.

   Examples: **(a)** The distance travelled is directly proportional to the time taken if the speed is constant.
   (b) The speed is inversely proportional to the time taken if the distance travelled is constant.

5. **Percentage**
- 'Per cent' means 'for each hundred' or 'out of a hundred'.
   The short form for of 'per cent' is %.
- Percentage can be converted to a decimal or a fraction.

   Examples: $35\% = 35 \times \dfrac{1}{100} = \dfrac{35}{100}$ or 0.35

   $100\% = 100 \times \dfrac{1}{100} = \dfrac{100}{100} = 1$

   $175\% = 175 \times \dfrac{1}{100} = \dfrac{175}{100}$ or 1.75

CHALLENGER 7

1. At noon, a car travels from A to B at a uniform speed of 60 km/h. At the same time, a van travels uniformly from B to A. At 3.30 p.m., the car and the van are 85 km apart after having passed each other earlier. If the car arrives at B at 5 p.m., find the time at which the van will arrive at A.

2. Three girls, A, B and C, shared a box of beads in the ratio 5 : 3 : 4, and there were 4 beads left over. Later, they shared these 4 beads together with a second box, containing $12\frac{1}{2}\%$ less beads than the first box, in the same ratio as before, and there was no remainder. If the additional number of beads they each received in the second round of sharing was the same as before, find the total number of beads each of them received.

3. 300 ml of pure alcohol is poured from a bottle containing 2 l of pure alcohol. Then, 300 ml of water is added into the bottle. Again 300 ml of the diluted alcohol is poured out and 300 ml of water is added into the bottle. Find the percentage of pure alcohol in the solution now.

4. The pupils in a certain class are divided equally into 3 groups A, B and C. The number of boys in group A is equal to the number of girls in group B. 25% of the boys in the class are in group C. Find the ratio of the number of boys to the number of girls in the class.

5. Mary prepared some milk from milk powder using the proportion recommended below.

> *Mixing Instructions*
> To prepare one litre of milk,
> add 130 g of milk powder to
> 900 g of water.

(a) What percentage (by mass) of the milk is the milk powder?

(b) What percentage (by volume) of the milk is the milk powder?
(*Note:* Volume of 1 g of water = 1 m*l*.)

(c) Mary said that she only used coffee cups of unknown capacity as 'measuring instrument' to prepare the milk. Do you think this is possible? Give reasons.

6. The following was a telephone conversation between Mr Tan, a contractor, and Mr Wang, an electrical engineer.

Mr Tan : 'Hello, Mr Wang. Do you remember how long you took to complete the electrical work for my 12 factories the last time?'

Mr Wang : '10 weeks because I had only 4 electricians.'

Mr Tan : 'Now, I have 16 similar factories. Can you complete the job in 8 weeks?'

Mr Wang : 'I may not have enough men to complete the job on time.'

Mr Tan : 'How many hours a day did your men work the last time?'

Mr Wang : 'On the average, each man worked 6 hours a day.'

Mr Tan : 'Can they work for longer hours?'

Mr Wang : '10 hours at most.'

Mr Tan : 'At least how many men do you need to complete the job on time?'

Mr Wang : 'I'll let you know later after lunch.'

Study the above conversation and calculate the number of electricians needed to complete the electrical work for 16 factories in 8 weeks if each of them works 10 hours a day.

Problem Solving 7

Sharing Drinks

At a cross-country race, a company donated 100 *l* of health drinks to the school. Each runner was given an amount equal to 230 m*l* except John who received an amount which was less than 230 m*l*. What percentage less than the normal share did John get?

Let us use the strategy **think of a related problem**.

Ask yourself: How many cups of 230 m*l* each can I fill with 100 *l* of water?
What percentage of a cup can I fill with the amount left over?

We may solve the related problem in a scrapbook. This will help us devise a plan to solve the original problem.

Suppose each runner is given a cup of 230 m*l* of the health drinks.

Number of cups = 100 000 ÷ 230 = 434.782 6

So, John received 0.782 6 cup, i.e. 78.26% of a cup.

Therefore, John received (100 – 78.26)%, i.e. 21.7% less than the normal share.

Alternatively, we **restate the problem in another way** as

'At a cross-country race, a company donated 100 *l* of health drinks to the school. Each runner was given an amount equal to 230 m*l* except John who received the amount left over. What percentage less than the normal share did John get?'

Then, we find the remainder of 100 000 ÷ 230 and express it as a percentage of 230 m*l*.

$$
\begin{array}{r}
434 \\
230\overline{)\,100\ 000} \\
92\ 0 \\
\hline
8\ 00 \\
6\ 90 \\
\hline
1\ 100 \\
920 \\
\hline
180
\end{array}
$$

So, as a percentage, the remainder = $\dfrac{180}{230} \times 100\% = 78.26\%$ and so on.

Problems...

1. **Changing Money**   Samy wants to buy as many Canadian dollar notes as he can with 70 Singapore dollars from a money changer. If the exchange rate is $1.35 Singapore money to one Canadian dollar, how much Singapore money will he have left?

2. **Making Fruit Cakes**   Mary has 20 cups of pecans. She wants to make as many cakes as she can with the pecans. Each cake requires $2\frac{1}{4}$ cups of pecans. After making the cakes, how many cups of pecans will she have left?

3. **Colour Cards**   In a box, there is 1 red card for every 2 cards, 1 blue card for every 6 cards, 1 yellow card for every 8 cards and the rest are white cards. If there are 10 white cards, how many cards are there in the box altogether?

4. **Dotty Pattern** **(a)** In the answer space, draw the 4th pattern of dots in the sequence.

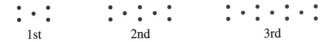

1st   2nd   3rd

(b) How many dots are there in the 5th pattern?

(c) How many dots are there in the 41st pattern?   *(C)*

REVISION EXERCISE 2

Revision 2A *(answers on p. 430)*

1. Water flows at 95 l in one minute from tap A and 105 l from tap B. How much water flows from the 2 taps in half an hour?

2. **(a)** Add $(3x^2 + 2x - 5)$ to $(-8x^4 - 2x + 8)$.
   (b) Subtract $(2x^4 + 3x^2 - 10)$ from $(18x^5 - 7x^3 - x^2 - 15)$.

3. For each of the sentences, state whether it is true if the variable has the suggested value.

   (a) $7 + 4x \leq 15$; $x = 2$ **(b)** $3x - 2\left(\dfrac{4}{5}x\right) \geq 23$; $x = -5$

   (c) $\dfrac{6x}{5} + 4 \leq \dfrac{23}{5}$; $x = \dfrac{1}{2}$

4. If $a^2 - 3ab = b + 2$, find b when $a = 3$.

5. The diagram shows a picture of a fuel gauge of a car. If the petrol tank can hold 36 l when full,
   (a) how much petrol is in the tank,
   (b) how far can the car go (approximately) if it travels 8 km on 1 l of petrol?

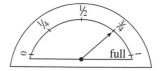

6. An article costs $72.80. If this cost is increased by 25%, find the new cost.

7. A certain number was doubled and the result was then multiplied by 3. If the product was 138, find the number.

8. Two numbers are in the ratio 7 to 11. Express the smaller as a percentage of their total correct to 1 decimal place.

9. The sum of 2 numbers is 3 and their difference is 7. Find the numbers.

10. Mary is $\dfrac{2}{5}$ as heavy as Mabel, find the mass of Mabel if their total mass is 84 kg.

Revision 2B *(answers on p. 430)*

1. How much of each ingredient in the recipe would you require to make a similar ice cream to serve 5 persons?

> *Recipe for ice cream to serve 3 persons*
>
> • *300 g sweet corn*
> • *120 g sugar*
> • *105 g cream*
> • *60 g water*

2. For each of the sentences, state whether it is true if the variable has the suggested value.

   (a) $5 + x > 2; x = 4$

   (b) $2x - 5\left(\frac{2}{3}x\right) > 2; x = -\frac{3}{4}$

3. Simplify the following expressions.

   (a) $\frac{al}{bcd} \times \frac{bm}{ac} \div \frac{cm}{dp}$

   (b) $\dfrac{\dfrac{st}{pq}}{\dfrac{rs}{p}}$

   (c) $\dfrac{\dfrac{mn}{a} \div \dfrac{ap}{m}}{\dfrac{m}{n}}$

4. Solve the equation $2x + \frac{1}{8} = \frac{4}{3}x - 7$.

5. (a) If $F = \frac{9}{5}(C + 25) - 20$, find F when $C = 15$.

   (b) Evaluate $(x - y)^2 - w^2$ if $x = \frac{1}{2}$, $y = \frac{1}{4}$ and $w = \frac{3}{4}$.

6. After paying 5 bills with a $50 note, there was change of $1.55. The receipt for one bill was lost and the amounts of the others were $10.20, $9.40, $11.45 and $8.50. What was the amount of the lost bill?

7. In an election, candidate A received 65% of the votes cast and secured 2 400 votes more than candidate B. How many people voted?

8. Three men started a business with a capital of $300 000. If their shares of the business are in the ratio 3 : 5 : 7, how much has each to subscribe?

9. There are 19 sweets to be shared between Ali and his sister. If Ali gets 5 more sweets than his sister, how many sweets will each get?

10. The sum of 2 numbers is 28. Three times the first plus the second is 40. Find the numbers.

Revision 2C   *(answers on p. 430)*

1. If 12 men can unload 360 tonnes of goods in 5 hours, find the rate of unloading in tonnes/man-hour. How many men are needed to unload 72 tonnes in 4 hours?

2. For each of the sentences, state whether it is true if the variable has the suggested value.

   (a) $\frac{5x}{3} + 6 \neq -\frac{11}{3}; x = 1$

   (b) $5 + 2x \geq 11; x = 3$

3. Solve the equation $0.4\,(2x - 1) = 0.6$

4. **(a)** Evaluate $(p + q)^2 - (p - q - 2r)^2$ if $p = \frac{1}{3}$, $q = \frac{1}{6}$ and $r = \frac{1}{9}$.

   (b) Evaluate $\sqrt{5\left(\dfrac{x^2 - y^2}{x}\right)}$ if $x = 5$ and $y = 4$.

5. The watchman works $7\frac{1}{2}$ hours a night in a factory. He starts work at 23 00 and earns \$41.25 per night.
   (a) At what time does he finish work?
   (b) How much is he paid an hour?

6. A man received \$264 for working a normal 44-hour week. How much was he paid for working a 52-hour week if the overtime rate was $1\frac{1}{4}$ times the normal rate?.

7. 10 men can complete a job in 14 days. How long will it take 4 men to finish the same job if they work at the same rate?

8. There are three numbers such that the second is three times the first, and the third is 3 less than four times the first. If the sum of the numbers is 37, find these numbers.

9. Henry has twice as much money as James. Thomas has three times as much money as Henry and James together. How much more money has Thomas than Henry if James has \$25.70?

10. Mrs Li bought 50 books for \$50. She paid \$4 for each of the big books and \$1 for 4 smaller ones. How many big books and how many small books did she buy?

Revision 2D   *(answers on p. 430)*

1. Simplify the following.
   (a) $3x^2 + 6xy - 3y^2 + 4x^2 - 8xy + 2y^2$
   (b) $6a^2 + 5ab - 6b^2 - 6a^2 + ab + 2b^2$
   (c) $3(a + 3b) + 4(a - 3b)$

2. Solve the equation $7 - \frac{3}{4}(p - 5) = \frac{1}{2}(p + 1)$.

3. **(a)** Given that $x = \frac{a}{b} - \left(\dfrac{c - d}{e}\right)$, find e if $x = 1$, $a = 2$, $b = 3$, $c = 4$ and $d = 5$.

   (b) Given that $\frac{1}{a} + \frac{1}{b} = 1$, find a if $b = 1\frac{1}{2}$.

4. A fruiterer bought 8 boxes of apples at \$95 per box and the cost of transporting them to his shop was \$3 per box. If he wished to make a profit of \$152 by selling all of them, how much should he sell each box of apples?

5. An 8-m long bus, travelling at a speed of 30 km/h, entered a tunnel. It took 3 minutes to come out completely at the other end. Find the length of the tunnel.

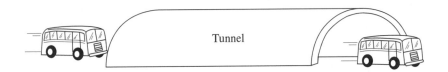

6. (a) If a man's salary is increased from $550 to $627, find the percentage increase.
   (b) A certain type of rice costs 78 cents per kg. What will be the new cost to the nearest cent if its cost is decreased by 5%?

7. A man travelling an hour by car and another hour by plane covered a total distance of 850 km. If the average speed of the plane taken by the man was 16 times that of the car, what was the distance covered by the car?

8. Mary is 12 years old and her mother is 42 years old. How old was Mary when her mother was 4 times as old as her?

9. The average mass of 24 boys in a class is 35.5 kg and that of 15 girls is 29 kg. A new boy joins the class and his mass is 1.4 kg heavier than the average mass of the whole class of 39 pupils. Find the average mass of the new class of 40 pupils after the new boy joined the class.

10. Sue has a total of 16 Singapore and Malaysian stamps. If she exchanges every Singapore stamp for 2 Malaysian stamps, she will have 21 Malaysian stamps. How many Singapore stamps and how many Malaysian stamps does Sue have?

Revision 2E   *(answers on p. 430)*

1. Simplify
   (a) $2(4 - b) + 3(b - 2b)$
   (b) $2x(x - 3y) + y(3x - y)$
   (c) $2a(1 - a) + 3a^2(1 + a)$

2. Solve the equation $2.1t - 1.4 = 1.6t + 1.2$.

3. (a) Evaluate $\frac{a + c}{2} - 8d \times b$ if $a = 4$, $b = -2$, $c = 3$ and $d = 7$.
   (b) Evaluate $[2c(b + d) + a]\, b + 5c$ if $a = 4$, $b = -2$, $c = 3$ and $d = 7$.

4. (a) Subtract $(45m^2 + 3m - 2)$ from $(m^4 + 3m^3 - 10m^2 + 8)$.
   (b) Subtract $(t^4 - 5t^5 - 10t^3 - 4)$ from $(12t^6 - 8t^3 - 4t^2 + 2t - 8)$.
   (c) Subtract the sum of $\left(\frac{a}{3} + \frac{b}{4}\right)$ and $\left(\frac{a}{6} - \frac{3b}{4}\right)$ from $[2(a - b)]$.

5. The ratio of the number of boys to the number of girls in a class of 42 pupils was 4 : 3. When some boys left the class, the number of girls was the same as the number of boys. How many boys left the class?

6. A man earns $11 250 a year and saves $150 monthly.
    (a) What are his total savings?
    (b) What percentage of his income are his savings?

7. School *A* and school *B* had a friendly basketball match. At the end of the match, the total score was 120 points. If school *A* scored 21 points more than half of the points that school *B* scored, what was the final score of each team?

8. A father was 27 years old when his son was 3 years old. In how many years time would the father be 3 times as old as the son?

9. Peter and Paul had $340 altogether. Peter spent $\frac{3}{4}$ of his money and Paul spent $\frac{2}{5}$ of his money. Then, they found that they each had an equal amount of money left. How much money did each of them have at first?

10. Tom and Jerry have some money. If Jerry gives $5 to Tom, then they will have the same amount of money. If Tom gives $5 to Jerry, then Jerry will have twice as much as Tom. How much money does each have at first?

MISCELLANEOUS EXERCISE 2

(answers on p. 430)

1. **(a)** Draw the 4th pattern of dots in the sequence.

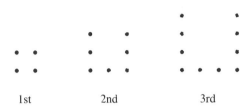

1st   2nd   3rd

    (b) How many dots are there in the 5th pattern?
    (c) How many dots are there in the 10th pattern?

2. One number is a more than the other. If the larger number is increased by b, the result is c times the smaller number. Find the sum of the two numbers in terms of a, b and c.

3. The number of textbooks on the desk is 5 less than twice the number of workbooks. If there are 15 textbooks, how many workbooks are there?

4. A motorist travels a distance of d_1 km at a uniform speed of v_1 km/h and then travels a distance of d_2 km at a uniform speed of v_2 km/h. If $d_1 : d_2 = 2 : 3$ and $v_1 : v_2 = 3 : 2$, find $t_1 : t_2$, where t_1 and t_2 are the times taken for the two parts of the journey.

5. The length and breadth of rectangle A are in the ratio $3 : 2$. The length and breadth of rectangle B are in the ratio $5 : 3$. If the perimeters of rectangles A and B are in the ratio $5 : 4$, find the ratio of the area of rectangle A to the area of rectangle B.

6. Grade A tea costs 10% more than grade B tea and grade B tea costs 10% more than grade C tea.
    (a) By what percentage does grade A tea cost more than grade C tea?
    (b) By what percentage does grade C tea cost less than grade A tea?

7. Every year, the monthly rent for a shop increases by 10%. The shopkeeper finds that he has to pay $168 more per month for the rent than he did 2 years ago. Find his present rent per month.

8. Peter gives his parents $\frac{1}{6}$ of his monthly salary.
    (a) How much does he give his parents if he earns $ 2 400?
    (b) Peter has a 6% pay rise the following month.
       (i) How much extra money does he earn a month?
       (ii) How much more does he give to his parents if he still gives them $\frac{1}{6}$ of his salary?
    (c) Peter saves 15% of his pay each month.
       (i) Express his first month's savings as a fraction of his second month's savings.
       (ii) Find the percentage increase of his savings.

9. A box contains some marbles of three different colours. If $\frac{3}{5}$ of them are red, $\frac{3}{8}$ of them are blue and the rest are yellow, calculate
   (a) the fraction of marbles that are yellow,
   (b) the percentage of marbles that are blue,
   (c) the smallest possible number of marbles in the box,
   (d) the ratio of the number of red marbles to the number of blue marbles.

10. There were 18 more women than men who joined the conducted tour to Malaysia.
    (a) The ratio of the number of men to the number of women in the group was 2 : 3. How many men were there in the group?
    (b) $\frac{2}{3}$ of the men and $\frac{5}{9}$ of the women were retirees. The rest were young adults. How many young adults were there?
    (c) A young adult paid $350 for the tour and a retiree paid 15% less than a young adult. How much money did the tour company collect?

11. (a) In 1993, a certain brand of oil cost 90 cents per litre. How many litres could be bought for $45?
    (b) In 1994, the price increased by 20%.
        (i) What was the price per litre then?
        (ii) How many litres of oil could be bought for $17.28?
    (c) In 1995, the price was increased further by 27 cents per litre.
        (i) Express the increase in price per litre in 1995 as a percentage of the price per litre in 1994.
        (ii) How much oil could be bought for $37.80 at the 1995 price?

12. A factory needs to send 150 cases of soft drinks to a supermarket. There are 12 cans of drinks in each case. One can of drink weighs 0.54 kg and an empty case weighs 1.2 kg.
    (a) Find the ratio of the mass of a can of drink to the mass of an empty case.
    (b) Find the mass of all the cans of drinks.
    (c) Express the mass of all the empty cases as a fraction of the mass of all the cans of drinks.
    (d) The transport company charges $0.25 per kg for transportation of goods. Find the cost of transporting all the cases of drinks to the supermarket.

13. In a chess tournament, each player must play one game with every other player. There are 8 players. Ahmad has already played 1 game, Bill 2 games, Chenghua 3 games, Dennis 4 games, Eddie 5 games, Freddy 6 games and Gomez 7 games. How many games has Henry already played?

14. Paul was a child for $\frac{1}{12}$ of his life, a student for $\frac{1}{6}$ of his life and a bachelor for $\frac{1}{9}$ of his life. 3 years after his marriage, he had a daughter. When he died, his only grandson was 2 years old. How long had he lived?

15. Complete the following division by finding a digit in each *.

```
              *7***
        ) ********
          ****
           ***
           ***
           ****
            ***
            ****
            ****
               0
```
***) ********

INVESTIGATION 2

1. **(a)** Copy and complete the following.

$$\frac{1}{7} = 0.\dot{1}4285\dot{7} \qquad \frac{4}{7} = \underline{\quad}$$

$$\frac{2}{7} = \underline{\quad} \qquad \frac{5}{7} = \underline{\quad}$$

$$\frac{3}{7} = \underline{\quad} \qquad \frac{6}{7} = \underline{\quad}$$

Describe your observation.

(b) Investigate for $\frac{1}{13}, \frac{2}{13}, \frac{3}{13}, \frac{4}{13}, \ldots, \frac{12}{13}$.
Describe your observation.

2. Copy and complete the following table. (Use calculator to help you investigate.)

		Divisible by		
	Number	**7**	**11**	**13**
Given number ⟶	11 855 844	Yes	Yes	Yes
11 855 – 844 ⟶	11 011	Yes		
11 – 11 ⟶	0	Yes		
Given number ⟶	233 080 848			Yes
233 080 – 848 ⟶	232 232			Yes
232 – 232 ⟶	0			Yes
Given number ⟶	8 082 844	Yes		
8 082 – 844 ⟶	7 238			No
238 – 7 ⟶	231	Yes		No

(a) Study the table and describe your observation.
(b) Explain how you can tell whether the following is divisible by 7, by 11 and by 13 without using the calculator.

2 020 711	58 264 206
1 084 941	100 098 999
98 896 798	5 321 589

3. **(a)** Start with the four numbers from the innermost ring. Write down the difference between each pair of adjacent numbers to complete the second ring. Repeat to complete the third ring and so on. What have you noticed?

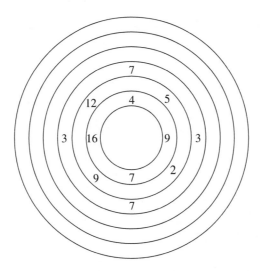

(b) Repeat (a) with four other numbers. Describe your observation.

(c) Will you get the same result if you start off with 3 numbers or 5 numbers or 6 numbers or 7 numbers or 8 numbers? Investigate.

4. **(a)** Verify

(i) $\left(2 + \dfrac{1}{4}\right) \div \dfrac{3}{4} = \left(2 + \dfrac{1}{4}\right) + \dfrac{3}{4}$,

(ii) $\left(3 + \dfrac{1}{5}\right) \div \dfrac{4}{5} = \left(3 + \dfrac{1}{5}\right) + \dfrac{4}{5}$.

(b) Is there a rule for finding strange examples as those given in (a)? Investigate.

Chapter 8

Solving Problems Involving Financial Transactions

Chapter Highlights

- Solving problems involving earnings, commission, rebate, profit and loss and discount.
- Solving problems involving simple interest, compound interest and hire purchase.
- Solving problems involving taxes and money exchange.

8.1 EARNINGS, PROFIT AND LOSS, COMMIS-SIONS AND DISCOUNTS

Earnings

Example

Mr Lin saves $5 400 which is 15% of his annual income. Mr Tan spends $2 800 a month which is $87\frac{1}{2}$% of his monthly income. Who earns more?

Let $x be Mr Lin's income per year.

Then, $\qquad$ 15% of $x = \$5\ 400$

$$\$x = \frac{\$5\ 400}{15\%}$$

$$= \frac{\$5\ 400}{0.15}$$

$$= \$36\ 000$$

Let $y be Mr Tan's income per month.

Then, $\qquad$ $87\frac{1}{2}$% of $y = \$2\ 800$

$$\$y = \frac{\$2\ 800}{87.5\%}$$

$$= \frac{\$2\ 800}{0.875}$$

$$= \$3\ 200$$

Mr Tan's annual income is $3\ 200 \times 12 = \$38\ 400$.

Therefore, Mr Tan earns more than Mr Lin.

Profit and Loss

When goods are bought and sold later, the result can be a **profit** (**gain**) or a **loss**. What do you think the result will be if the cost price is more than the selling price? What will it be if the selling price is more than the cost price?

Thus, we can calculate the profit or loss as follows:

Profit = Selling price – Cost price
Loss = Cost price – Selling price

In business transactions, the actual profit or loss does not give a 'true picture' about the transactions. For instance, consider the following.

(a)   A set of books which cost $25 was sold at $30.

(b)   Another set of books which cost $75 was sold at $80.

In each case, as you will notice, the actual profit is $5, but one of the transactions is more favourable than the other. To find out which, we can express the profit as a percentage of the cost.

In the first case, the percentage is 20%, as

$$\frac{5}{25} = \frac{5}{25} \times 100\%$$
$$= 20\%.$$

In the second case, the percentage is $6\frac{2}{3}\%$, as

$$\frac{5}{75} = \frac{5}{75} \times 100\%$$
$$= 6\frac{2}{3}\%.$$

Hence, the first transaction is more profitable. Notice that the profit has been calculated with reference to the cost price.

Commissions

The selling and buying of goods may be done by an agent on behalf of another person. The agent is paid a fee called a **commission** for his services. The commission is a sum calculated as a percentage of the sum received (when selling) or paid (when buying) by the agent on behalf of his employer.

Example

A book salesman is paid a commission of 15% of the selling price of a set of books. If he sells the set of books for $100, his commission is 15% of $100 or $15.

Discounts

Shop owners and storekeepers often allow some reduction for cash payment of goods bought. Such a reduction is normally calculated as a percentage of the original price and is called a **discount**.

A discount is a reduction in the regular price of an item when it is put on sale.

Example

During a sale, goods were sold at a discount of 10%. In such a case, goods originally priced at $10 were sold at 90% of the price, i.e.

$10 \times \dfrac{90}{100}$ or $9.

A discount called a **rebate** is also given to a person for a sum of money which he owes to another person if the debt is paid at an earlier date.

Worked Example 1

A salesman received $192 commission for selling a TV set at $3 200. Express his commission as a percentage of his sale.

Solution:

$$\text{Percentage} = \frac{192}{3\ 200} \times 100\%$$
$$= 6\%$$

His commission was 6% of the selling price.

Worked Example 2

A man bought an article for $240 and sold it for $276. Find his percentage gain.

Solution:

$$\text{Profit} = \text{Selling price} - \text{Cost price}$$
$$= \$276 - \$240$$
$$= \$36$$

$$\therefore \ \text{percentage gain} = \frac{36}{240} \times 100\%$$
$$= 15\%$$

Worked Example 3

A trader bought 20 bicycles for $1 200 and sold them at $80 each. Find his percentage gain or loss.

Solution:

$$\text{Selling price of 20 bicycles} = \$80 \times 20$$
$$= \$1\ 600$$
$$\text{Gain} = \$1\ 600 - \$1\ 200$$
$$= \$400$$

$$\therefore \ \text{percentage gain} = \frac{400}{1\ 200} \times 100\%$$
$$= \frac{40\ 000}{1\ 200}\%$$
$$= \frac{100}{3}\% \text{ or } 33\frac{1}{3}\%$$

Worked Example 4
An article which cost $150 is sold at a loss of 5%. What is the selling price?

Solution:
$$\text{Selling price} = \text{Cost price} - \text{Loss}$$
$$= \$150 - \left(\$150 \times \frac{5}{100}\right)$$
$$= \$150 - \$7.50$$
$$= \$142.50$$

Alternative solution:
The selling price is 100% − 5% or 95% of $150.
$$\text{Selling price} = \$150 \times \frac{95}{100}$$
$$= \$142.50$$

Worked Example 5
By selling goods for $168, a profit of 12% was made by a merchant. How much did the goods cost him?

Solution:
$$112\% \text{ of the original price} = \$168$$
$$1\% \text{ of the original price} = \$\frac{168}{112}$$
$$100\% \text{ of the original price} = \$\frac{168}{112} \times 100$$
$$= \$150$$

Thus, the goods cost $150.

Alternative solution:
Let the cost of the goods be x dollars.

The profit, 12% of x, can also be expressed as $\frac{12}{100}x$.

Now, $\quad\quad\quad\quad$ Cost price + Profit = Selling price
$$x + \frac{12}{100}x = 168$$
$$\left(1 + \frac{12}{100}\right)x = 168$$
$$\frac{112}{100}x = 168$$
$$x = 168 \times \frac{100}{112}$$
$$= 150$$

Therefore, the goods cost $150.

Exercise 8.1 ✍

answers on p. 431

1. A man saves $500 which is 20% of his annual income. How much does he earn in one year?

2. A man whose salary is $2 580 a month receives an increment of 8%. Find his new monthly salary.

3. Mr Li's salary is raised from $1 570 to $1 805.50 a month. Calculate his salary increase as a percentage of his old salary.

4. A man spends 70.5% of his income and saves $885 a month. Find his monthly income.

5. Peter spends $87\frac{1}{2}$% of his income and saves $240 a month. Paul saves $330 which is 15% of his monthly income. Who earns more and by how much?

6. An increase in wages of 15% makes the monthly wage bill of a company $59 800. What is the amount of the increase?

*7. If the salaries are increased by $12\frac{1}{2}$% all round, the yearly salary bill paid by a company becomes $51 300. What is the increase per month in the bill?

8. A man bought a car for $87 500 and sold it for $75 000. Find his percentage loss, giving your answer correct to two decimal places.

9. A trader bought eggs at 8 cents each and sold them at 10 cents each. Find his percentage profit.

10. By selling goods for $175.50, a profit of 17% was made by a merchant. How much did the goods cost him?

11. By selling goods for $250, a merchant lost 25% on his outlay. For how much should he have sold the goods in order to have a gain of 10%?

12. By selling his goods at $8.50, the shopkeeper makes a profit of 20%. At what price, to the nearest cent, should he sell his goods in order to make a profit of 30%?

*13. Mr Bala bought 960 handkerchiefs at $1.80 per dozen. He sold 780 of them at 3 for $1.00 and the rest at 4 for $1.00. Find his percentage profit, giving your answer correct to the nearest whole number.

*14. Eggs are bought at $8.50 per 100. If 4% of the eggs bought are broken and discarded, how many eggs, to the nearest number, must be sold for 80¢ to gain 80%?

*15. Peter bought rose syrup at 100 litres for $86. He added sugar syrup to gain 10% of the volume, 10% of the mixture was spilt and wasted and he sold the rest at $2.10 per litre. If the sugar syrup cost 13¢ per litre, find his percentage profit correct to the nearest whole number.

16. A real estate agent receives a commission of $\frac{1}{2}$% of the selling price for any sale that he makes. What will his commission be if he sells a house for $625 000?

17. A bookseller receives $12\frac{1}{2}$% commission on the sale of books from a publisher. In a certain month, he received a commission of $250 from the publisher for selling a number of books. How much was his sale for that particular month?

18. A bookseller receives $90 commission for selling a set of books at $2 000. Express his commission as a percentage of his sale.

*19. A salesman is paid 6% commission on his weekly sales over $5 000, but $3\frac{1}{2}$% commission otherwise. In one particular month, his weekly sales were $4 800, $5 600, $3 200 and $8 200. Find **(a)** the total commission he received for the 4 weeks, and **(b)** his average percentage commission on the total sales.

20. The selling price of an article is $260 and its cost price is $160. What profit will a dealer make if he sells the article at a discount of 15%?

21. A departmental store gives 20% discount for cash payment. A woman paid $45 cash for a dress. What was the marked price of the dress?

22. How much money must a man pay to settle an account of $1 200 at 5% rebate?

23. When a discount of 15% of the marked price of an article is allowed, the article is sold for $29.75. Calculate the marked price.

24. A man bought an article for $300. By selling it at a discount of 25% on the list price, he made a profit of 15% on the cost. Find the list price.

*25. A dealer bought a TV set for $374 and he marked up the price to gain 40%. If he sold the set at a discount of 25%, find his percentage profit.

8.2 INTEREST AND HIRE PURCHASE

Simple Interest

When money is loaned, particularly for business purposes, the borrower is expected to pay a little extra for the use of the money. The amount of money lent is called the **principal**, and the extra payment for use of the money is called the **interest**.

If the interest is calculated leaving the principal unaltered throughout the whole term of the loan, it is called **simple interest**.

Worked Example 5

A sum of $2 000 is borrowed for 5 years at 3% per annum. Find the simple interest and amount paid back.

Solution:

Interest on $2 000 for 1 year at 3% is $\frac{3}{100} \times \$2\,000$ or $60.

Interest on $2 000 for 5 years at 3% is $\frac{3}{100} \times \$2\,000 \times 5$ or $300.

$$\begin{aligned} \text{Amount paid back} &= \text{Principal} + \text{Interest} \\ &= \$2\,000 + \$300 \\ &= \$2\,300 \end{aligned}$$

Therefore, the interest is $300 and the amount paid back is $2 300.

From the worked example above, it is easy to see that the simple interest is equal to the principal multiplied by the rate per cent and the number of years. Thus, if a principal of P dollars earns an interest of I dollars at the rate of R per cent per year for a period of T years, then

$$I = \frac{PRT}{100}.$$

Worked Example 6

A borrower had his rate of interest per annum reduced from $6\frac{1}{2}\%$ to 6% and so paid $76 less in simple interest in a year. Calculate
(a) the sum of money he borrowed,
(b) the interest he would have paid at $6\frac{1}{2}\%$ per annum.

Solution:

(a) Difference in rate $= 6\frac{1}{2}\% - 6\%$

$$= \frac{1}{2}\%$$

The custom of charging interest is found as early as 2000 BC, as recorded on ancient Babylonian clay tablets. Interest rates in Babylon ran as high as 33%. The origin of the word 'interest' is related to church policy, which forbade usury, payment for the use of money. The money-lender got around this restriction by collecting a fee only if the payment was late, which happened often enough even in those days.

MATHSTORY

$\frac{1}{2}$% of the sum borrowed   = $76

1% of the sum borrowed   = $76 × 2

                                        = $152

100% of the sum borrowed = $152 × 100

                                        = $15 200

Thus, the sum of money he borrowed was $15 200.

(b) The interest at $6\frac{1}{2}$% per annum $= \dfrac{13}{200} \times \$15\ 200$

                                              = $988

Compound Interest (Optional)

Example

A man borrowed $1 000 for 2 years at 8% interest per annum. The interest was compounded yearly as follows:

> At the end of the first year, the 8% interest on $1 000, i.e. $80, was to be added to the principal to become the loan for the second year. The loan for the second year will then be $1 080.

> At the end of the second year, the interest on $1 080 was 8% of $1 080, i.e. $86.40. The total interest, called **compound interest**, was $80 + $86.40 or $166.40.

Worked Example 7

Find the compound interest on $5 000 for 3 years at 4% per annum compounded annually.

Solution:

Principal for 1st year = $5 000

Interest at 4% $= \dfrac{4}{100} \times \$5\ 000 = \$200$

Principal for 2nd year = $5 200

Interest at 4% $= \dfrac{4}{100} \times \$5\ 200 = \$208$

Principal for 3rd year = $5 408

Interest at 4% $= \dfrac{4}{100} \times \$5\ 408 = \$216.32$

∴ compound interest = $200 + $208 + $216.32

                                  = $624.32

Note: The short form p.a. for per annum may be used.

Hire Purchase

Nowadays, many people buy goods by paying a deposit and then paying the rest of the amount in weekly or monthly instalments. This method of purchasing goods is called **hire purchase**.

In hire purchase transactions, the buyers have to pay more than the cash price of the goods in the long run because interest is charged on the amount that has yet to be paid.

Worked Example 8

The cash price of a washing machine is $820. The hire purchase price is a deposit of $172 and 24 monthly instalments of $32.
(a) Find the difference between the cash price and hire purchase price.
(b) Express this difference as a percentage of the cash price, giving your answer to the nearest one decimal place.

Solution:
(a) Deposit = $172
      Total of 24 monthly instalments of $32 = $32 × 24
$$= \$768$$

    Hire purchase price $= \$172 + \$768$
$$= \$940$$

    ∴ difference between cash price and hire purchase price $= \$940 - \$820$
$$= \$120$$

(b) Percentage difference $= \dfrac{120}{820} \times 100\%$
$$= 14.6\%$$

Exercise 8.2

answers on p. 431

1. Find the simple interest on
   (a) $300 for 3 years at 5% p.a.,
   (b) $500.50 for 4 years at $3\frac{1}{2}$% p.a.,

   (c) $1 000 for 3 years at $2\frac{1}{2}$% p.a.,
   (d) $750 for $2\frac{1}{2}$ years at 3% p.a.,

   (e) $500 for 4 years at 5% p.a.,
   (f) $525 for 4 years at $3\frac{1}{2}$% p.a.

2. If the simple interest on $500 at 4% per annum is $35.00, find the period of the loan.

3. If the simple interest on $250 for 5 years is $43.75, find the rate per cent per annum.

4. If \$350 amounts to \$385 at $2\frac{1}{2}$% per annum, find the duration of the loan.

5. If the simple interest on a sum of money invested at $3\frac{1}{2}$% per annum for 4 years is \$100, find the principal.

6. Find the principal which amounts, at simple interest, to \$729 in 4 years at 2% per annum.

7. Find the quarterly (three-monthly) interest on \$840 at $2\frac{1}{2}$% per annum.

8. A man borrows \$500 and agrees to repay \$750 at the end of 4 years. What is the rate of simple interest charged?

9. A man's statement of account from a bank showed \$9 as one year's interest from that bank which pays 3% interest. How much money had he in the bank before the interest was added?

10. A man lends a sum of money to his local council and receives \$63 interest on the loan each year. When the rate of interest rises by 0.5%, the annual interest is raised to \$67.50. Calculate the sum of money lent to the council and the new percentage rate of interest. *(C)*

11. A housewife invests \$5 000 at $5\frac{1}{2}$% per annum. Her husband wishes to invest enough money to have 8% interest so that their total interest will amount to \$1 000 in a year. How much should the husband invest?

*12. If the rate of interest on a loan is increased from $6\frac{1}{2}$% to 7%, the annual interest is increased by \$330. How much is the loan?

*13. If the simple interest on \$3 200 for $1\frac{1}{2}$ years is \$252, find the simple interest on \$12 000 for 4 months at the same rate of interest.

*14. A man invests a sum of money at simple interest. The total of the principal and interest is known as the *amount*. Study the table below and calculate the values of *a*, *b*, *x* and *r*.

Principal ($)	Rate of simple interest (%) p.a.	Length of time (year)	Amount ($)
x	r	1	30 240
x	r	2	a
x	r	3	34 720
x	r	4	b

15. What is the compound interest on $4 500 for 2 years at 10% per annum compounded yearly? (Optional)

16. What is the compound interest on $2 500 for 3 years at 12% per annum compounded yearly? Give your answer correct to the nearest dollar. (Optional)

17. A man borrowed $3 000 at 8% per annum compound interest compounded annually. How much must he repay in all at the end of 3 years? Give your answer correct to the nearest dollar. (Optional)

18. For each of the following, **(i)** find the difference between the cash price and the hire purchase price, and **(ii)** express this difference as a percentage of the cash price.
   (a) A transistor radio at $120 cash or $10 deposit and 12 monthly instalments of $12.50.
   (b) A television set priced at $2 400 cash or $600 deposit and 24 monthly instalments of $90.
   (c) A refrigerator priced at $1 200 cash or $200 deposit and 24 monthly instalments of $55.
   (d) A set of furniture priced at $3 200 cash or $200 deposit and 24 monthly payments of $140.
   (e) A piano priced at $2 600 or $625 down payment and 12 monthly payments of $190.

19. The list price of a car is $27 000.
   (a) If a buyer is allowed to pay this price by first paying a deposit of $9 000 followed by 12 equal monthly instalments, find the amount of each instalment.
   (b) If the discount is $10\frac{1}{2}$% for cash payment, how much has the buyer to pay?

20. A man borrows $336 from a finance company. The company adds, as interest, $6\frac{1}{2}$% of the amount owing at the beginning of each year including the first. During the first year, he pays back the loan by monthly instalments of $13.75. Calculate
   (a) the amount still owing at the end of the year,
   (b) the total amount he must pay back in the second year to clear the debt.
   (C)

*21. The same video camera is to be sold at the same price of $2 256 cash in shop *A* and shop *B*. But the shops offer different credit terms as follows:
   Shop *A* requires a deposit of 15% and 12 monthly instalments of $183.77.
   Shop *B* requires a deposit of 10% and 18 monthly instalments of $135.36.

Calculate in each shop the difference between the hire purchase price and the cash price. State which shop is offering the better deal.

*22. A shop sold a watch for $276.25 after offering a discount of 15%. Another customer bought the same type of watch from the same shop on hire purchase by paying a down payment of 10% of the usual price and 10 equal monthly instalments.
(a) How much was the usual price for the watch?
(b) How much was each monthly instalment?

8.3 TAXATION AND MONEY EXCHANGE

Taxation

In most countries, tax is collected to bear the cost of various public services such as health, defence and education. If a tax payer has to pay a tax of 6 cents for every dollar of his chargeable income (i.e. income after deduction and reliefs), we say that he pays tax at a rate of 6 cents/dollar. Some countries prefer to use the term 'percentage' to express tax rate. Thus, 6 cents/dollar = $\frac{6 \text{ cents}}{100 \text{ cents}}$ = 6%.

GST (Goods and Services Tax) is a tax on goods and services which are purchased. If the price quoted has not included the GST, then the price you pay will have the GST added in. The GST rate is determined by the government and may vary as the need arises.

Worked Example 9
If the rate of tax is 3 cents on the dollar, find the tax on an income of $4 000 of which the first $1 500 is exempted from tax.

Solution:
Chargeable income is $4 000 – $1 500 or $2 500.

The tax for $2 500 is $2\,500 \times \frac{3}{100}$ or $75.

Money Exchange

Each country has its own currency. If £1 (Sterling) is equivalent to $2.15 (Singapore), the **exchange rate** of the Singapore dollar to the Sterling pound is $\frac{1}{2.15}$ pound per dollar or approximately 0.47 pound per dollar.

Every major bank displays the exchange rates of foreign currency and the rates fluctuate daily.

The table below is an example.

	Currency	Selling	Buying
Local $ to 1 unit	US dollar (US$)	1.41	1.40
	Canadian dollar (C$)	1.05	1.02
	Sterling pound (£)	2.20	2.15
	Australian dollar (A$)	1.05	1.02
Local $ to 100 units	Deutschemark (DM)	95.86	93.46
	Swiss franc (SFR)	115.28	112.54
	French franc	28.06	27.19
	Japanese yen (¥)	1.45	1.42
	Philippine peso (P)	5.79	5.70
	Indonesian rupiah (R)	0.06	0.02
	Hong Kong dollar (HK$)	18.40	17.98
	Malaysian ringgit (M$)	57.17	56.13

Table 8.1

Notice that a bank uses a lower exchange rate when buying foreign currency as compared to selling, and hence makes profit from the transaction.

Worked Example 10
A Singapore merchant bought wine for S$14 000 at the rate of 40 francs per litre. If the exchange rate was S$28 to 100 francs, how many litres did he buy? If he sold the wine at S$16 per litre, find his gain per cent.

Solution:

$$\text{Cost per litre} = 40 \text{ francs}$$

$$= \text{S\$}\left(\frac{40 \times 28}{100}\right)$$

$$= \text{S\$}11.2$$

$$\therefore \text{ the number of litres bought} = \frac{14\ 000}{11.2}$$

$$= 1\ 250$$

$$\text{Profit} = \text{Selling price} - \text{Cost price}$$

$$= \text{S\$}16 - \text{S\$}11.2$$

$$\therefore \text{ gain per cent} = \frac{16 - 11.2}{11.2} \times 100\%$$

$$= \frac{4.8}{11.2} \times 100\%$$

$$\approx 42.9\%$$

Exercise 8.3 ✎

answers on p. 431

1. Find the tax on an income of $4 500 if the first $750 is exempted from tax and the tax is paid at 5 cents for every dollar on the remainder.

2. Find the tax on an income of $5 000 if the first $700 is exempted from tax and the tax is charged at 6% on the next $875 and at 8% on the remainder.

3. All prices at the P&P store are quoted exclusive of GST. Mr Wang bought a TV set at $1 680, a microwave oven at $920 and a blender at $80. Calculate his total bill, including 3% of GST.

*4. A retailer buys a piano for $1 800. He wants to make a profit of $45\frac{1}{2}$%. Find the selling price of the piano inclusive of 3% GST.

*5. A man's chargeable income is $22 888. How much of this amount is left after paying a tax of $1 375 for the first $20 000 and the remainder at the rate of 12%?

*6. Mr Tan earned $16 800 from his employment and $288 from other investments. His total tax reliefs amounted to $2 168.
   (a) Calculate his chargeable income?
   (b) If he is paying tax at the rate of $5\frac{1}{4}$% on the first $10 000 and the remainder at the rate of 8%, calculate his tax payable.

7. If the exchange rate of Singapore dollar to Sterling pound is S$2.15 = £1, copy and complete the following. (*Note:* £1 = 100 p)
   (a) S$1 = _____ p   (b) 45 p = S$ _____
   (c) 72 p = _____ ¢   (d) 265 ¢ = £ _____
   (e) £2.96 = _____ ¢   (f) S$5.35 = _____ p
   (g) S$12.60 = £ _____   (h) £17.25 = S$ _____
   (i) £25 and 45 p = S$ _____ and _____ ¢
   (j) S$38 and 72 ¢ = £ _____ and _____ p

8. On a certain day, the exchange rates of currency are as follows:

S$1.40 = US$1	S$27 = 100 Francs (French)
S$2.15 = £1.00	S$18 = HK$100
S$1.10 = A$1	

   Copy and complete the following.
   (a) US$2 = S$ _____   (b) £9 = S$ _____
   (c) A$7 = S$ _____   (d) US$9.40 = S$ _____

(e) £12.30 = S$ _____   **(f)** US$ _____ = S$1

(g) £ _____ = S$1   **(h)** A$ _____ = S$1

(i) US$ _____ = S$2.50   **(j)** £ _____ = S$6.30

(k) A$ _____ = S$15.40   **(l)** 450 francs = S$ _____

(m) _____ francs = S$95   **(n)** HK$745 = S$ _____

(o) HK$ _____ = S$108

9. A man and his family went for a holiday to Thailand. If the exchange rate was S$5.50 to 100 bahts, how many Singapore dollars were exchanged for 5 000 Thai bahts?

10. A Hong Kong garment manufacturer exported HK$200 000 worth of shirts to France. If the exchange rate was HK$1.60 to 1 French franc, how many francs must the French importer pay?

11. A man wishes to change S$2 500 for Sterling pounds (£) from a bank. How many Sterling pounds will he get if the exchange rate is S$2.20 to £1? A licensed money changer is willing to give £1 for S$2.10. How much more will the man get if he exchanges his money with the money changer?

12. A man went to a Singapore bank with 100 000 rupiahs. Find out how many Singapore dollars he would get if he sold 75% of his money. The exchange rates for that certain day is shown below.

BANK

Local $ to 1 000 units		Selling	Buying
	Indonesian Rupiahs	0.60	0.20

13. On a certain day, the exchange rates of currencies were as follows:

Local $ to 100 units of foreign exchange	
Hong Kong dollar	18.35
Malaysian ringgit	57.60
Danish kroner	23.65
French franc	28.10
Deutschemark	95.90
Japanese yen	1.45
Indian rupee	4.60

Convert

(a) HK$1 to Danish kroners,

(b) 10 French francs to Malaysian ringgits,

(c) 10 Deutschemarks to Japanese yen,

(d) 270 Indian rupees to Singapore dollars.

(*Note:* For simplicity, the difference between the 'buying' and 'selling' rates is ignored.)

*14. John changed $1\ 000 to Canadian dollars and $1\ 500 to US dollars. For some reason, his holiday trip was cancelled and he changed all his Canadian dollars and US dollars back to Singapore dollars. How much money (S$) did he lose?

Exchange rate Local $ to 1 unit		
	Bank buys	Bank sells
Canadian dollar (C$)	1.02	1.06
US dollar (US$)	1.42	1.47

Chapter Review

1. **Profit and Loss**
   - Profit or loss in a transaction is calculated with reference to cost price or is expressed as a percentage of the cost.
   - Profit (P) = Selling Price (SP) – Cost Price (CP)
   - Loss (L) = Cost Price (CP) – Selling Price (SP)

   Examples: **(a)** $CP = \$120$, $SP = \$150$

   $$P = SP - CP$$
   $$= \$150 - \$120$$
   $$= \$30$$

   Profit as a percentage of cost

   $$= \frac{SP - CP}{CP} \times 100\%$$

   $$= \frac{\$150 - \$120}{\$120} \times 100\%$$

   $$= \frac{30}{120} \times 100\%$$
   $$= 25\%$$

   (b) $CP = \$150$, $SP = \$110$

   $$L = CP - SP$$
   $$= \$150 - \$110$$
   $$= \$40$$

   Loss as a percentage of cost

   $$= \frac{CP - SP}{CP} \times 100\%$$

   $$= \frac{40}{150} \times 100\%$$

   $$= 26\frac{2}{3}\%$$

2. **Simple Interest**
   - Simple interest is the money charged or paid for a certain amount of money borrowed over a certain period of time.
   - The simple interest (I) charged on a principal sum of money ($\$P$) borrowed for a number of years (T) at a certain interest rate per year ($R\%$) is given by the formula

   $$I = \frac{PTR}{100}.$$

CHALLENGER 8

1. An article is sold at a profit equivalent to 20% of its sale price. Express this profit as a percentage of the cost price.

2. A man sold a radio to his friend at a discount of 40%. Find the percentage gain or loss if his usual profit, without discount, was 50%.

3. A man bought some eggs at x cents each. y of them were broken while the rest were sold at z cents each. If he made a total profit of w cents, find the number of eggs he bought in terms of x, y, z and w.

4. Alan bought a piece of land and sold it to Bill at a profit of 10%. Later on, Bill sold it back to Alan at a profit of 10%. What percentage would Alan have saved on the cost of the land had he not sold it to Bill? Give your answer correct to two decimal places.

5. A man would gain 20% by selling a T.V. set for \$840 and 15% by selling a tape recorder for \$460. If he sells the T.V. set at a special offer of \$650, what is the least price at which he must sell the tape recorder to avoid any loss on the two together?

6. A merchant pays his salesman 16% commission on the selling price of every article he sold. If he has to pay 4% more commission, by what percentage must the selling price be increased so that his actual percentage profit remains the same as before?

Problem Solving 8

Road Signs

John was travelling on a tourist bus. He saw a road sign as shown. Later, at 11.30 a.m., he asked the driver, 'When will we arrive at Beta City?' The driver said, 'Well, it depends on how much time you would like to spend for lunch at

Alpha Town. Anyway, it takes 1 hour to travel to Alpha Town and another hour to Beta City.' Assuming that the bus travelled at the same speed, when did John see the road sign?

The strategy to use is **use diagram**. A diagram is drawn to help you understand the problem and plan your solution.

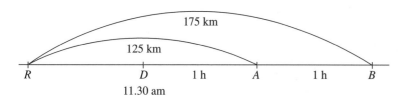

R: Road sign
D: Point where
  driver spoke
A: Alpha Town
B: Beta City

$DA = AB = (175 - 125)$ km $= 50$ km

From R to A, time taken $= \left(\dfrac{125}{50} \times 1\right)$ h $= 2\dfrac{1}{2}$ h

From R to D, time taken $= \left(2\dfrac{1}{2} - 1\right)$ h $= 1\dfrac{1}{2}$ h

Therefore, John saw the road sign at 10 a.m.

After you have solved the problem and checked the answer, you may think of more questions.

Ask yourself: When would John arrive at Beta City if he was allowed 40 minutes for lunch at Alpha Town? Where did John question the driver?

 Problems...

1. **Up and Down a Ladder** A construction worker stood on the middle rung of a ladder. He stepped down 4 rungs, climbed up 9 rungs, stepped down 6 rungs and finally stepped down 7 rungs to get to the floor. How many rungs did the whole ladder have?

2. **Speed** John was travelling to Beta City via Alpha Town. At 10 30, he noted from a road sign that Alpha Town was 105 km away and Beta City was 155 km away. At 12 30, he stopped for lunch at a place midway between Alpha Town and Beta City. At what average speed did John travel before he stopped?

3. **Shopping Together** Ann had $20 more than Betty. They went shopping together. Ann spent twice as much as Betty and her remainder was $\frac{2}{3}$ as much as Betty's. If they had $156 altogether, how much did Betty spend?

4. **Same Total** Copy the figure. Fill in all the circles with all the numbers 1 to 7 such that the numbers on each straight line have the same total.

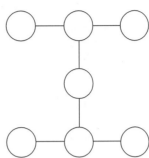

Chapter 9

Introducing Geometry

Chapter Highlights

- Understanding the terms 'supplementary' and 'complementary angles'.
- Properties of adjacent angles on a straight line, vertically opposite angles and angles at a point.
- Drawing perpendicular bisectors and parallel and perpendicular lines.
- Properties of corresponding, alternate and interior angles between parallel lines.

9.1 LINE SEGMENT, LINE AND ANGLES

MATHSTORY

Line Segment

If we mark two points and join them with a straight edge, we have a **line segment**. The two points we marked are called **endpoints**. If we name these two points A and B, we get a line segment AB. Fig. 9.1 shows a line segment AB.

Fig. 9.1

The ruler is used for measuring length and drawing line segments.

The measurement of length should start from the mark, 0, on the ruler.

Fig. 9.2

In Fig. 9.2, line segment AB is 6·4 cm long.

Line

If we extend the line segment in both directions on and on without end, we will get what we call, in geometry, a **line**. A line AB may be represented like this:

Fig. 9.3

Line segment AB, line AB or the length of AB may simply be written as AB. Instead of using different ways to show them, we may simply represent them like this:

Fig. 9.4

The word 'geometry' comes from two Greek words, ge and metria, which may literally be translated as 'earth measuring'. Over the years, geometry has been adapted to serve as the first mathematics course in which students encounter logic as a deductive way to develop theorems – mathematical theorem.

In Euclidean geometry, a line extends indefinitely in both directions and is considered to be 'straight'. Arrowheads indicate the direction of the line.

Angle

In the environment, we find many examples that suggest the idea of an angle. Fig. 9.5 shows some examples.

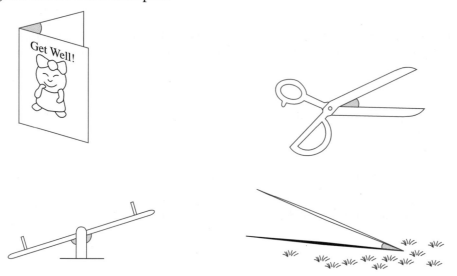

An angle is the union of two rays with a common endpoint. The rays of an angle are called the sides of the angle.

Fig. 9.5

If a boy facing north makes a quarter turn so that he faces east while standing on the same spot, we say that he has turned through an angle of 90°.

An angle of 90° is called a **right angle**. A right angle is usually marked with a small square corner as shown in Fig. 9.6.

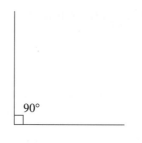

90°

Fig. 9.6

MATHSTORY

In 1634, Pierre Herigone used a symbol for an angle. It was not until 1923 that the Mathematical Association of America recommended ∠ as the standard symbol for angle in the United States. The use of 360° to measure angles seems to date to the Babylonian culture from 4000–3000 BC.

We can make a right angle by folding a piece of paper as shown in Fig. 9.7.

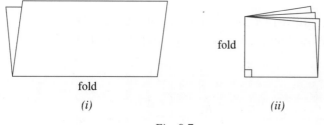

fold

fold

(i)

fold

(ii)

Fig. 9.7

The square corner obtained is a right angle.

In Fig. 9.8, the two hands of the clock make a right angle.

Fig. 9.8

In Fig. 9.9, the point *A* is called the **vertex** of the angle. *AB* and *AC* are called the **sides** or **arms** of the angle. We name this angle as angle *BAC* or angle *CAB* and write it as $B\hat{A}C$ or $C\hat{A}B$.

Another way of writing this angle is $\angle BAC$ or $\angle CAB$.

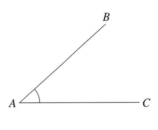

Fig. 9.9

Notice that when naming an angle, we always put the letter for the vertex in the middle.

Another way of indicating an angle is shown in Fig. 9.10, where one letter of the alphabet is used. This angle is written as $\hat{p}$.

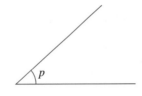

Fig. 9.10

There are three types of angles:
1. An **acute angle** is less than 90°.
2. An **obtuse angle** is greater than 90° but less than 180°.
3. A **reflex angle** is greater than 180° but less than 360°.

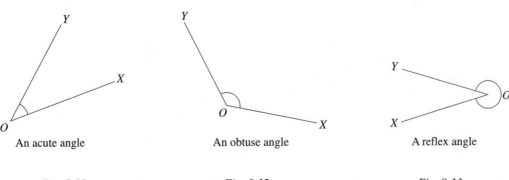

An acute angle	An obtuse angle	A reflex angle
Fig. 9.11	*Fig. 9.12*	*Fig. 9.13*

Two angles are said to be **supplementary** if their sum is 180°. In Fig. 9.14, the angles 151° and 29° are supplementary angles. So are the angles 55° and 125° in Fig. 9.15.

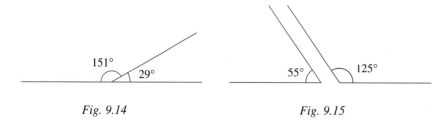

Fig. 9.14   Fig. 9.15

Two angles are said to be **complementary** if their sum is 90°. The angles 25° and 65° in Fig. 9.16 are complementary angles and so are the angles 70° and 20° in Fig. 9.17.

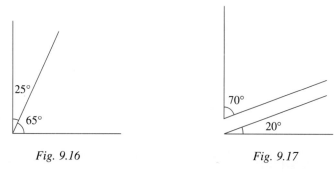

Fig. 9.16   Fig. 9.17

To measure the size of an angle, we use the protractor. The protractor is a semicircle. The centre of the circle is the midpoint of the base line.

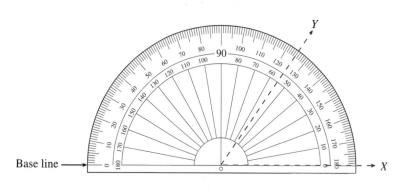

Fig. 9.18

To measure an angle, follow these steps:
1. Place the centre point of the protractor on the vertex of the angle to be measured.
2. Align the base line of the protractor with one arm of the angle.
3. Read the appropriate scale, that is, the scale that starts with 0 from the aligned arm.

In Fig. 9.18, the size of $X\hat{O}Y$ should read 55° (not 125° nor 135° nor 65°).

Fig. 9.19 shows the correct ways of measuring with a protractor.

(i)

(ii)

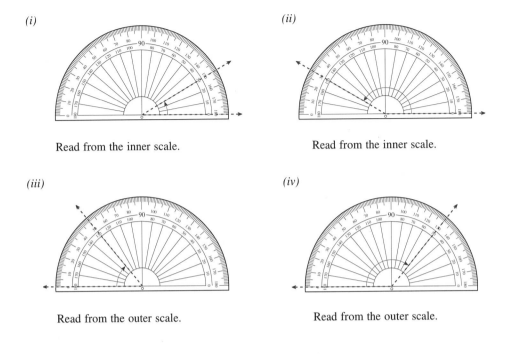

Read from the inner scale.

Read from the inner scale.

(iii)

(iv)

Read from the outer scale.

Read from the outer scale.

Fig. 9.19

Fig. 9.20 shows some incorrect ways of measuring with a protractor.

(i)

(ii)

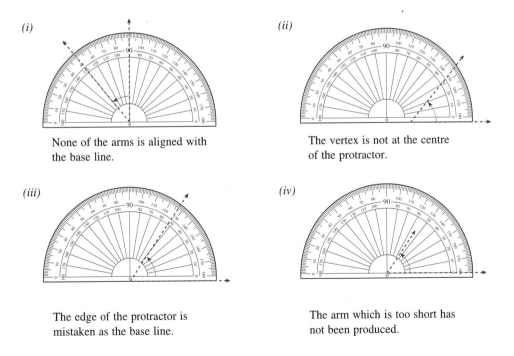

None of the arms is aligned with the base line.

The vertex is not at the centre of the protractor.

(iii)

(iv)

The edge of the protractor is mistaken as the base line.

The arm which is too short has not been produced.

Fig. 9.20

Class Activity 1

1. Name and measure the angles marked with arcs.

   (a)

   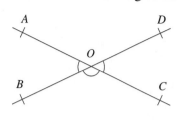

   (b)

   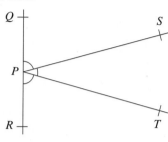

   (c)

   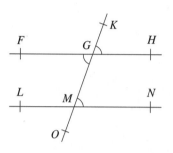

   (d)

   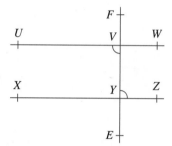

2. In the following figures, measure all angles marked with letters. Then, name **(i)** all pairs of complementary angles, **(ii)** all pairs of supplementary angles, and **(iii)** all pairs of equal angles.

   (a)

   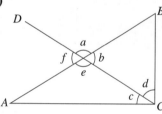

   (b)

   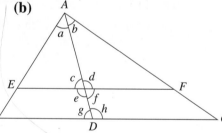

   (c)

   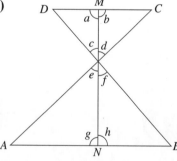

   (d)

   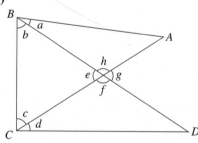

3. **(a)** Measure $A\hat{B}C$.

   (b) Make a copy of $A\hat{B}C$.

   (c) Draw $X\hat{Y}Z$ such that $X\hat{Y}Z = \frac{1}{2} A\hat{B}C$.

4. **(a)** Measure $P\hat{Q}R$.

(b) Make a copy of $P\hat{Q}R$.

(c) On the diagram in (b), draw line segment QS between QR and QP such that $S\hat{Q}R = \frac{1}{2} P\hat{Q}R$. Notice that QS **bisects** $P\hat{Q}R$ (i.e. QS divides $P\hat{Q}R$ into halves). QS is called the **angle bisector** of $P\hat{Q}R$.

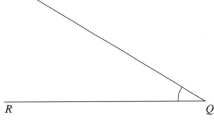

(d) Produce RQ to T.

(e) Draw the bisector QU of $P\hat{Q}T$.

(Make necessary measurement before answering **(f)** and **(g)**.)

(f) Name all pairs of complementary angles.

(g) Name all pairs of supplementary angles.

Exercise 9.1

answers on p. 431

1. Use your protractor to draw angles having the following measures.

   (a) 60°   **(b)** 115°   **(c)** 21°

   (d) 150°   **(e)** 195°   **(f)** 5°

   (g) 56°   **(h)** 160°   **(i)** 245°

Classify the angles into acute, obtuse and reflex angles.

2. What are the supplements of the angles whose measures are given below?

   (a) 10°   **(b)** 117°   **(c)** 82°

   (d) 90°   **(e)** 165°   **(f)** 22°

   (g) 68°   **(h)** 131°   **(i)** $92\frac{1}{2}°$

3. What are the complements of the angles whose measures are given below?

   (a) 37°   **(b)** 48°   **(c)** 45°

   (d) 9°   **(e)** 90°   **(f)** 22°

   (g) 39°   **(h)** 87°   **(i)** $22\frac{1}{2}°$

4. Name and measure the angles marked with arcs in the figure. Which angles **(a)** have equal measure, **(b)** are supplementary?

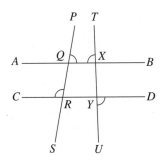

5. **(a)** Use a protractor to construct the following angles.

    (i)   15°   **(ii)**   30°   **(iii)** 45°

    (iv) 60°   **(v)**   90°   **(vi)** 130°

    (vii) 70°   **(viii)** 120°   **(ix)** 160°

   (b) Construct a bisector for each of the angles in (a).

6. **(a)** Use a protractor to draw an angle $A\hat{O}B$ of 60°.

   (b) Draw a bisector OX of AOB.

   (c) Produce BO to D.

   (d) Draw a bisector OY of $A\hat{O}D$.

   (Make necessary measurement before answering **(e)** and **(f)**.)

   (e) Name all pairs of complementary angles.

   (f) Name all pairs of supplementary angles.

9.2 ANGLE PROPERTIES RELATED TO STRAIGHT LINES

Class Activity 2

1. In the figure, ACB is a straight line. $\hat{a}$ and $\hat{b}$ are **adjacent angles**. Thus, we call $\hat{a}$ and $\hat{b}$ adjacent angles on a straight line.

   Draw a figure similar to the one on the right.

   (a) Measure $\hat{a}$ and $\hat{b}$.

   (b) Do they add up to 180°?

   (c) Do you agree that the sum of adjacent angles on a straight line is 180°?

   (d) What can you say about adjacent angles on a straight line?

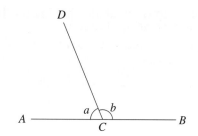

2. Draw any two lines to intersect at T as shown. In the figure, $\hat{a}$ and $\hat{c}$ are called **vertically opposite angles**. $\hat{b}$ and $\hat{d}$ are also vertically opposite angles.

   (a) Are $\hat{a}$ and $\hat{c}$ equal?

   (b) Are $\hat{b}$ and $\hat{d}$ also equal?

   (*Hint:* Check your answers by placing a traced copy of one on the other or by measuring them with a protractor.)

   (c) What can you say about vertically opposite angles?

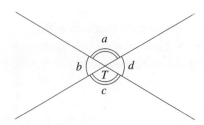

3. **(a) (i)** Measure all the angles marked in Fig. a.
 (ii) What is the total degree measure of all the angles?

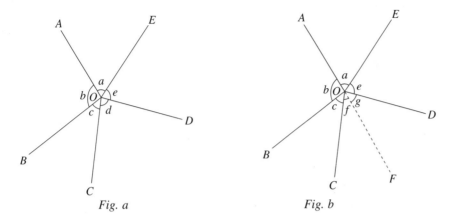

Fig. a   Fig. b

(b) In Fig. b, AO is produced to F. $\hat{d}$ is replaced by $\hat{f}$ and $\hat{g}$.
 (i) What is the degree measure of $\hat{a} + \hat{e} + \hat{g}$?
 (ii) What is the degree measure of $\hat{f} + \hat{c} + \hat{b}$?
 (iii) Is $\hat{a} + \hat{e} + \hat{g} + \hat{f} + \hat{c} + \hat{b} = 360°$ true?
 (iv) Replace $\hat{f} + \hat{g}$ by $\hat{d}$ in (iii).
   What can you say about $\hat{a} + \hat{b} + \hat{c} + \hat{d} + \hat{e}$?
 (v) Notice that $\hat{a}$ is adjacent to $\hat{b}$, $\hat{b}$ is adjacent to $\hat{c}$, . . . , and $\hat{e}$ is
   adjacent to $\hat{a}$. Notice also that they all have the same vertex O.
   These angles are called **angles at a point**.
   'The sum of angles at a point is equal to 360°.'
   Is this statement true?

From the above class activity, we observe the following.

- **The sum of the adjacent angles on a straight line is 180°
  (adj. ∠s on st. line).**
- **Vertically opposite angles are equal (vert. opp. ∠s).**
- **The sum of angles at a point is equal to 360° (∠s at a
  point).**

Note: The abbreviations are indicated within the brackets.

Worked Example 1
AOB and COD are straight lines. Find the values
of x, y and z.

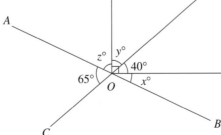

Solution:

$$65° = 40° + x° \text{ (vert. opp. } \angle s)$$
$$\therefore x = 65 - 40$$
$$= 25$$

$$y° + 40° = 90°$$
$$\therefore y = 50$$

$$65° + z° + y° = 180° \text{ (adj. } \angle s \text{ on st. line)}$$
$$65° + z° + 50° = 180°$$
$$\therefore z = 65$$

Worked Example 2

AB and CD are straight lines. Form an equation
in x and solve the equation.

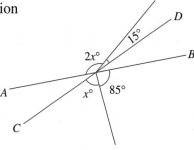

Solution:

$$2x° + 15° = x° + 85° \text{ (vert. opp. } \angle s)$$
$$\therefore x = 70$$

Exercise 9.2 ✍

answers on p. 432

In this exercise, AB, CD, EF and GH are straight lines.

1. Find the values of x and y.

(a)

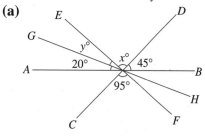

(b)

(c)

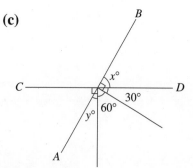

(d)

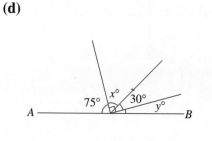

2. Form an equation in x in each case and solve the equation.

(a)

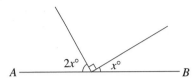

(b)

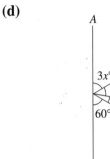

(c)

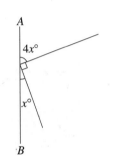

(d)

(e)

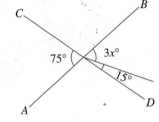

(f)

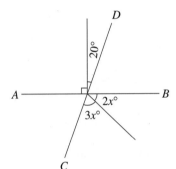

(g)

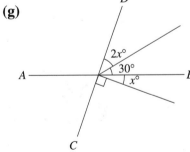

(h)

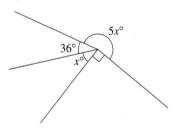

(i)

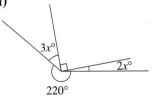

(j)

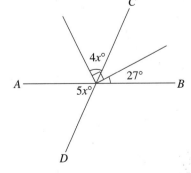

(k)

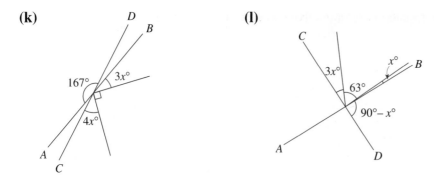

(l)

9.3 PERPENDICULAR AND PARALLEL LINES

When two line segments cut to form right angles (90°), we say that the line segments are **perpendicular** to each other.

Two straight lines are **parallel** if they are both perpendicular to another straight line.

It is easy to draw parallel lines. First, draw a line like in Fig. 9.21 on a piece of paper.

First line

Fig. 9.21

When the four angles formed by two interesecting lines all measure 90°, i.e. they are all right angles, the lines are perpendicular.

When two distinct lines in a plane do not intersect, the lines are parallel.

Draw a second line that is perpendicular to it as in Fig. 9.22 (this is easily done with your set-square).

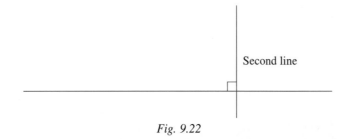

Second line

Fig. 9.22

Then, draw a third line that is perpendicular to the second line (see Fig. 9.23).

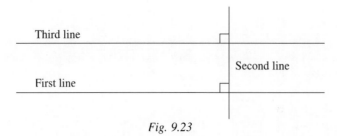

Third line

Second line

First line

Fig. 9.23

The first and third lines are parallel since the second is perpendicular to each of them.

Another way of drawing parallel lines is by sliding a set-square along a ruler as shown in Fig. 9.24. You will find that parallel lines can also be drawn as shown in Fig. 9.25.

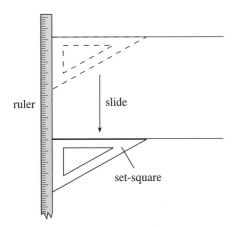

Fig. 9.24

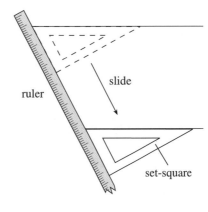

Fig. 9.25

Class Activity 3

1. **(a)** Measure *AB*.
    (b) Make a copy of *AB*.
    (c) Bisect *AB* at *M* (i.e. mark a point *M* on *AB* such that *AM = BM*).
    (d) Through *M*, draw *LM* perpendicular to *AB*. *LM* is called the **perpendicular bisector** of *AB*.

A   *B*

2. **(a)** Measure *PQ*.
    (b) Make a copy of *PQ*.
    (c) Mark a convenient point *R* above *PQ*.
    (d) Draw a perpendicular from *R* to *PQ*.

P   *Q*

3. **(a)** Measure *XY*.
    (b) Make a copy of *XY*.
    (c) Make a point *Q* on *XY* such that *QX* = 4 cm.
    (d) Mark a point *P* 4 cm directly above *Q* (i.e. *PQ* is perpendicular to *XY* and *PQ* = 4 cm). We say that the distance from *P* to *XY* is 4 cm.

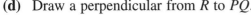

X   *Y*

4. **(a)** Make a copy of *AB*.
   (b) Mark a point *P* such that *P* is 3 cm from *AB* (i.e. the distance from *P* to *AB* is 3 cm).
   (c) Draw a line *CD* through *P* and parallel to *AB*. We say that the distance between the parallel lines *AB* and *CD* is 3 cm.

   A ———————————————— B

5. Provide examples of perpendicular and parallel lines in the environment.

Exercise 9.3
answers on p. 432

1. **(a)** Copy these line segments. Then, using a ruler, bisect each of them.

   (i) A ———————————— B

   (ii) C ————————————————————————— D

   (b) Copy these line segments. Then, using a ruler and a set square, draw a perpendicular bisector for each.

   (i) E ————————————————————— F

   (ii) G ——————————————————————————— H

   (iii) I ———————————— J

2. Draw the following line segments, and then draw the perpendicular bisector of each line segment.
   (a) $AB = 3$ cm   **(b)** $PQ = 4 \cdot 5$ cm
   (c) $ST = 5 \cdot 5$ cm   **(d)** $XY = 6 \cdot 5$ cm

3. Draw a line segment *AB*, 6 cm long. Draw its perpendicular bisector. Mark a point *P* on the perpendicular bisector 4 cm from the midpoint of *AB*. Measure *AP* and *BP*.

4. Draw a line segment *XY*, 10 cm long, and mark a point *N* on *XY*, 4 cm from *X*. Through *N*, draw a perpendicular to *XY*.

5. Draw a line segment *MN*, 5 cm long. Draw through *N* a perpendicular to *MN*.

6. Draw a line *PQ* and mark a point *R* not lying on *PQ*. Draw a perpendicular from *R* to the line *PQ*.

7. **(a)** Draw *BC* perpendicular to *AB* such that *AB* = 3 cm and *BC* = 4 cm. Draw and measure *AC*.

   (b) Draw *ZX* perpendicular to *XY* such that *XY* = 5 cm and *ZX* = 12 cm. Draw and measure *YZ*.

8. **(a)** Draw two parallel lines *AB* and *XY* such that they are 4 cm apart.

   (b) Draw two parallel lines *PQ* and *ST* such that the distance between them is 5 cm. Draw a third parallel line *XY* which is exactly between *PQ* and *ST*.

   (c) Draw *AB*, 5 cm long. At *A*, draw *AC*, 4 cm long, such that it is perpendicular to *AB*. At *C*, draw *CD*, 6 cm long, such that it is perpendicular to *AC* and such that *D* is on the same side of *AC* as *B*. Is *CD* parallel to *AB*? Draw and measure *DB*.

9. In the figure, *OC* is perpendicular to *AB*. Copy the figure and draw the bisectors of *AÔC* and *CÔB*. Name the bisectors *OD* and *OE* respectively. What is the size of *DÔE*? Again draw the bisectors of *DÔC* and *CÔE*. Name these new bisectors *OF* and *OG* respectively. What is the size of *FÔG*?

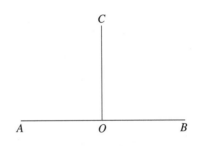

9.4 ANGLES PROPERTIES RELATED TO PARALLEL LINES

Class Activity 4

1. Draw two parallel lines. Then, draw a third line perpendicular to either one of your parallel lines. Is the third line also perpendicular to the other line?

2. Draw two parallel lines. Then, draw a third line parallel to either one of the two lines. Is the third line also parallel to the other line?

3. Draw two parallel lines. Then, draw a **transversal** (i.e. a line that cuts them both) as shown.

   AP̂Q and *PQ̂D* are called **alternate angles**

   BP̂Q and *PQ̂C* are also alternate angles.

   Measure the angles with your protractor. What can you say about alternate angles?

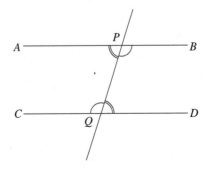

4. Draw lines *AB* and *CD* intersecting at *M*. (Choose any convenient size such as 70°, 85°, 110°, etc. for $A\hat{M}D$.) Then, draw a third line *LF* cutting the line *CD* at *R* so that $A\hat{M}R = M\hat{R}F$ as shown. Are lines *AB* and *LF* parallel? Check this by using a set-square and a ruler.

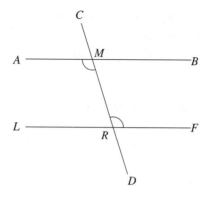

5. In the figure, $\hat{a}$ and $\hat{b}$ are called **corresponding angles** and $\hat{b}$ and $\hat{c}$ are called **interior angles** on the same side of the transversal.

   Are the following statements true?

   If *AB // CD*, then $\hat{a} = \hat{b}$ and vice versa.

   If *AB // CD* then $\hat{b} + \hat{c} = 180°$ and vice versa.

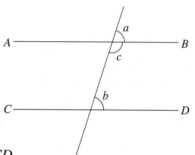

Note: *AB // CD* means *AB* is parallel to *CD*.

From the above class activity, we observe the following.

- **A line that is perpendicular to one of two parallel lines is also perpendicular to the other.**
- **A line that is parallel to one of two parallel lines is also parallel to the other.**
- **When a transversal cuts two parallel lines,**
  (a) the alternate angles are equal (alt. ∠s),
  (b) the corresponding angles are equal (corr. ∠s),
  (c) the interior angles on the same side of the transversal are supplementary (int. ∠s).
- **Two lines in a plane are parallel if they are cut by a transversal in such a way that**
  (a) the alternate angles are equal, or
  (b) the corresponding angles are equal, or
  (c) the interior angles on the same side of the transversal are supplementary.

Note: To indicate parallel lines or segments, we usually make use of arrow-heads like the ones in Fig. 9.26.

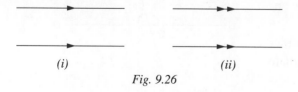

(i)   (ii)

Fig. 9.26

Worked Example 3
Find the value of x.

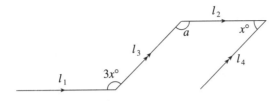

Solution:

$$\hat{a} = 180° - x° \text{ (int. } \angle s, \, l_3 \,/\!/ \, l_4)$$

Also, $\qquad 3x° = \hat{a} \text{ (alt. } \angle s, \, l_1 \,/\!/ \, l_2)$

i.e. $\qquad 3x° = 180° - x°$

$\qquad\qquad 4x° = 180°$

$$\therefore x = \frac{180}{4}$$

$$= 45$$

Worked Example 4
In each of the figures below, find the angle marked x.

(a)

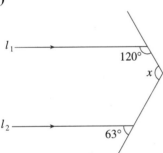

(b)

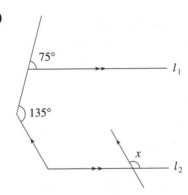

Solution:

(a) Draw a horizontal line l_3 parallel to l_1 and l_2
as shown.

$\hat{a}$ and $120°$ are supplementary (int. $\angle s$, $l_1 \,/\!/ \, l_3$).

$\therefore \quad \hat{a} = 180° - 120°$

$\qquad = 60°$

Also, $\hat{b} = 63°$ (corr. $\angle s$, $l_2 \,/\!/ \, l_3$)

$\therefore \quad \hat{x} = \hat{a} + \hat{b}$

$\qquad = 60° + 63°$

$\qquad = 123°$

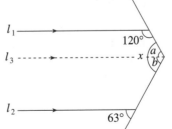

(b) Draw l_3 parallel to l_1 and l_2 and mark l_4, l_5, $\hat{a}$, $\hat{b}$, $\hat{c}$ and $\hat{d}$ as shown.

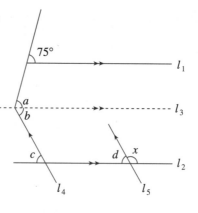

$\hat{a} = 75°$ (alt. $\angle$s, $l_1 \parallel l_3$)
$\hat{b} = 135° - \hat{a}$
$\quad = 135° - 75°$
$\quad = 60°$

Also, $\hat{c} = \hat{b} = 60°$ (alt. $\angle$s, $l_3 \parallel l_2$)
$\quad \hat{d} = \hat{c} = 60°$ (corr. $\angle$s, $l_4 \parallel l_5$)
$\therefore \quad \hat{x} = 180° - \hat{d}$ (adj. $\angle$s on st. line)
$\quad = 180° - 60°$
$\quad = 120°$

Exercise 9.4

answers on p. 432

1. Below is a diagram of a transversal crossing two parallel lines.
   (a) Use your knowledge of vertically opposite angles and of alternate angles to name all the angles that are equal to $H\hat{B}R$.
   (b) What angles are equal to $B\hat{Q}N$?

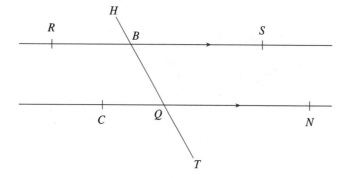

2. In the figure, $AB \parallel ED$. Calculate $\hat{x} + \hat{y} + \hat{z}$.
   (*Hint:* Draw a line through C parallel to BA.)

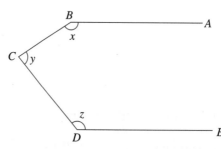

3. In the figure, if $BA \parallel ED$ and $BC \parallel EF$, is $A\hat{B}C = D\hat{E}F$?

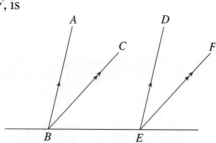

4. In the figure, if AB bisects $Q\hat{A}C$ and CD bisects $A\hat{C}S$, is $AB \parallel CD$?

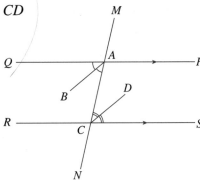

5. Study the figure shown.
   (a) Is $A\hat{B}C = D\hat{C}E$?
   (b) Is $A\hat{D}C = D\hat{C}E$?
   (c) Is $A\hat{B}C = A\hat{D}C$?
   (d) What can you say about $B\hat{A}D$ and $B\hat{C}D$?

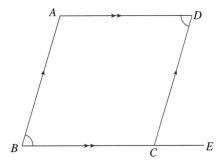

6. Study the figure shown. Then, write down all the pairs of equal angles (other than the right angles indicated).
   (*Hint:* Produce AB and CB to meet CG and AF produced respectively.)

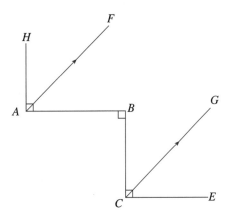

7. In the figure, $\hat{a} = \hat{b} = \hat{c} = \hat{d}$. Write down four pairs of parallel lines.

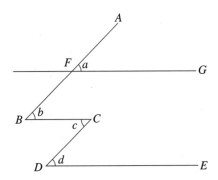

8. Find the value of x in each of the following figures.

(a)

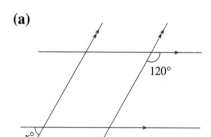

(b)

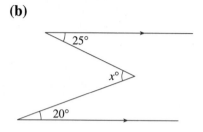

(c)

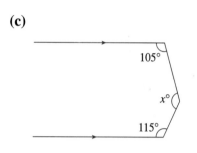

(d)

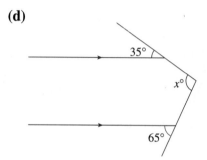

(e)

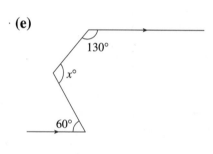

(f)

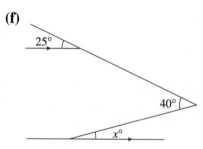

(g)

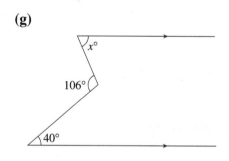

(h)

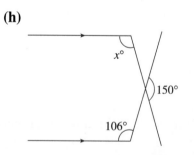

(i)

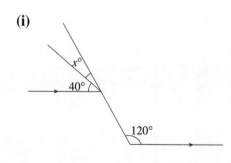

(j)

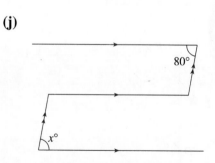

9. Find the value of x in each of the following.

(a)

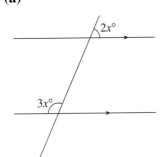

(b)

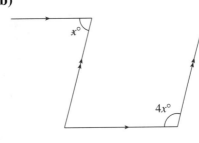

(c)

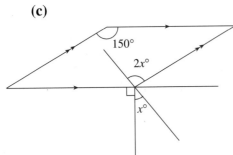

(d)

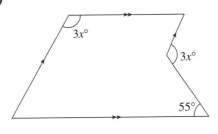

10. Find $\hat{a}$ in each of the following.

(a)

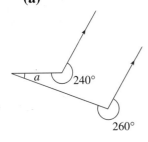

(b)

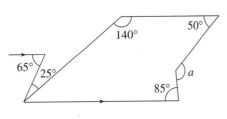

(c)

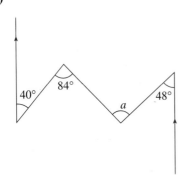

(d)

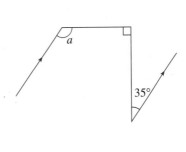

11. Name the pairs of parallel lines in each of the following.

(a)

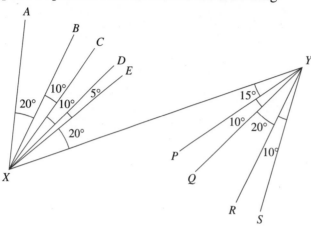

(b)

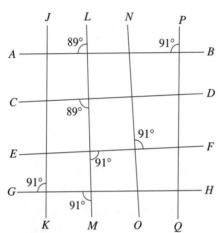

Chapter Review

1. **Adjacent Angles**

The sum of adjacent angles on a straight line is 180° (adj. ∠s on a st. line).

Example:

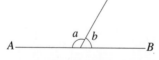

$$\hat{a} + \hat{b} = 180°$$

2. **Vertically Opposite Angles**

Vertically opposite angles are equal (vert. opp ∠s).

Example:

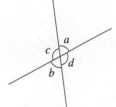

$$\hat{a} = \hat{b}$$
$$\hat{c} = \hat{d}$$

3. Angles at a Point

The sum of angles at a point is equal to 360° (∠s at a point).

Example:

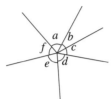

$$\hat{a} + \hat{b} + \hat{c} + \hat{d} + \hat{e} + \hat{f} = 360°$$

4. Perpendicular Lines

A line that is perpendicular to one of the two parallel lines is also perpendicular to the other.

Example:

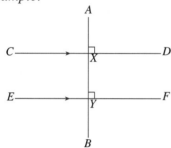

CD // EF (given).
If $A\hat{X}D = 90°$, then $A\hat{Y}F = 90°$.

5. Parallel Lines

- A line that is parallel to one of the two parallel lines is also parallel to the other.

  Example:

  A ——————→—————— B

  C ——————→—————— D

  E ——————→—————— F

  AB // EF (given).
  If *CD // AB*, then *CD // EF*.

- When a transversal cuts two parallel lines,
  (a) the alternate angles are equal (alt. ∠s),
  (b) the corresponding angles are equal (corr. ∠s),
  (c) the interior angles on the same side of the transversal are supplementary (int. ∠s).

  Example:

  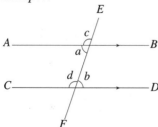

  AB // CD
  EF is a transversal (given)
  $\hat{a} = \hat{b}$ (alt. ∠s)
  $\hat{c} = \hat{d}$ (corr. ∠s)
  $\hat{a} + \hat{d} = 180°$ (int. ∠s)

- Two lines in a plane are parallel if they are cut by a transversal in such a way that
  - **(a)** the alternate angles are equal, or
  - **(b)** the corresponding angles are equal, or
  - **(c)** the interior angles on the same side of the transversal are supplementary.

To illustrate:

(a)

If $\hat{x} = \hat{y}$ (alt. $\angle$s),
then $AB \mathbin{/\mkern-4mu/} CD$.

(b)

If $\hat{a} = \hat{b}$ (corr. $\angle$s),
then $AB \mathbin{/\mkern-4mu/} CD$.

(c)

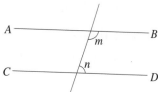

If $\hat{m} + \hat{n} = 180°$,
then $AB \mathbin{/\mkern-4mu/} CD$.

CHALLENGER

1. **(a)** a, b and c are given line segments such $c > b > a$. Explain how you would construct a line segment equal to $a - b + c$ using ruler and compasses only.

   (b) a and b ($a > b$) are two given line segments. Explain how you would construct a line segment equal to $\frac{1}{2}[a - (2b - a)]$.

2. Draw AB and CD to cut at a point O. Mark any two points P and Q on AB and CD respectively. Construct points R and S on AB and CD respectively such that $PO = OR$ and $QO = OS$. Join PQ, QR, RS and SP. What relationships have you observed between PQ, QR, RS and SP?

3. Draw AT of any length. Through A, draw $AF = 10$ cm exactly. Construct points B, C, D and E on AF such that $AB = BC = CD = DE = 2$ cm. Join FT and draw lines through E, D, C and B parallel to FT to cut AT at S, R, Q and P. Measure AP, PQ, QR, RS and ST. Have you discovered a way to divide a given line segment into equal parts?

4. Draw a triangle ABC of any size. Construct the bisectors of angle A and angle B. If these bisectors meet at a point O, is O equidistant (same distance away) from the three sides of the triangle? Can you find another point which is equidistant from the lines AB, BC and CA? If so, construct it on the same diagram. (*Hint:* Produce the sides of triangle ABC.)

5. (a) The figure on the right is constructed by John using a ruler and a pencil only. Measure $\hat{a}$ and $\hat{b}$ with your protractor. What have you noticed?

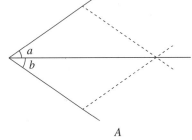

(b) $A\hat{O}B$ is a given angle. Think of a way to bisect $A\hat{O}B$ using a pencil and a ruler only. Explain your method.

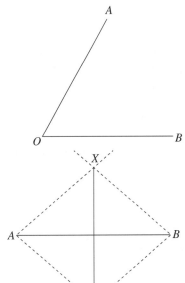

6. (a) The figure on the right shows the method invented by Sani to construct the perpendicular bisector XY of a given line segment AB, using a pencil and a ruler only. Study the construction carefully. Describe this method briefly.

(b) Draw a line segment AB. Construct the perpendicular bisector XY of AB using the method suggested in (a).

Problem Solving 9

Denominations of Coins

A sum of $3.60 is formed by 20 coins of denominations 10¢, 20¢ and 50¢. Find the number of coins of each denomination. Give all possible sets of answers.

Chapter 9

Let us use the strategies **use tabulation** and **look for pattern**

Let us first consider the case where one 50¢ coin is used.

Number of coins			Amount
50¢	20¢	10¢	
1	1	18	$2.50
1	2	17	$2.60
1	3	16	$2.70
.	.	.	.
.	.	.	.
.	.	.	.
.	.	.	.
.	.	.	.
1	12	7	$3.60

Notice from the pattern that in each step, the number of 20¢ coins increases by 1 while the amount increases by 10¢. Similarly, after considering cases where two, three, four, . . . 50¢ coins are used, we have the following sets of answers.

    1 50¢ coin, 12 20¢ coins and 7 10¢ coins;
    2 50¢ coins, 8 20¢ coins and 10 10¢ coins;
    3 50¢ coins, 4 20¢ coins and 13 10¢ coins.

We can also use the strategies **use equation** and **guess and check** as follows:

Let x and y be the numbers of 50¢ coins and 20¢ coins respectively.
Then, the number of 10¢ coins is $20 - x - y$.
So, we have
$$50x + 20y + 10(20 - x - y) = 360.$$
This reduces to
$$4x + y = 16$$
$$x = \frac{16 - y}{4} = 4 - \frac{y}{4}.$$

Since x and y are positive integers, we observe that
$$y = 4, 8, 12$$
$$x = 3, 2, 1$$
$$20 - x - y = 13, 10, 7$$

These values will give the same sets of answers as above.

 **Problems...**

1. **Chickens and Rabbits** The total number of rabbits and chickens is 39 and the total number of their legs is 100. How many rabbits are there?

256

2. **Monks and Buns** There are 100 buns for 100 monks. A senior monk is served with 3 buns and 3 junior monks are to share 1 bun. How many senior monks are there?

3. **Buying Stamps** Peter bought 12 stamps of denominations 15¢, 20¢ and 50¢. If the stamps costs $2.60, find the number of each type of stamp. (Give all possible sets of answers.)

4. **Ceramic Art** At a school funfair, Ali had 6 pieces of ceramic art to sell. They were priced at $15, $16, $18, $19, $20 and $31. Ali sold 3 pieces in the morning and 2 pieces in the afternoon. The amount collected in the morning was twice as much as the amount collected in the afternoon. Which piece of ceramic art was left unsold?

Chapter 10

Polygons

Chapter Highlights

- Constructing a triangle or quadrilateral with given data.
- Classifying triangles into acute-angled, obtuse-angled, right-angled, equilateral, isosceles and scalene triangles and knowing their properties.
- Recognising the various quadrilaterals (parallelogram, rhombus, rectangle, square, kite and trapezium) and knowing their properties.
- Finding interior/exterior angles, their sum and number of sides of a polygon using given information.
- Solving geometrical problems involving triangles, quadrilaterals and other polygons.

10.1 TRIANGLES

MATHSTORY

Euclid of Alexandria in around the year 300 BC introduced an equilateral triangle as a triangle 'which has its three sides equal' and an isosceles triangle as a triangle 'which has two of its sides alone equal'.

A **triangle** is a three-sided plane figure.

Triangles can be classified into three types according to their sides:
1. A triangle which has three equal sides is called an **equilateral triangle**.
2. A triangle in which two sides are equal is called an **isosceles triangle**.
3. A triangle having none of its sides equal is called a **scalene triangle**.

Note: An equilateral triangle can be considered as a special kind of isosceles triangle.

Triangles can also be classified according to their angles as follows:
1. A triangle whose three angles are acute is called an **acute-angled triangle**.
2. A triangle having one obtuse angle is called an **obtuse-angled triangle**.
3. A triangle which has a right angle is called a **right-angled triangle**.

Remember these:

Classification of triangles	
By sides	**By angles**
Equilateral triangle	Acute-angled triangle (All angles are acute.)
Isosceles triangle	Obtuse-angled triangle (One angle is obtuse.)
Scalene triangle	Right-angled triangle

Table 10.1

Worked Example 1
Construct $\triangle ABC$ such that $AB = 6$ cm, $\hat{A} = 45°$ and $\hat{B} = 65°$. Measure AC and BC.

Solution:

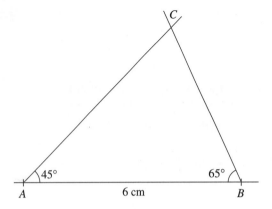

By measurement, AC = 5.8 cm and BC = 4.5 cm.

Note: △ABC means a triangle with vertices A, B and C.
The steps for construction are as follows:
1. Draw a line segment AB, 6 cm long.
2. Use the protractor to construct $\hat{A}$ equal to 45° and $\hat{B}$ equal to 65°.
3. Produce the arms of $\hat{A}$ and $\hat{B}$ to meet at C.
Thus, △ABC is the required triangle.

Worked Example 2

Construct △XYZ such that XY = 5 cm, XZ = 4 cm and YZ = 3 cm. Measure $X\hat{Z}Y$.

Solution:

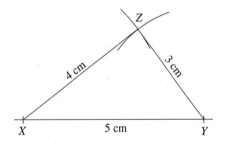

By measurement with a protractor, $X\hat{Z}Y$ = 90°.

Note: The steps for construction are as follows:
1. Draw a line segment XY, 5 cm long.
2. Set the compasses with radius 4 cm and with X as centre, draw an arc.
3. Similarly, with Y as centre and radius 3 cm, draw an arc to cut the first arc at Z.
4. Join XZ and YZ.
Thus, △XYZ is the required triangle.

answers on p. 432

Exercise 10.1

1. Make an exact copy of the given triangle *ABC* using a ruler, pencil and compasses only.

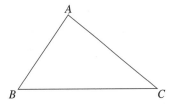

2. Construct a right-angled triangle such that the two sides of the right angle are 5 cm each. Is the figure an isosceles triangle? Find the other two angles by measurement.

3. Construct $\triangle ABC$ such that $\hat{A} = 60°$, $AB = 5$ cm and $AC = 5$ cm. Is $\triangle ABC$ an isosceles triangle? Measure BC, $\hat{B}$ and $\hat{C}$. Is $\triangle ABC$ an equilateral triangle?

4. Draw triangles *ABC* with the data given below. For each triangle, measure the sides and angles which are not given. Classify each triangle (i) by sides, and (ii) by angles.
   (a) $AB = 3$ cm, $BC = 5$ cm, $CA = 3$ cm
   (b) $AB = 4$ cm, $\hat{A} = 45°$, $\hat{B} = 45°$
   (c) $AB = 2$ cm, $BC = 3$ cm, $CA = 4$ cm
   (d) $AB = 4$ cm, $BC = 4$ cm, $CA = 4$ cm
   (e) $AB = 5$ cm, $\hat{A} = 40°$, $\hat{B} = 80°$
   (f) $AB = 3$ cm, $BC = 4$ cm, $CA = 5$ cm
   (g) $AB = 3$ cm, $CA = 3$ cm, $\hat{A} = 120°$

5. Construct $\triangle XYZ$ such that $XY = 6$ cm, $\hat{X} = 50°$ and $\hat{Y} = 60°$. Measure XZ, YZ and $\hat{Z}$. What is the sum of $\hat{X}$, $\hat{Y}$ and $\hat{Z}$?

6. Construct $\triangle PQR$ such that $PQ = 6$ cm, $QR = 5.5$ cm and $PR = 5$ cm. Measure $\hat{P}$, $\hat{Q}$ and $\hat{R}$. What is the sum of $\hat{P}$, $\hat{Q}$ and $\hat{R}$?

7. Construct $\triangle STU$ such that $\hat{S} = 90°$, $ST = 4$ cm and $TU = 6$ cm. Measure SU, $\hat{T}$ and $\hat{U}$. What is the sum of $\hat{S}$, $\hat{T}$ and $\hat{U}$?

8. Construct a triangle with two sides equal to 5 cm each and the third side equal to 7.5 cm. Measure the angles of the triangle. What is their sum?

9. Construct a right-angled triangle such that two sides of the right angle are 6 cm each. Measure the other two angles. Are these two angles complementary angles?

10. For each set of data given below, draw the $\triangle ABC$. For each triangle, measure the angles which are not given and write down the value of $\hat{A} + \hat{B}$. Produce *BC* to a point *X*. Find the value of $A\hat{C}X$ by measurement,

compare the value of $A\hat{C}X$ with that of $\hat{A} + \hat{B}$ and describe your finding in each case.

(a) $AB = 4$ cm, $\hat{A} = 20°$, $\hat{B} = 50°$
(b) $BC = 3$ cm, $CA = 3$ cm, $\hat{C} = 30°$
(c) $AB = 2$ cm, $BC = 5$ cm, $\hat{B} = 70°$
(d) $AB = 4$ cm, $\hat{A} = 30°$, $\hat{B} = 90°$

10.2 ANGLE PROPERTIES OF A TRIANGLE

Class Activity 1

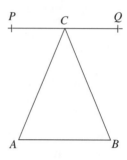

1. Consider $\triangle ABC$. The line PQ is parallel to AB.
    (a) Is $P\hat{C}A + A\hat{C}B + B\hat{C}Q$ equal to 180°? Why?
    (b) Is $P\hat{C}A$ equal to $C\hat{A}B$? Why?
    (c) Is $B\hat{C}Q$ equal to $C\hat{B}A$? Why?
    (d) Is the statement below true?
         'The sum of three angles of a triangle is 180°.'

2. In $\triangle ABC$, the side BC is produced to a point X. As a result, $A\hat{C}X$ is formed. $A\hat{C}X$ is called an **exterior angle** of the triangle. $C\hat{A}B$ and $A\hat{B}C$ are called the **interior opposite angles** of $A\hat{C}X$.
    (a) Is $A\hat{C}X + B\hat{C}A$ equal to 180°? Why?
    (b) Is $A\hat{B}C + C\hat{A}B + B\hat{C}A$ equal to 180°? Why?
    (c) Is $A\hat{C}X$ equal to $A\hat{B}C + C\hat{A}B$?
    (d) Do you agree with the statement below?
         'In any triangle an exterior angle is equal to the sum of the interior opposite angles.'

From the preceding discussion, the following useful properties are observed.

> *   *The sum of the angles of a triangle is $180°$ ($\angle$ sum of $\triangle$).*
> *   *An exterior angle of a triangle is equal to the sum of the interior opposite angles (ext. $\angle$ of $\triangle$).*

Worked Example 3
Find the value of x in the figure.

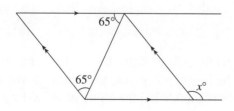

Solution:

Mark $y°$, $z°$, l_1, l_2, l_3 and l_4 as shown.

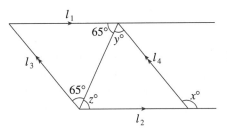

$\qquad y° = 65°$ (alt. $\angle$s, $l_3 \mathbin{/\!/} l_4$)

Also, $\quad z° = 65°$ (alt. $\angle$s, $l_1 \mathbin{/\!/} l_2$)

$\qquad x° = y° + z°$ (ext. $\angle$ of $\triangle$)

$\qquad\quad = 130°$

$\therefore \; x = 130$

Worked Example 4

Form an equation in x and solve the equation.

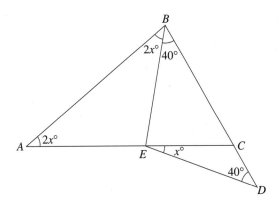

Solution:

$$B\hat{E}C = 2x° + 2x° \text{ (ext. } \angle \text{ of } \triangle)$$
$$= 4x°$$

In $\triangle BED,$ $\quad 40° + 4x° + x° + 40° = 180°$ ($\angle$ sum of $\triangle$)
$$5x = 180 - 40 - 40$$
$$\therefore \; x = \frac{100}{5}$$
$$= 20$$

Exercise 10.2

answers on p. 432

1.

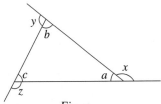

Fig. a

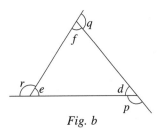

Fig. b

Copy and complete the following.

(a) $\hat{b}$ and $\hat{c}$ are the interior opposite angles of $\hat{x}$.

$\hat{c}$ and $\hat{a}$ are the interior opposite angles of _____.

$\hat{a}$ and $\hat{b}$ are the interior opposite angles of _____.

(b) $\hat{e}$ and $\hat{f}$ are the interior opposite angles of $\hat{p}$.

_____ and _____ are the interior opposite angles of $\hat{q}$.

_____ and _____ are the interior opposite angles of $\hat{r}$.

2. State whether the following statements are true or false.

   (a) Every right-angled triangle has two complementary angles.

   (b) It is possible to draw a triangle with two right angles.

   (c) An acute-angled triangle can never have an acute exterior angle.

3. Find the value of x in each case.

(a)

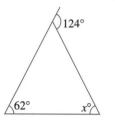

(b)

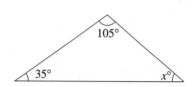

(c)

(d)

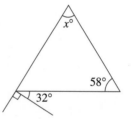

(e)

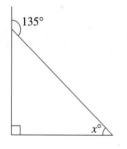

(f)

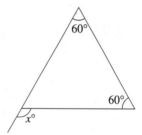

(g)

(h)

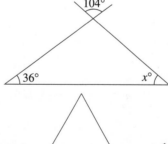

(i)

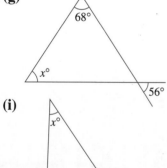

(j)

4. Form an equation in x in each case and solve the equation.

(a)

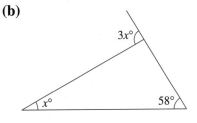

(b)

(c)

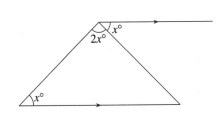

(d)

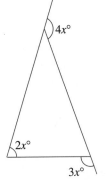

(e)

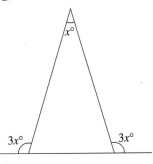

(f)

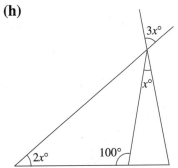

(g)

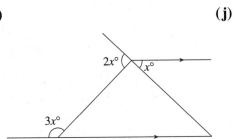

(h)

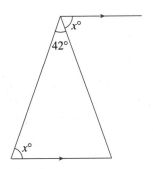

(i)

(j)

(k)

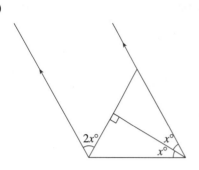

(l)

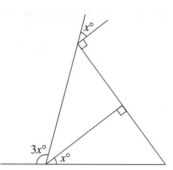

(m)

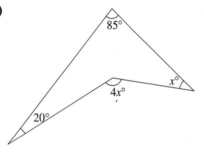

(n)

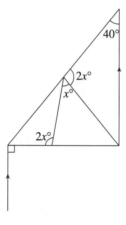

(o)

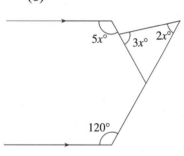

(p)

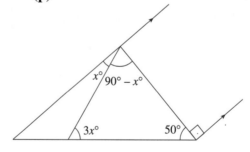

10.3 ISOSCELES AND EQUILATERAL TRIANGLES

Class Activity 2

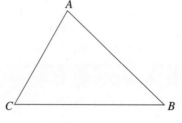

1. In $\triangle ABC$, AB is said to be the side opposite $\hat{C}$ and $\hat{C}$ is said to be the angle opposite AB.
   What side is opposite $\hat{B}$?
   What angle is opposite BC?

2. The figure shows a triangle *ABC* such that *AB* = *AC*.
△*ABC* is an isosceles triangle.

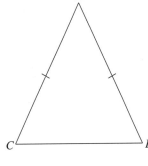

(a) Measure the angles that are opposite the two equal sides.

(b) Are these two angles equal?

(c) Draw a different triangle with two equal sides and repeat (a) and (b) above. Then, compare your findings with your classmates.

(d) Do you agree with the statement below?

'If two sides of a triangle are equal, then the angles opposite them are equal.'

3. The figure shows a triangle *ABC* such that $\hat{B} = \hat{C}$.

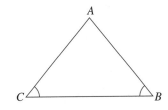

(a) Measure the two sides that are opposite the two equal angles.

(b) Are these two sides equal?

(c) Draw a different triangle with two equal angles and repeat (a) and (b) above. Then, compare your findings with your classmates.

(d) Do you agree with the statement below?

'If two angles of a triangle are equal, then the sides opposite these angles are equal.'

4. The figure shows a triangle *ABC*.
Are the following statements true? Why?

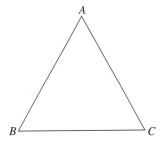

(a) If *AB* = *BC* = *CA*, then $\hat{A} = \hat{B} = \hat{C}$.

(b) If $\hat{A} = \hat{B} = \hat{C}$, then *AB* = *BC* = *CA*.

(c) If △*ABC* is an equilateral triangle, then $\hat{A} = \hat{B} = \hat{C} = 60°$.

From the above class activity, the following useful properties are observed.

1. 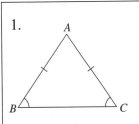 In △*ABC*, if *AB* = *AC*, then $\hat{B} = \hat{C}$.	2. 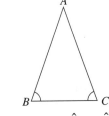 In △*ABC*, if $\hat{B} = \hat{C}$, then *AB* = *AC*.	3. 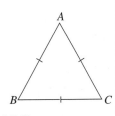 In △*ABC*, if *AB* = *BC* = *CA*, then $\hat{A} = \hat{B} = \hat{C} = 60°$ and vice versa.

Worked Example 5

Find the value of x.

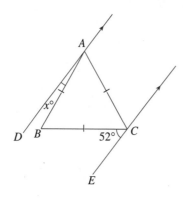

Solution:

$$B\hat{A}C = A\hat{C}B = 60° \text{ (equilateral } \triangle)$$
$$D\hat{A}C + E\hat{C}A = 180° \text{ (int } \angle\text{s, } DA \text{ // } EC)$$
$$x° + 60° + 60° + 52° = 180°$$
$$\therefore \ x = 8$$

Worked Example 6

In the figure, O is the centre of the circle. Form an equation in x and solve the equation.

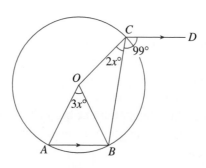

Solution:

$$O\hat{B}C = 2x° \text{ (iso } \triangle OBC)$$

$$A\hat{B}O = \frac{1}{2}(180° - 3x°) \text{ (iso } \triangle ABO \text{ and } \angle \text{ sum of } \triangle)$$

$$A\hat{B}C = B\hat{C}D \text{ (alt } \angle\text{s, } AB \text{ // } CD)$$

$$A\hat{B}O + O\hat{B}C = 99°$$

$$\frac{1}{2}(180° - 3x°) + 2x° = 99°$$

$$180° - 3x° + 4x° = 198°$$

$$\therefore \ x = 18$$

Exercise 10.3 ✐

answers on p. 433

1. Find the value of x in each case.

    (a)

    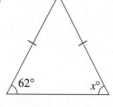

    (b)

    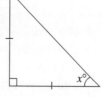

    (c)

    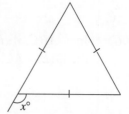

(d)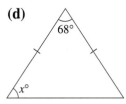

(e)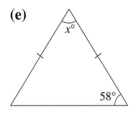

(f)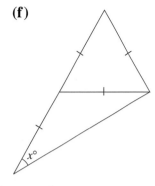

2. Form an equation in x for each case and solve the equation.

(a)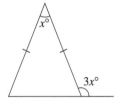

(b)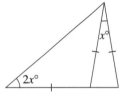

(c)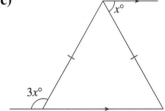

(d)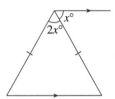

3. In each figure, O is the centre of the circle. Form an equation in x and solve the equation.

(a)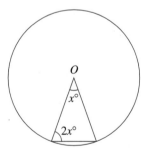

(b)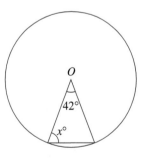

(c)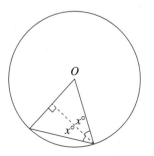

(d)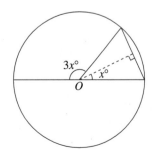

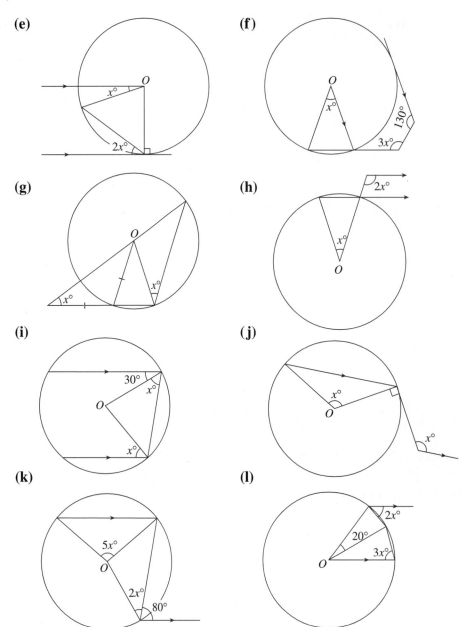

(e)

(f)

(g)

(h)

(i)

(j)

(k)

(l)

10.4 ANGLE PROPERTIES OF A POLYGON

Here are some closed figures made up of line segments.

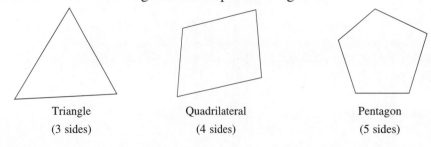

Triangle
(3 sides)

Quadrilateral
(4 sides)

Pentagon
(5 sides)

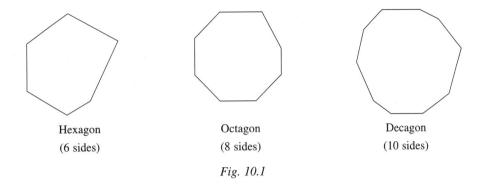

Hexagon	Octagon	Decagon
(6 sides)	(8 sides)	(10 sides)

Fig. 10.1

Plane figures with 3, 4, 5 or more sides such as the above are known as **polygons**.

Let us name the different parts of a polygon.

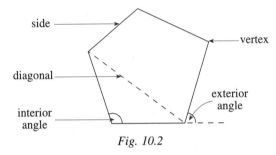

Fig. 10.2

Note: As you can see from the above, the diagonal is the line joining one vertex to another which is not an adjacent vertex.

We have learnt that the sum of the angles of a three-sided polygon (triangle) is 180°. If we draw any four-sided polygon (quadrilateral), we will find by measurement that the sum of the interior angles is 360°. Instead of measuring the angles, we can prove this by reasoning.

Example

In Fig. 10.3, *ABCD* is a four-sided polygon. If we choose any vertex, say *A*, and from *A* draw a diagonal, we will notice that the figure is divided into two triangles. Let us name the angles as shown in the figure. The angle sum of the quadrilateral is $B\hat{A}D + A\hat{D}C + D\hat{C}B + C\hat{B}A$, i.e. $(\hat{a} + \hat{f}) + \hat{e} + (\hat{d} + \hat{c}) + \hat{b}$ or $(\hat{a} + \hat{b} + \hat{c}) + (\hat{d} + \hat{e} + \hat{f})$. Since these are angle sums of the two triangles, we can conclude that the angle sum of a quadrilateral is equal to $2 \times 180°$ or 360°.

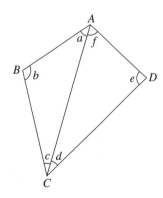

Fig. 10.3

Note: There are many ways to name the quadrilateral in Fig. 10.3, for example, in anticlockwise direction as *ABCD*, *BCDA*, etc. or in clockwise direction as *ADCB*, *DCBA*, etc. But it should never be named as *ACBD*, *ABDC*, etc.

Class Activity 3

1. Draw a polygon with five sides. Choose any one vertex and from it draw the diagonals. How many triangles are thus obtained?

    Repeat the preceding activity for polygons with more sides. Then, copy and fill in the table.

Name of polygon	No. of sides	No. of triangles obtained	Sum of angles
Quadrilateral	4	2	$2 \times 180°$
Pentagon	5		
Hexagon	6		
Heptagon	7		
Octagon	8		
Nonagon	9		
Decagon	10		
n-gon	n		

2. The figure on the right is a pentagon whose sides are produced in order. The exterior angles are $\hat{a}$, $\hat{b}$, $\hat{c}$, $\hat{d}$ and $\hat{e}$. Since we speak of exterior angles of the polygon, we shall now, for emphasis, refer to $\hat{p}$, $\hat{q}$, $\hat{r}$, $\hat{s}$ and $\hat{t}$ as interior angles. Find, by calculation, the sum of the following angles.

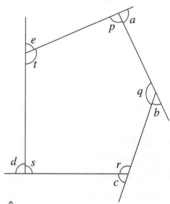

    (a) $\hat{a} + \hat{p} + \hat{b} + \hat{q} + \hat{c} + \hat{r} + \hat{d} + \hat{s} + \hat{e} + \hat{t}$

    (b) $\hat{p} + \hat{q} + \hat{r} + \hat{s} + \hat{t}$

    (c) $\hat{a} + \hat{b} + \hat{c} + \hat{d} + \hat{e}$

    Repeat the above for a hexagon and a heptagon. Do you agree that the sum of the exterior angles of any polygon is four right angles?

We observe from the above discussion the following results.

> * **The sum of the interior angles of an n-sided polygon is $(n-2) \times 180°$ or $(2n-4)$ right angles.**
> * **The sum of the exterior angles of an n-sided polygon is $360°$ or four right angles.**

Note that if all the sides and all the angles of a polygon are equal, the polygon is said to be **regular**, otherwise it is irregular.

Regular pentagon

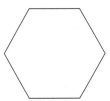

Regular hexagon

Regular octagon

Fig 10.4

An interior angle of a regular n-gon is equal to

$$\frac{(n-2) \times 180°}{n} \text{ or } \frac{(2n-4)}{n} \text{ right angles.}$$

Worked Example 7
Find the sum of the interior angles of a polygon with fifteen sides.

Solution:
The sum of the interior angles of an n-sided polygon is $(n-2) \times 180°$.
When $n = 15$, the sum is $(15-2) \times 180° = 13 \times 180°$
$$= 2\,340°$$

Worked Example 8
How many sides has a regular polygon if its interior angles are $120°$ each?

Solution:
The sum of interior angles of an n-sided polygon is $(n-2) \times 180°$. Each interior angle of an n-sided regular polygon is $\frac{(n-2) \times 180°}{n}$.

We have
$$\frac{(n-2) \times 180°}{n} = 120°$$
$$180n - 360 = 120n$$
$$60n = 360$$
$$\therefore \ n = 6$$

Hence, the polygon has six sides.

Alternative solution:

$$\text{Each exterior angle} = 180° - \text{interior angle}$$
$$= 180° - 120°$$
$$= 60°$$

$$\text{But the sum of the exterior angles} = 360°$$
$$\therefore \quad \text{the number of sides} = \frac{360°}{60°}$$
$$= 6$$

Thus, the polygon has six sides.

Worked Example 9

The ratio of the angles of a quadrilateral is $1 : 2 : 2 : 4$. Find the largest angle.

Solution:

$$\text{Sum of angles} = (4 - 2) \times 180°$$
$$= 360°$$

$$\text{Largest angle} = \frac{4}{1 + 2 + 2 + 4} \times 360°$$
$$= 160°$$

Exercise 10.4

answers on p. 433

1. Find the sum of the interior angles of a polygon with **(a)** 20 sides, **(b)** 30 sides, and **(c)** 50 sides.

2. If the sum of the interior angles of a polygon is 20 right angles, find the number of sides the polygon has.

3. Find the size of an exterior angle of a regular polygon with **(a)** 20 sides, **(b)** 30 sides, and **(c)** n sides.

4. Find the size of an interior angle of a regular octagon.

5. How many sides has a regular polygon if its interior angles are **(a)** 144° each, and **(b)** 135° each?

6. Find the remaining angle of a quadrilateral if three of its angles given are 85°, 95° and 110°.

7. *PQRS* is a quadrilateral in which $\hat{P} = \hat{Q} = \hat{R}$. If $\hat{S} = 60°$, find $\hat{P}$.

8. *PQRST* is a regular pentagon. *PQ* and *SR* are produced to meet at *X*. Find $Q\hat{X}R$.

9. *PQRS* is a quadrilateral in which $\hat{Q} + \hat{S} = 180°$. If *SP* is produced to *X*, show that $Q\hat{P}X = \hat{R}$.

10. Form an equation in *x* in each case and solve the equation.

(a)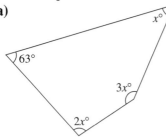

(b)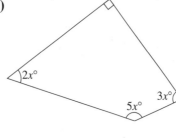

(c)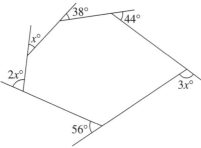

(d)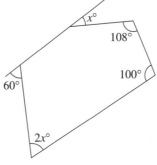

11. In the figure, $\hat{a} + \hat{b} + \hat{c} = 170°$. Calculate $\hat{p}$.

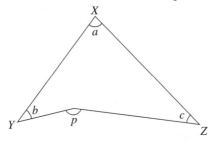

12. Find the sum of the marked angles in each figure.

(a)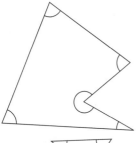

(b)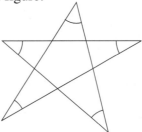

(c)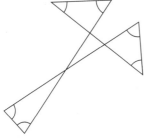

(d)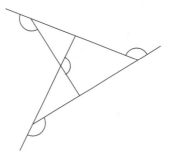

13. The ratio of the angles of a quadrilateral is 2 : 3 : 3 : 4. Find the smallest angle.

14. The ratio of the angles of a pentagon is 1 : 2 : 2 : 3 : 4. Find the largest angle.

10.5 QUADRILATERALS

A **quadrilateral** is a four-sided plane figure. Fig. 10.5 shows some special quadrilaterals.

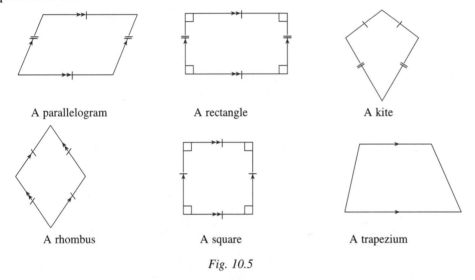

Fig. 10.5

- pentagon
- hexagon
- heptagon
- octagon
- nonagon
- decagon

A **parallelogram** is a quadrilateral in which opposite sides are parallel.
A **rhombus** is a quadrilateral in which all its sides are equal.
A **rectangle** is a quadrilateral having four right angles.
A **square** is a special rectangle in which all its sides are equal.
A **kite** is a quadrilateral with two pairs of equal adjacent sides.
A **trapezium** is a quadrilateral with a pair of parallel sides.

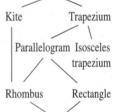

Worked Example 10
Construct a rectangle *ABCD* such that *AB* = 4 cm and *BC* = 3 cm. Measure the diagonal *AC*.

Solution:

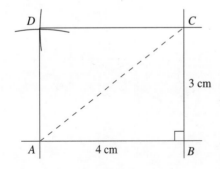

By measurement, *AC* = 5 cm.

Note: The steps for construction are as follows:
1. Draw line segment *AB*, 4 cm long.
2. Draw line segment *BC*, 3 cm long, such that $A\hat{B}C = 90°$ (use a protractor).
3. With *A* as centre and radius 3 cm, draw an arc with a pair of compasses.
4. With *C* as centre and radius 4 cm, draw an arc to cut the first arc at *D*.
5. Join *AD* and *CD*.

We can check, by measurement, to confirm that all the four angles of the figure drawn are right angles. Thus, *ABCD* is the required rectangle.

Worked Example 11

Construct a quadrilateral *ABCD* such that *AB* = 3 cm, *BC* = 4 cm, *CD* = 6 cm, *DA* = 5 cm and diagonal *AC* = 5 cm. Measure diagonal *BD* and $A\hat{B}C$.

Solution:

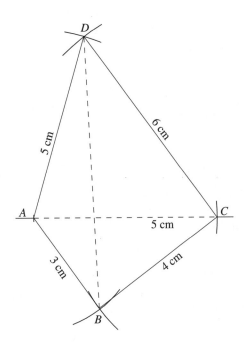

By measurement, *BD* = 7.2 cm and $A\hat{B}C = 90°$.

Note: The steps for construction are as follows:
1. Draw *AC*, 5 cm long.
2. With *A* and *C* as centres and radii 5 cm and 6 cm respectively, draw arcs to cut at *D*.
3. With *A* and *C* as centres and radii 3 cm and 4 cm respectively, draw arcs to cut at *B*.
4. Join *AD*, *CD*, *AB* and *CB*.

Thus, *ABCD* is the required quadrilateral.

Before an accurate drawing is made, it is advisable to draw a sketch first. If the diagonal is given, draw the diagonal first. Then, complete the figure.

Exercise 10.5

answers on p. 433

1. Draw a quadrilateral *STUV* as follows:
   Draw *ST* = 5 cm. At *T*, draw *TU* = 4 cm such that it is perpendicular to *ST*. At *U*, draw an arc of radius 5 cm. At *S*, draw an arc of radius 4 cm to cut the first arc at *V*. Complete the quadrilateral. Measure all the angles of the figure. Is the figure a rectangle?

2. Draw a square *PQRS* as follows:
   Draw *PQ* = 5 cm. At *Q*, draw *QR* = 5 cm such that it is perpendicular to *PQ*. At *R*, draw an arc of radius 5 cm. At *P*, draw an arc of radius 5 cm to cut the first arc at *S*. Complete the square. Draw the diagonals. Measure an angle where the two diagonals meet.

3. Construct a rectangle which is 4 cm by 6 cm. Measure the length of each diagonal.

4. Construct a quadrilateral *ABCD* such that *AB* = 4 cm, *BC* = 6 cm, *CD* = 4 cm, *DA* = 6 cm and diagonal *AC* = 5 cm.
   Are *AB* and *DC* parallel? Are *AD* and *BC* parallel?
   Is this quadrilateral a parallelogram?

5. Construct a quadrilateral *ABCD* such that *AB* = 3 cm, *BC* = 4 cm, *CD* = 4.5 cm, *DA* = 9 cm and diagonal *AC* = 6 cm.
   Does this quadrilateral have a pair of parallel sides?
   Is this quadrilateral a trapezium?

6. Construct a quadrilateral *ABCD* such that *AB* = *BC* = *CD* = *DA* = 3 cm and diagonal *DB* = 5.2 cm.
   Is this quadrilateral a rhombus?
   Draw *AC*. Measure an angle where the two diagonals meet.

7. Construct a quadrilateral *ABCD* such that *AB* = *BC* = 3 cm, *CD* = *DA* = 5 cm and diagonal *AC* = 4 cm.
   Is this quadrilateral a kite?
   Draw *DB*. Measure an angle where the two diagonals meet.

8. Construct exact copies of the following figures.

(a)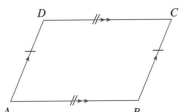

(b)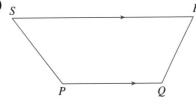

10.6 **PROPERTIES OF QUADRILATERALS**

Class Activity 4

Make the necessary measurements before answering the following questions.

1. The figure shows a quadrilateral *ABCD* such that *AB* // *DC* and *AD* = *BC*. This figure is an isosceles trapezium.

    (a) Draw *XY*, the perpendicular bisector of *AB*.

    (b) Is *XY* also the perpendicular bisector of *DC*?

    (c) Are $\hat{A}$ and $\hat{B}$ equal?

    (d) Are $\hat{D}$ and $\hat{C}$ equal?

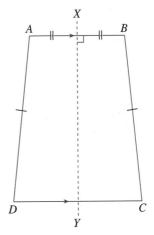

2. The figure shows a quadrilateral *ABCD* such that *AD* = *AB* and *DC* = *BC*. This figure is a kite.

    (a) Are the diagonals *AC* and *DB* perpendicular to each other?

    (b) What can you say about $A\hat{D}C$ and $A\hat{B}C$?

    (c) Does *AC* bisect $\hat{A}$ and $\hat{C}$?

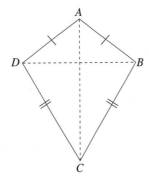

3. The figure shows a quadrilateral *ABCD* such that *AB* // *DC* and *AD* // *BC*. This figure is a parallelogram.

    (a) Are the opposite sides of the parallelogram equal?

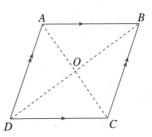

(b) Are the opposite angles of the parallelogram equal?

(c) Do the diagonals *AC* and *DB* of the parallelogram bisect each other?

4. The figure shows a quadrilateral *ABCD* such that $\hat{A} = \hat{B} = \hat{C} = \hat{D} = 90°$. This figure is a rectangle.

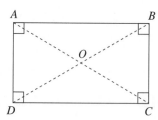

(a) Are the opposite sides of the rectangle parallel? (Check by sliding a set-square along a ruler.)

(b) Is the rectangle a special parallelogram?

(c) Are the opposite sides of the rectangle equal?

(d) Do the diagonals of the rectangle bisect each other?

(e) Are the diagonals equal?

5. The figure shows a quadrilateral *ABCD* such that $AB = BC = CD = DA$. This figure is a rhombus.

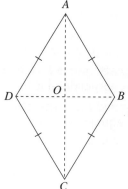

(a) Is the rhombus a special kite?

(b) Are the diagonals of the rhombus perpendicular to each other?

(c) Are the opposite sides of the rhombus parallel?

(d) Is the rhombus a special parallelogram?

(e) Are the opposite angles of the rhombus equal?

(f) Do the diagonals of the rhombus bisect each other?

(g) Are the diagonals bisectors of the angles of the rhombus?

6. The figure shows a quadrilateral *ABCD* such that $AB = BC = CD = DA$ and $\hat{A} = \hat{B} = \hat{C} = \hat{D} = 90°$. This figure is a square.

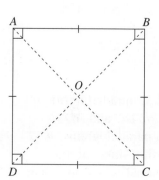

(a) Is the square a special rectangle and a special rhombus?

(b) Are the opposite sides of the square parallel?

(c) Do the diagonals of the square bisect each other?

(d) Are the diagonals of the square equal in length?

(e) Are the diagonals of the square perpendicular to each other?

(f) Are the diagonals bisectors of the angles of the square?

Remember these:

- A **trapezium** is a quadrilateral in which there is a pair of parallel sides.

- A **kite** is a quadrilateral in which
  (a) there are two pairs of equal adjacent sides,
  (b) the diagonals are perpendicular to each other,
  (c) there is a pair of equal opposite angles,
  (d) there is a diagonal which bisects a pair of opposite angles.

- A **parallelogram** is a quadrilateral in which
  (a) opposite sides are parallel,
  (b) opposite sides are equal,
  (c) opposite angles are equal,
  (d) diagonals bisect each other.

- A **rectangle** is a quadrilateral having all the properties of a parallelogram and the following as well:
  (a) It has four right angles.
  (b) Its diagonals are equal.

- A **rhombus** is a quadrilateral having all the properties of a parallelogram and a kite as well. In addition,
  (a) its sides are all equal,
  (b) its diagonals are bisectors of opposite angles of the figure.

- A **square** is a quadrilateral having all the properties of a rectangle and a rhombus as well.

Exercise 10.6

answers on p. 433

1. State whether the following statements are true or false.
   (a) In a rectangle, opposite sides are equal.
   (b) In a square, all four sides are equal.
   (c) It is possible to draw a quadrilateral which is not a square but has four equal sides.
   (d) If the opposite sides of a quadrilateral are equal, the quadrilateral is a rectangle.
   (e) A quadrilateral can have exactly three right angles.
   (f) A rectangle is a special square.
   (g) A rectangle is a special parallelogram and it must have all the properties of a parallelogram.
   (h) If $ABCD$ is a quadrilateral in which $\hat{A} = \hat{B} = \hat{C} = 90°$, then it is a rectangle.
   (i) A square is a special rhombus.

(j)   A rhombus is a special kite.

(k)   If the diagonals of a quadrilateral intersect at right angles, then it is a rhombus.

(l)   If the diagonals of a rectangle intersect at right angles, then it is a square.

2.   Copy and complete the table below. Put 'T' to indicate true and 'F' to indicate false.

Note: True means always true. False means not true or not always true. For example, the property in (k) is taken as false for the trapezium although there are special cases where the diagonals of the trapezium can be equal. For example, in the trapezium *ABCD* shown, *AC = BD*.

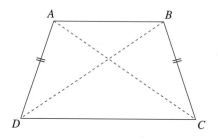

Properties	Trapezium	Kite	Parallelogram	Rectangle	Rhombus	Square
(a) There is a pair of parallel sides.						
(b) There are two pairs of equal adjacent sides.						
(c) The diagonals are perpendicular to each other.		T				
(d) There is a pair of equal opposite angles.					T	T
(e) There is a diagonal which bisects a pair of opposite angles.						
(f) The opposite sides are parallel.			T			
(g) The opposite sides are equal.	F					
(h) The opposite angles are equal.						
(i) The diagonals bisect each other.		F				
(j) There are four right angles.			F	T		
(k) The diagonals are equal.	F				F	T
(l) The sides are all equal.						
(m) The diagonals are bisectors of opposite angles.				F		

3. Find the values of *x* and *y*.

(a)

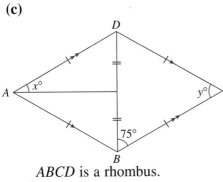

ABCD is a trapezium.

(b)

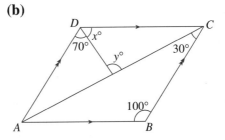

ABCD is a parallelogram.

(c)

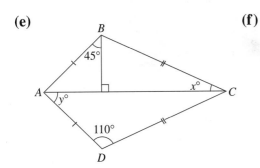

ABCD is a rhombus.

(d)

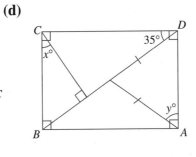

ABCD is a rectangle.

(e)

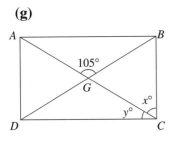

ABCD is a kite.

(f)

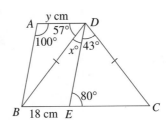

ABCD is a quadrilateral.
BEC is a straight line.

(g)

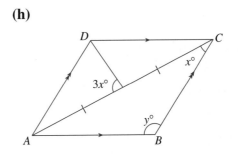

ABCD is a rectangle.

(h)

ABCD is a rhombus.

(i)

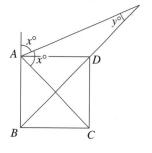

ABCD is a square.

(j)

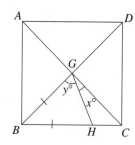

ABCD is a square.

Chapter Review

1. **Classification of Triangles**

By sides		By angles	
	All the sides are equal. Equilateral triangle		All the angles are acute. Acute-angled triangle
	Two sides are equal. Isosceles triangle		One angle is obtuse. Obtuse-angled triangle
	No sides are equal. Scalene triangle		One angle = 90° Right-angled triangle

2. **Sum of Angles**

   The sum of the angles of a triangle is 180° (∠ sum of △).

   Example:

   $$\hat{a} + \hat{b} + \hat{c} = 180°$$

3. **Exterior Angle**

   An exterior angle of a triangle is equal to the sum of the interior opposite angles (ext $\angle$ of $\triangle$).

   Example:

   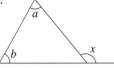

   $$\hat{x} = \hat{a} + \hat{b}$$

4. **Some Properties of Triangles**

   - Isosceles triangle:

   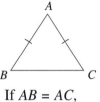

   If $AB = AC$,
   then $\hat{B} = \hat{C}$.

   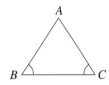

   If $\hat{B} = \hat{C}$,
   then $AB = AC$.

   - Equilateral triangle

   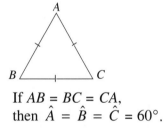

   If $AB = BC = CA$,
   then $\hat{A} = \hat{B} = \hat{C} = 60°$.

   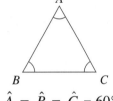

   If $\hat{A} = \hat{B} = \hat{C} = 60°$,
   then $AB = BC = CA$.

5. **Angle Properties of a Polygon**

   - The sum of the interior angles of an n-sided polygon is $(n-2) \times 180°$ or $(2n-4)$ right angles.
   - The sum of the exterior angles of an n-sided polygon is $360°$ or 4 right angles.

6. **Some Properties of Quadrilaterals**

   - Trapezium:

     It has a pair of parallel lines, i.e. $AD \,/\!/\, BC$.

   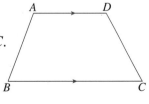

   - Kite:

     $AB = AD$,
     $BC = DC$,
     $AC \perp BD$,
     AC bisects $B\hat{A}D$ and $B\hat{C}D$.

   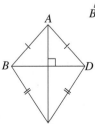

- Parallelogram:
  $AD \parallel BC$, $AD = BC$,
  $AB \parallel DC$, $AB = DC$,
  $A\hat{B}C = A\hat{D}C$,
  $B\hat{A}D = B\hat{C}D$,
  AC and BD bisect each other.

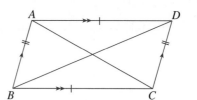

- Rectangle:
  It has all the properties of a parallelogram and in addition
  $\hat{A} = \hat{B} = \hat{C} = \hat{D} = 90°$,
  $AC = BD$.

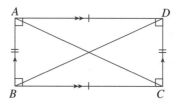

- Rhombus:
  It has all the properties of a parallelogram and a kite as well.
  In addition,
  $AB = BC = CD = DA$,
  AC bisects $\hat{A}$ and $\hat{C}$,
  BD bisects $\hat{B}$ and $\hat{D}$.

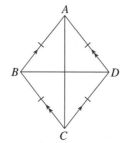

- Square:
  It has all the properties of a rectangle and a rhombus as well.

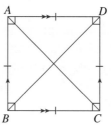

CHALLENGER 10

1. In $\triangle ABC$, AD bisects $B\hat{A}C$, $\hat{B} = 58°$ and $A\hat{D}C = 96°$. Find $\hat{C}$.

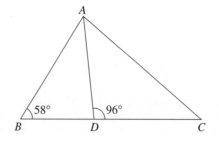

2. In the figure, CD bisects $A\hat{C}B$, $AB = BC$, $B\hat{E}C = 90°$ and $D\hat{C}E = 39°$. Find $\hat{A}$.

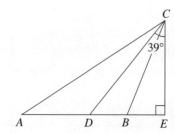

3. In the figure, QP and CM are perpendicular to AB, $P\hat{Q}B = C\hat{M}N$, $B\hat{A}C = 40°$ and $M\hat{N}C = 108°$. Find $\hat{B}$.

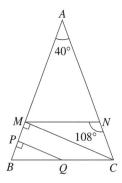

4. A polygon has n sides. If one of its interior angles is $84°$ and the other interior angles are each equal to $156°$, find the value of n.

5. Find the sum of angles A, B, C, D, E, F, G and H.

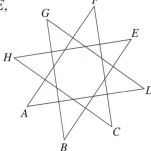

6. A polygon has only one unknown obtuse interior angle A. The remaining interior angles are each equal to $93°$. John says, '$\hat{A}$ is $160°$.' Ali says, 'Impossible!'. What do you think? If $\hat{A}$ is not equal to $160°$, find the correct measure of $\hat{A}$. Explain your method.

Problem Solving 10

Treasure Hunt

To play a treasure hunt game, 60 girls and 105 boys divided themselves exactly into mixed groups with the same proportion of boys and girls in each group.
(a) Find the largest number of groups that could be formed.
(b) How many boys and girls were in each group in this case?

Since there are no boys or girls left over, the number of groups must be an exact divisor of both 60 and 105. The required answer for (a) is the largest common divisor, i.e. the HCF of 60 and 105.

So, we may present the answers as follows:
(a) The HCF of 60 and 105 is 15.
    Therefore, the largest number of groups that could be formed is 15.

(b) The number of boys in each group is $105 \div 15$, i.e. 7.
    The number of girls in each group is $60 \div 15$, i.e. 4.

The strategy used is **make connection** between the problem context and specific area of mathematical knowledge which is, in this case, the concept of HCF.

Alternatively, we use the concept of equivalent ratios. So, we have

$$\begin{aligned} \text{number of boys : number of girls} &= 105 : 60 \\ &= 21 : 12 \\ &= 7 : 4. \end{aligned}$$

To form the largest number of groups, we use 7 boys and 4 girls for each group and this gives the answer for (b).

So, for (a), the answer is

$$60 \div 4 = 15 \text{ (groups).}$$

 **Problems...**

1. **Telephone Cards** Samy has $1\frac{1}{2}$ times as many telephone cards as Peter has. If Samy collects another 25 telephone cards and Peter collects another 10 telephone cards, then Peter will have half as many telephone cards as Samy. How many telephone cards has Samy at first?

2. **How Heavy Are the Cakes?** Two cakes A and B weigh 13 kg altogether. $\frac{2}{3}$ of cake A and $\frac{3}{4}$ of cake B are sold. The remaining part of cake A was $\frac{4}{5}$ kg less than the remaining part of cake B. Find the original mass of each cake.

3. **At a Party** Mr Li distributed the same number of sweets to each of the pupils at a party. Each pupil also received the same number of biscuits. He gave out 220 sweets and 300 biscuits in all.
    (a) Find the largest possible number of pupils at the party.
    (b) How many sweets and biscuits did each pupil receive in this case?

4. **Making Bouquets** Mrs Wang used 90 red flowers, 105 blue flowers and 120 white flowers to make bouquets. Each bouquet had the same number of red flowers, the same number of blue flowers and the same number of white flowers as every other bouquet. Find the greatest number of bouquets that could be made.

Symmetries and Nets of Solid Figures

Chapter Highlights

- Identifying line and rotational symmetries of plane figures and, plane symmetry and axis of rotational symmetry of solid figures.
- Giving the number of planes and axes of symmetry and the order of rotational symmetry of given figures.
- Constructing nets of solid figures and identifying solid figures from their nets.

11.1 LINE SYMMETRY

MATHSTORY

Aristotle stated: "The chief forms of beauty are order and symmetry and precision which the mathematical sciences demonstrate in a special degree". Radial symmetry (the basis being the circle, an ancient symbol of perfection) is found in many flowers and sea creatures, e.g. in certain varieties of starfish. Bilateral symmetry is found in bivalves, in many varieties of plants and animals (leaves, butterflies, etc.) and many insects.

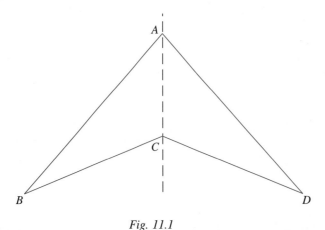

Fig. 11.1

Look at Fig. 11.1. If you make a copy of the figure and fold it along *AC*, you will find that one half of the figure will fit the other. We say that the figure possesses **line symmetry**. The line *AC* is called the **line of symmetry**. If you join *BD*, you will find that *AC* is the perpendicular bisector of *BD*.

The butterfly shown below not only has a well-balanced symmetrical shape, but also has a beautiful symmetrical pattern.

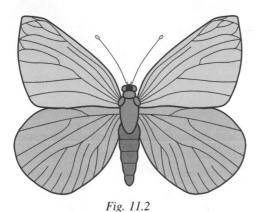

Fig. 11.2

Class Activity 1

1. Fold a piece of paper in halves. Cut out a design on the folded paper and then open it out. Do you get a symmetrical design? Repeat this activity to get several more designs.

2. Fold a piece of paper in halves and than in quarters. Cut out a design on the folded paper and then open it out. Do you get a symmetrical design? If so, how many lines of symmetry does your design have? Repeat this activity to get several more designs.

3. Fold a piece of paper twice and cut across the corner as shown. When the 'corner piece' is opened out, what is the resulting shape? How many lines of symmetry does it have. (Use mental visualisation to predict the answers before using actual paper folding and cutting.)

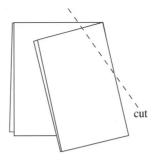

cut

4. Can you make a design by folding and cutting paper so that your design will have three lines of symmetry? Investigate.

Exercise 11.1

answers on p. 433

1. Which of the following have **(a)** one line of symmetry, **(b)** more than one line of symmetry, and **(c)** no lines of symmetry at all?

(i)

(ii)

(iii)

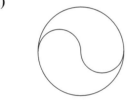

(iv)

(v)

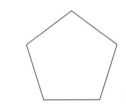

(vi)

(vii)

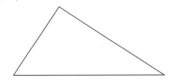

(viii)

(ix)

(x)

2. Using graph paper, copy the figure in each case and complete it to form a symmetrical figure with respect to the line *m*.

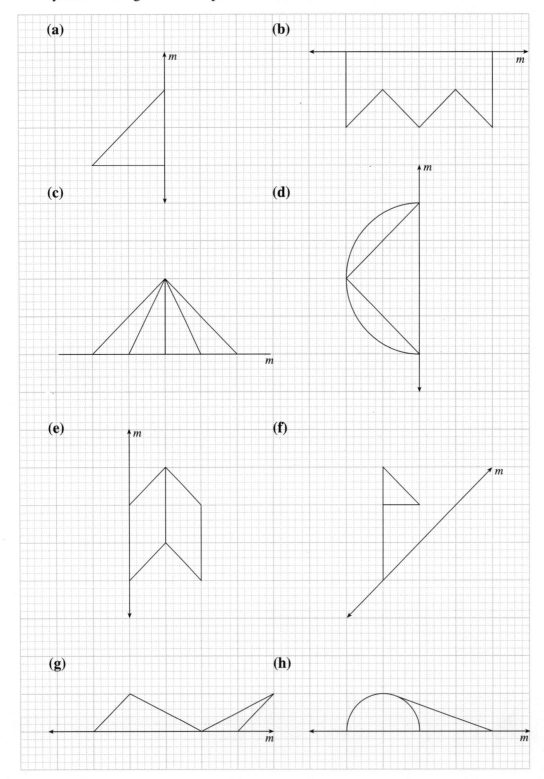

3. Use your geometrical instruments to copy and complete each of the following figure to form a symmetrical figure with respect to the line *m*.

(a)

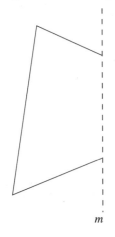

m

(b)

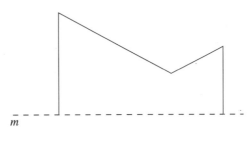

m

(c)

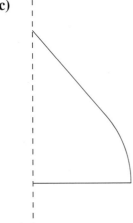

m

(d)

m

(*Hint:* Use 2.7 cm as radius to draw the arc.)

4. The figure has four lines of symmetry.

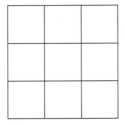

Shade exactly two of the nine small squares so that the resulting pattern has
(a) only two lines of symmetry, one horizontal and one vertical;
(b) only two lines of symmetry about the diagonals;
(c) only one horizontal line of symmetry;
(d) only one line of symmetry about a diagonal;
(e) no line of symmetry at all.

11.2 ROTATIONAL SYMMETRY

If a traced copy of the figure in Fig. 11.3 is made and rotated through 120° about O, the copy will coincide with the figure. This figure is said to possess **rotational symmetry**. The point O is referred to as the **centre of rotational symmetry**. Notice that the copy can be placed in position with the figure in three different ways within 360° rotation. We say that the order of rotational symmetry is 3.

A figure has rotational symmetry when the traced figure can be rotated less than 360° about some point so that it matches the original figure. Note that the condition 'less than 360°' is necessary because any figure will coincide with itself after being rotated 360°.

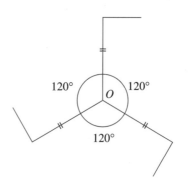

Fig. 11.3

The following figures possess rotational symmetry of different orders.

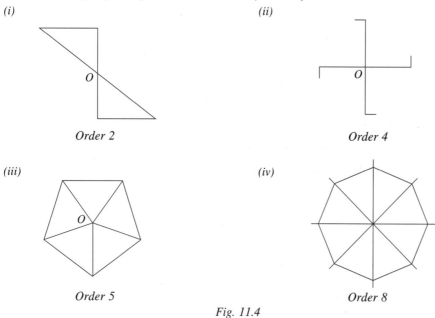

(i) Order 2

(ii) Order 4

(iii) Order 5

(iv) Order 8

Fig. 11.4

Note: When we say that a figure possesses rotational symmetry, we mean that it has rotational symmetry of order 2 or more.

Example

A hexagon has a rotational symmetry of order 6. If the shading is taken into consideration, this pattern has a rotational symmetry of order 3.

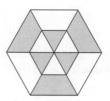

Fig. 11.5

Exercise 11.2 ✎ *answers on p. 433*

1. Here are some symmetrical figures. Which of the following figures have
   (a) line symmetry, **(b)** rotational symmetry, and **(c)** no symmetry at all?

   (i)  **(ii)**

   (iii) **(iv)**

   (v) **(vi)**

   (vii) **(viii)**

   (ix) **(x)**

   (xi) **(xii)**

2. Which of the following figures have **(a)** rotational symmetry, and **(b)** line
   symmetry?
   (i) An isosceles triangle **(ii)** A rectangle
   (iii) A circle **(iv)** A regular hexagon

(v)   A trapezium   (vi)   A rhombus
(vii)   An equilateral triangle   (viii)   A regular pentagon
(ix)   A kite   (x)   A right-angled triangle
(xi)   A square   (xii)   A parallelogram

3.

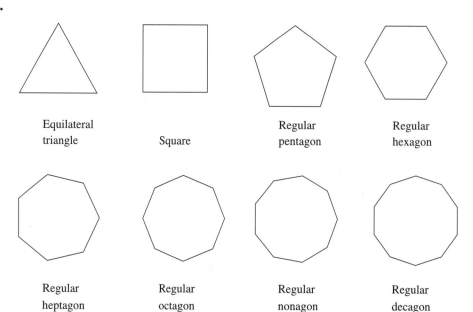

| | Equilateral triangle | Square | | Regular pentagon | Regular hexagon |

Regular heptagon   Regular octagon   Regular nonagon   Regular decagon

Study the symmetrical properties of the regular polygons above. Then, copy and complete the following table.

		Number of lines of symmetry	Order of rotational symmetry
(a)	Equilateral triangle	3	
(b)	Square		4
(c)	Regular pentagon		
(d)	Regular hexagon		
(e)	Regular heptagon		7
(f)	Regular octagon		
(g)	Regular nonagon	9	
(h)	Regular decagon		

4. Copy the figures on graph paper.
   (a) Draw all the lines of symmetry for each of them where possible.
   (b) Mark with a cross (×) the centre of rotational symmetry where possible.

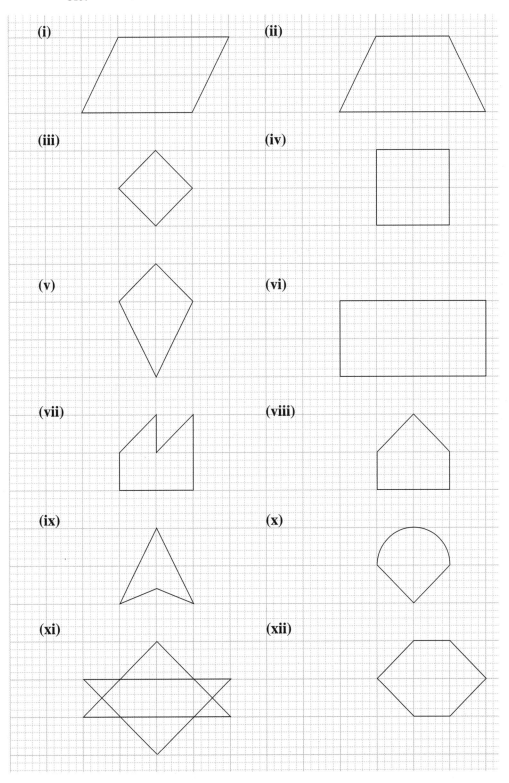

5. Copy and complete the following table.

Name of quadrilateral	Number of lines of symmetry	Order of rotational symmetry
Parallelogram	Nil	2
Rectangle		
Kite		
Rhombus		
Square		
Trapezium		

6. Copy the figure. Shade certain parts of the figure so that the resulting pattern has a rotational symmetry of
(a) order 8,
(b) order 4,
(c) order 2.

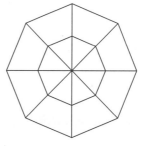

*7. State whether each of the following statements is true or false. Give an example if the answer is false.
(a) If a figure has 2 lines of symmetry, it must have rotational symmetry of order 2.
(b) If a figure has 3 lines of symmetry, it must have rotational symmetry of order 3.
(c) If a figure has 4 lines of symmetry, it must have rotational symmetry of order 4.
(d) If a figure has rotational symmetry of order 2, it must have 2 lines of symmetry.
(e) If a figure has rotational symmetry of order 3, it must have 3 lines of symmetry.
(f) If a figure has rotational symmetry of order 4, it must have 4 lines of symmetry.

11.3 PATTERNS

We often see patterns of flowers, animals and other objects on textiles or wallpaper. Some of these patterns can be made using geometrical constructions.

Examples

(a) Fig. 11.6(i) shows a magic square. Notice that if you add three numbers horizontally, vertically or diagonally, the answer is always 15.

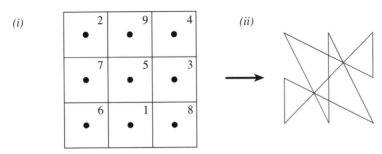

Fig. 11.6

If you use pencil to make a copy of the magic square and then use ink to join the dots 1 to 2, 2 to 3, . . . , 9 to 1, you will get a pattern like in Fig. 11.6(ii) after the pencil marks are erased. Notice that the pattern has rotational symmetry of order 2.

(b) If you use pencil to draw a triangle like in Fig. 11.7(i) and then use ink to join the 1's, the 2's, the 3's and so on, you will get a pattern like in Fig. 11.7(ii) after the pencil marks are erased. Notice that the pattern has 3 lines of symmetry and also rotational symmetry of order 3.

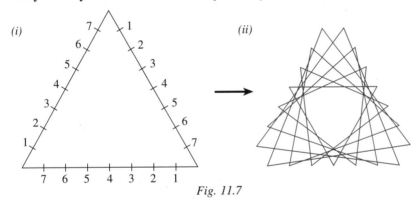

Fig. 11.7

(c) If you draw a square like in Fig. 11.8(i) and then draw $\hat{a}$, $\hat{b}$, $\hat{c}$, $\hat{d}$, $\hat{e}$, . . . , each of $10°$ and continue until you cover the whole square, you will get a pattern like in Fig. 11.8(ii).

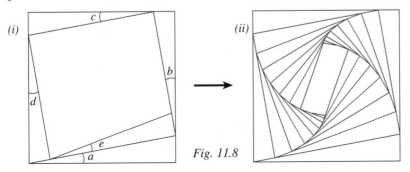

Fig. 11.8

A careful examination reveals that the pattern does not have symmetry at all.

Exercise 11.3 ✐

answers on p. 434

1. For each of the following, use pencil to copy the magic square. Use ink to join the dots 1 to 2, 2 to 3, 3 to 4, . . . , 16 to 1. Then, erase the pencil marks to obtain a pattern.

   Does the pattern have any symmetries? If so, give a full description.

   (a)

1	14	15	4
8	11	10	5
12	7	6	9
13	2	3	16

   (b)

10	11	6	7
5	8	9	12
3	2	15	14
16	13	4	1

2. For each of the following, use pencil to copy and complete the magic square. Then, follow the method used in question 1 to draw a pattern.

   Does the pattern have any symmetries? If so, give a full description.

   (a)

8	13	12	1
3	10		6
9		5	
14	7		11

   (b)

13	10	7	4
		3		9
12		2	5
	6	11	16

3. For each of the following, use pencil to copy the figure. Use ink to join all the points marked with the same number. Then, erase the pencil marks to obtain a pattern.

   Does the pattern have any symmetries? If so, give a full description.

   (a)

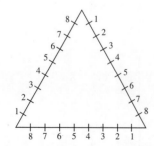

   (b)

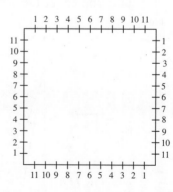

4. Copy and complete the pattern by drawing angles of constant value.
    Does the pattern obtained have any symmetries? If so, give a full description.

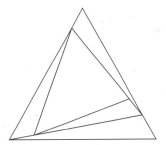

5. For each of the following, make a copy (the size may be enlarged) and use colours of your choice to colour it.
    Does your design have any symmetries? If so, give a full description.

    (a)

    (b)

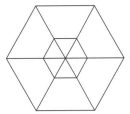

    (c)

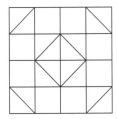

    (d)

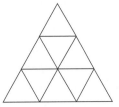

6. For each of the following, use a pair of compasses to make a copy of the pattern.
    Does the pattern have any symmetries? If so, give a full description.

    (a)

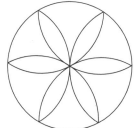

    (b)

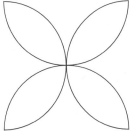

    (c)

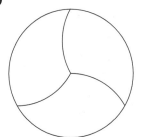

    (d)

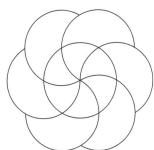

11.4 SYMMETRIES OF SOLID FIGURES

MATHSTORY

Solid Figures

Examples

(a) Plane surfaces which bound a solid are called **faces** of a solid. A line where two faces meet is called an **edge**. A point at which edges meet is called a **vertex** (plural, vertices). A **cube** is bounded by six square faces as shown. It has eight vertices and twelve edges.

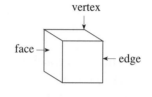

Fig. 11.9

The Taj Mahal is the most famous of all Islamic mausoleums. It was built by one of the Moslem rulers in India as a memorial to his wife. Symmetry is seen in the structure of the building and in the reflecting pools.

(b) A **cuboid** is bounded by six rectangular faces as shown. It has eight vertices and twelve edges. A cuboid is also known as a *rectangular prism*.

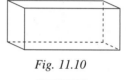

Fig. 11.10

(c) A **triangular prism** is bounded by three rectangular faces and two triangular faces as shown. It has six vertices and nine edges.

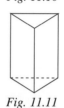

Fig. 11.11

Each of the triangular faces is called a **base**. Notice that these bases are identical. If the bases are general polygons, we referred to the solid as a **polygonal prism** or simply a prism.

(d) A **triangular pyramid** is bounded by four triangular faces as shown. It has four vertices and six edges. A triangular pyramid is also known as a *tetrahedron*.

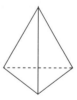

Fig. 11.12

(e) A **pyramid with a square base** is bounded by four triangular faces and a square face as shown. It has five vertices and eight edges.

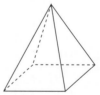

Fig. 11.13

(f) A **cylinder** is shaped like a circular tin. It is bounded by two circular faces and a curved surface as shown.

Fig. 11.14

(g) A **cone** is shaped like a clown's hat. It is bounded by a circular face and a curved surface as shown. It has one vertex.

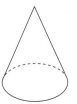

Fig. 11.15

(h) A **sphere** is shaped like a ball. It is bounded by a curved surface.

Fig. 11.16

Class Activity 2

1. Name the geometrical shapes of the following objects.
   (a) A football
   (b) A matchbox
   (c) A tin of milk
   (d) An exercise book
   (e) A scout tent
   (f) The roof of a house
   (g) A marble
   (h) An ice cream cornet (unfilled)
   (i) A megaphone
   (j) The tomb of an ancient Egyptian king

2. Study the following solid shapes. Then, copy and complete the table.
   (a) 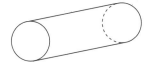 **(b)** **(c)**

   (d)  **(e)** 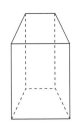 **(f)**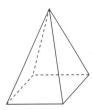

   (g) 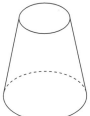 **(h)** 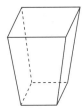 **(i)**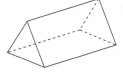

(j) 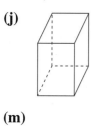 **(k)**  **(l)**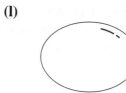

(m) 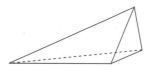 **(n)** 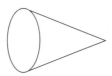 **(o)**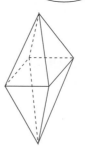

Solid shapes	Prism	Pyramid	Cylinder	Cone	Sphere	Others
(a)						
(b)						
(c)	✓					
(d)						
(e)						
(f)		✓				
(g)						
(h)						
(i)						
(j)						
(k)						
(l)						
(m)						
(n)						
(o)						

3.

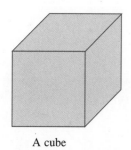 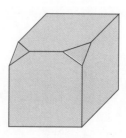

A cube A cube with 1 corner truncated A cube with 2 corners truncated

(a) Copy and complete the table.

Type of solid	Number of faces (F)	Number of vertices (V)	Number of edges (E)	Value of F + V – E
Cube	6	8	12	2
Cube with 1 corner truncated	7	10	15	
Cube with 2 corners truncated	8			
Cube with 3 corners truncated	9			
Cube with 4 corners truncated	10			
Cube with 5 corners truncated	11			
Cube with 8 corners truncated	14			

(b) Write down a formula connecting F, V and E.

(c) Does this rule apply to other solids like prisms and pyramids? Investigate.

Symmetries in Space

Examples

(a) Fig. 11.17 shows how a cube can be cut by a plane in many different ways.

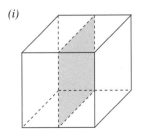 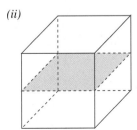 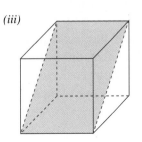

(i)   *(ii)*   *(iii)*

(iv) 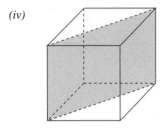   *(v)*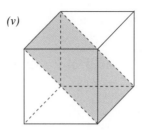

Fig. 11.17

We say that a cube is symmetrical about a plane if that part of the cube on one side of the plane is a mirror image of the part on the other side of the plane. We call the plane a **plane of symmetry**. You will find that there are a few more planes of symmetry other than those shown above.

(b) Every face of a cube has a centre of rotational symmetry. Imagine that an axis *XY* passes through the centres of two parallel faces as shown.

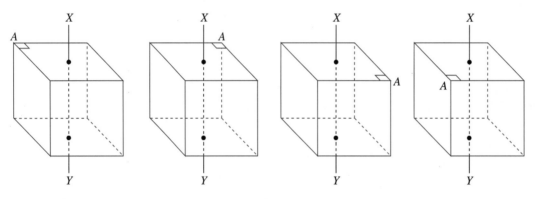

Fig. 11.18

If the solid is rotated about the axis *XY*, there are four different ways to make the solid look the same before a particular point of the solid returns to its original position (look at the vertex *A*). We say that the cube has a rotational symmetry of order 4 about the axis *XY*. We refer to *XY* as the **axis of rotational symmetry**. You will find that there are a few more axes other than *XY*.

(c) Fig. 11.19 shows a solid whose 4 faces are equilateral triangles. This solid is called a **regular tetrahedron**.

Notice that this solid has six equal edges. You will find that there is a plane of symmetry through each edge. The shaded plane *ADE* is one of them.

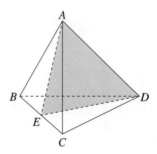

Fig. 11.19

Fig. 11.20 shows that the face *BCD* is horizontal and the vertical line *XY* is an axis of rotational symmetry of the tetrahedron. Notice also that *PQ*, which passes through the midpoints of edges *AD* and *BC*, is another axis of rotational symmetry. You will find that there are a few more axes of rotational symmetry.

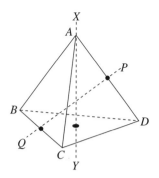

Fig. 11.20

Exercise 11.4

answers on p. 434

1. How many of the following solids have at least **(a)** one plane of symmetry, and **(b)** one axis of rotational symmetry?

(i)

Parallelepiped
(Every face is a parallelogram.)

(ii)

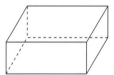

Rectangular solid

(iii)

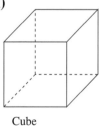

Cube

(iv)

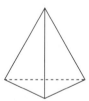

Regular tetrahedron

(v)

Right cylinder

(vi)

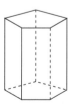

Right prism
(Given that each base of the prism is a regular pentagon.)

(vii)

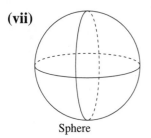

Sphere

(viii)

Oblique circular cone

(ix)

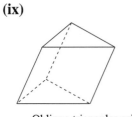

Oblique triangular prism

(x)

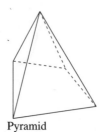

Pyramid

2. Which of the following objects have at least one plane of symmetry?
   (a) A rugby ball
   (b) A chair
   (c) Your desk
   (d) A drinking glass
   (e) A spring
   (f) A hand glove
   (g) Your mathematics textbook
   (h) Your left shoe

3. Study the symmetrical properties of the solids. Then, copy and complete the table.

(a)

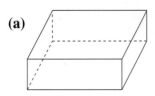

Rectangular prism

(b)

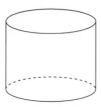

Right circular cylinder

(c)

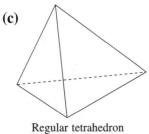

Regular tetrahedron

(d)

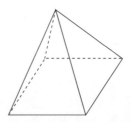

Right square pyramid

(e)

Hemisphere

(f)

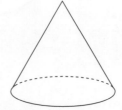

Right circular cone

(g)

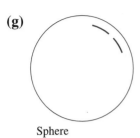

Sphere

(h)

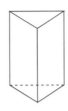

Right prism
(Given that each base of the prism is an
equilateral triangle.)

(i)

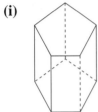

Right prism
(Given that each base of the
prism is a regular pentagon.)

(j)

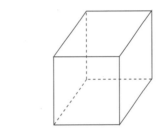

Cube

		Number of planes of symmetry	Number of axes of rotational symmetry
(a)	Rectangular prism	3	
(b)	Right circular cylinder		
(c)	Regular tetrahedron	6	
(d)	Right square pyramid		
(e)	Hemisphere	Infinitely many	
(f)	Right circular cone		1
(g)	Sphere		
(h)	Right prism (Given that each base of the prism is an equilateral triangle)		4
(i)	Right prism (Given that each base of the prism is a regular pentagon)	6	
(j)	Cube		

11.5 NETS OF SOLID FIGURES

On the right is a **net** of a cube. (It can be made from cardboard.) If you fold along the dotted lines you can make a cube.

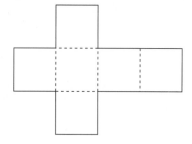

Fig. 11.21

There are different nets to make a cube. Here are two examples.

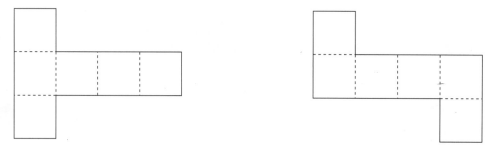

Fig. 11.22

Notice that any net of a cube is made up of 6 equal squares.
Look at the common solids you have learnt in section 11.4 on page 302 again.

Except for the sphere, you will find that the nets of the other solids are made up of the following plane figures.

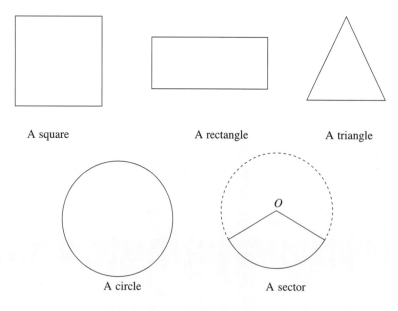

A square   A rectangle   A triangle

A circle   A sector

Fig. 11.23

Here is a net of a triangular prism not drawn accurately. If you want to make the solid, you have to draw the net accurately.

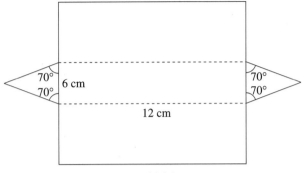

Fig. 11.24

In the following exercise, you will have practice in making accurate constructions using a ruler, a pair of compasses, a protractor and set-squares.

Exercise 11.5

answers on p. 434

1. What solids can be formed by the following nets?
   Draw a sketch for each of these solids.

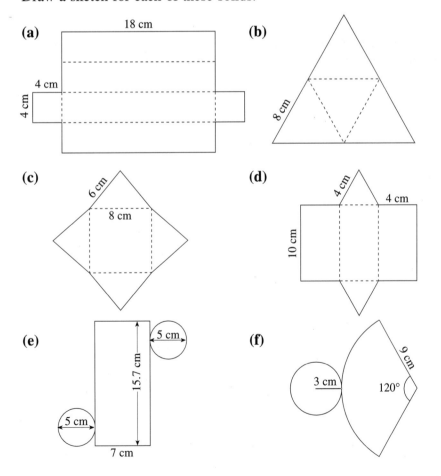

2. Sketch a different net for each case in question 1.

3. The net for a certain solid is shown below. All measurements are in centimetres.

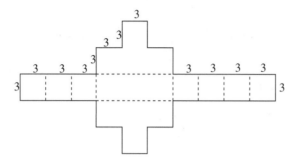

(a) Make a sketch of the solid.
(b) How many planes of symmetry has the solid?
(c) Does the solid have rotational symmetry? If so, what is the order of rotational symmetry?

4. If an ant walks from vertex *A* to vertex *Z* of a solid cube of edge 6 cm shown on the right, what is the shortest distance the ant would have to walk? Make an appropriate drawing and use it to find your answer by measurement.

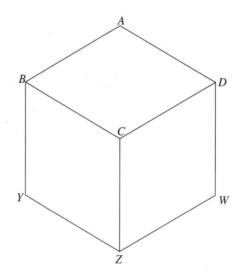

5. The following are the nets of 3 solids, *A*, *B* and *C*. All measurements are in centimetres.

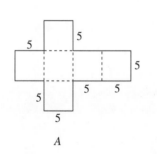

A

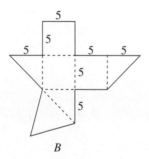

B

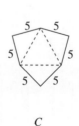

C

Describe the relationship between the three solids.

6. The figure shows a rectangular box. Three of its faces are marked with black stripes.

(a) Which of the following nets can you use to make this box with the same arrangement of black stripes?

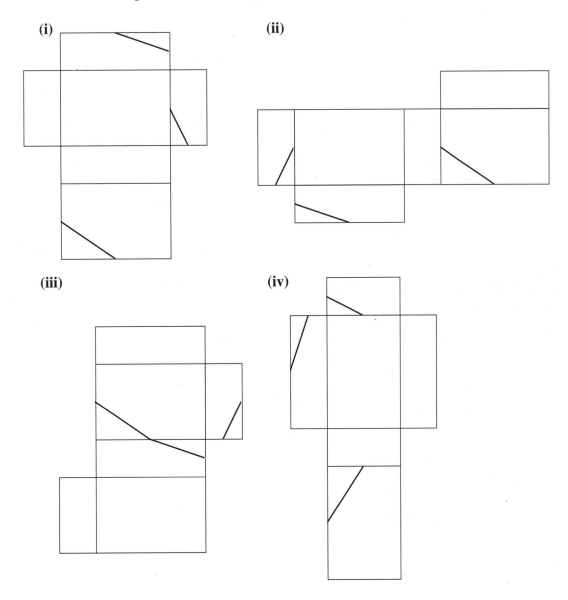

(i)   **(ii)**

(iii)   **(iv)**

(b) Sketch other nets that can be used to make this box with the same arrangement of black stripes.

7. Make an accurate copy of each net in question 1 on a piece of cardboard. Cut out the net and fold along the dotted lines to form the solid. Name the solids made.

8. **(a)** Draw full size on a piece of cardboard the nets for solid *B* and solid *C* mentioned in question 5. Cut out the nets and make the solids.

    (b) Does each of the solids have any symmetries? If so, give a full description.

---

1. **Symmetry**
    *   A figure possesses **line symmetry** if one half of the figure is a mirror image of the other along a line of symmetry.
        Example:

        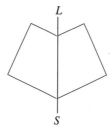

        The figure has line symmetry with *LS* as the line of symmetry

    *   A figure possesses **rotational symmetry** if it can be made to look the same as before when rotated about an angle less than 360°.
        Example:

        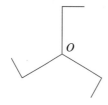

        The figure has rotational symmetry of order 3 with *O* as the centre of rotation.

    *   A solid possesses **plane symmetry** if one half of the solid is a mirror image of the other along a plane.
        Example:

        The shaded portion shows a plane of symmetry of a cube. (The cube also possesses other planes of symmetry).

- A solid possesses an **axis of rotational symmetry** if it can be made to look the same as before when rotated about that axis.
  Example:

  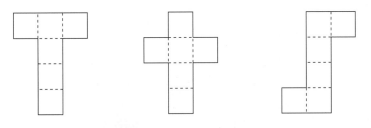

  The line *XY* is an axis of rotational symmetry of the solid.

2. **Nets**

  A solid can have one or several different nets.
  Example: Here are some of the nets of a cube.

CHALLENGER 11

1. Draw a hexagon which has rotational symmetry of order 3.

2. Draw a hexagon which has 3 lines of symmetry.

3. Draw an octagon which has 4 lines of symmetry.

4. The diagram is a net of a certain solid.
   (a) Make a sketch of the solid.
   (b) How many axes of symmetry does the solid have?
   (c) How many plane of symmetry does the solid have?

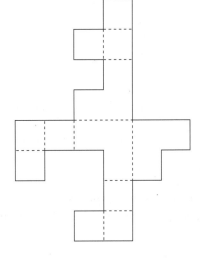

5. In the figure, $\triangle ABC$ is an equilateral triangle. If $AE = CD$, what is the measure of $B\hat{G}D$?
    (*Hint:* Add in a line segment to the figure so that the resulting figure has rotational symmetry.)

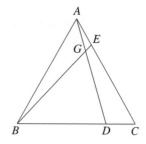

6. The solid is made up of 6 cubes. Draw a net of the solid.

Problem Solving 11

Flowering Plant

Lamp posts are put at intervals of 84 m along a road and flowering plants are placed at intervals of 60 m. The first flowering plant is placed at the foot of the first lamp post.

(a) How far along the road is the next flowering plant that is placed at the foot of a lamp post?

(b) How many lamp posts and flowering plants are there in between before they are together for the second time?

Let us use the strategy **make connection** between this problem and the concept of LCM.

The distance between the first plant and the next plant that is placed at the foot of a lamp post must be a common multiple of both 60 and 84. The required answer is the smallest common multiple, i.e. the LCM of 60 and 84. So, the solution for (a) is:

(a) The LCM of 84 and 60 is 420.
    Therefore, the next flowering plant that is placed at the foot of a lamp post is 420 m from the first plant.

The strategy **use diagram** can be used for (b).

The diagram shows that the number of lamp posts in between is 1 fewer than the number of 'intervals of 84 m' etc.

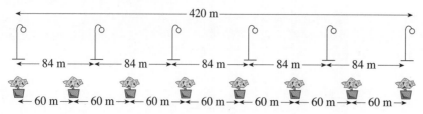

So the solution for (b) is:

(b) The number of lamp posts in between is $420 \div 84 - 1$, i.e. 4.

The number of flowering plants in between is $420 \div 60 - 1$, i.e. 6.

Problems...

1. **Grading Tests** In a class test, $\frac{1}{8}$ of the pupils obtained grade A, $\frac{1}{5}$ obtained grade B, $\frac{1}{2}$ obtained grade C and the rest obtained grade D. How many pupils obtained each grade? (Assume that the number of pupils in a class does not exceed 43.)

2. **Which Class Has More Boys?** Class A and class B have the same number of pupils. The number of boys in class A is equal to $\frac{1}{2}$ the number of girls in class B. The number of boys in class B is equal to $\frac{1}{3}$ the number of girls in class A. Express the number of girls in class A as a fraction of the number of girls in class B. Which class has more boys?

3. **Night Duty** In a club house, Peter was on night duty once in every 6 days and Paul was on night duty once in every 9 days. On a certain night, they were both on duty.
   (a) After how many days would they be together on night duty again?
   (b) How many times had they each been on night duty in between before they were together for the second time?

4. **Circular Track** 3 boys, Ali, Minfa and Samy, started from the same point and went round a circular track 1 km in circumference, in the same direction. Ali took 5 minutes to cycle one round, Minfa took 9 minutes to run round and Samy took 15 minutes to walk one round. After how many minutes will they be together again at the starting point?

REVISION EXERCISE 3

Revision 3A *(answers on p. 435)*

1. Draw a triangle ABC such that $AB = 5$ cm, $BC = 4$ cm and $CA = 6$ cm.

2. One angle of a polygon is $140°$ and the rest are each $40°$ smaller. Find the number of sides of the polygon.

3. Find the values of x and y.

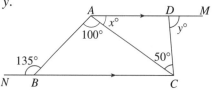

4. John went to a money changer to buy some foreign currencies.
   (a) How many US$ would he get for S$437.50?
   (b) How much did he pay for £45?

Money Changer
US$1 — S$ 1.75
£1 — S$ 3.70
HK$100 — S$22.30

5. Form an equation in x for each of the following and solve the equation.
   (a)

   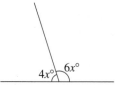

   (b)

   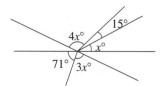

6. The interior angles of a polygon are in the ratio $1 : 2 : 3 : 4 : 5$. Find the degree measure of the second largest angle.

7. Find the value of x in each case.
   (a)

   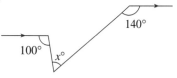

   (b)

   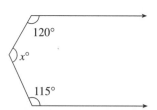

8. Find the simple interest on $500 borrowed for 3 years at 8% per annum.

9. Form an equation in x for each of the following and solve the equation.
   (a)

   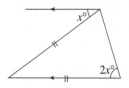

   (b)

   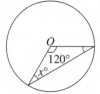

10. A man bought 510 greeting cards at 3 for $4. He sold $\frac{2}{3}$ of them at 2 for $3 and the rest at 5 for $6.50. What profit did he make?

11. Find the value of x in each case.
    (a)
    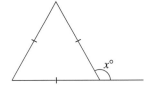
    (b)
    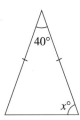

Revision 3B *(answers on p. 435)*

1. Construct an angle of 120°. Divide it into four equal angles.

2. One of the angles of an octagon is 86°. If the remaining angles are all equal, find the size of each.

3. Form an equation in x for each of the following and solve the equation.
    (a)
    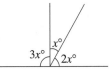
    (b)
    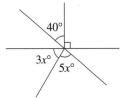

4. Form an equation in x and solve the equation.
    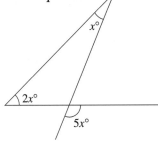

5. Find the value of x in each case.
    (a)
    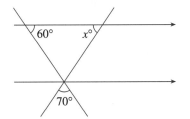
    (b)
    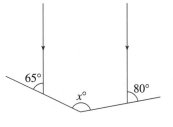

6. **(a)** The figure has a rotational symmetry about a point.
    What is the order of symmetry of the figure?
    (b) Draw a plane geometrical figure which has exactly 5 axes of symmetry.

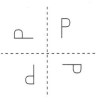

7. A T-shirt normally costs $40 in the two shops shown.
   (a) By how many dollars is the T-shirt reduced in each shop?
   (b) Find the difference between the two reductions.

AA's	BB's
SALE	SALE
All Items	All Goods
25% OFF	$\frac{1}{5}$ OFF

8. Each diagram shows part of a complete figure which has a rotational symmetry of order 3 with O as the centre of the symmetry. Copy the diagrams and then complete the figures.
   (a)
   (b)

9. (a) Ali bought the radio recorder on credit terms. How much did he pay?
   (b) If he paid by cash, how much would he save?

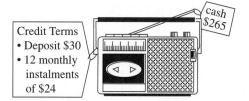

10. Find the angles marked x.
    (a)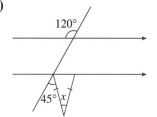
    (b)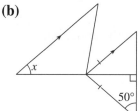

11. The list price of a TV set is $1 600.

    (a) If a customer pays cash, he is entitled to $9\frac{1}{2}$% discount. How much has he to pay?

    (b) If he pays by 12 monthly instalments, he is entitled to $5\frac{1}{2}$% discount. How much has he to pay per month?

Revision 3C   (answers on p. 435)

1. Draw a line XY, 2 cm long. Construct a point Z on XY produced such that YZ = 3XY. Construct an equilateral △AYZ with YZ as a side. Bisect the angle AYX.

2. If one angle of a pentagon is a right angle, find the size of each of the remaining angles if they are equal to one another.

3. Find the angles marked x.

(a)

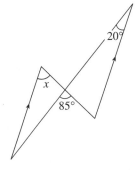

(b)

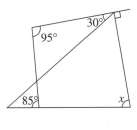

4. Form an equation in x and solve the equation.

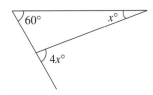

5. Form an equation in x for each of the following and solve the equation.

(a)

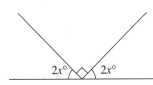

(b)

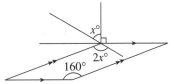

6. Find the value of x in each case.

(a)

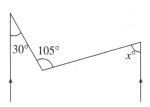

(b)

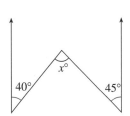

7. A man earns \$850 per month.

(a) If he receives a bonus of $1\frac{1}{2}$ month's salary at the end of the year, find his annual salary.

(b) If he saves 15% of his salary for the first 6 months and 10% of his salary for the remaining months of the year, including the bonus, find his annual savings.

8. A certain bank pays $12\frac{1}{2}$% per annum simple interest. How much money must a man have in the bank if he will receive \$650 as interest in 2 years?

9. How many axes of symmetry have the following figures?

(a)

(b)

10. By selling an article for $2 450, a shopkeeper made a profit of 12%. Find the cost of the article.

11. A publisher sold 6 500 copies of a textbook at $5.50 each. If the author was paid 6% of the selling price for the first 3 000 copies sold and 8% of the selling price of the remaining copies, find the amount of money the author received.

Revision 3D *(answers on p. 435)*

1. Draw a triangle *XYZ* such that $\hat{Y} = 60°$, $\hat{Z} = 70°$ and *YZ* = 5 cm. Construct the bisectors of $\hat{Y}$ and $\hat{X}$ to meet at *O*. Construct a perpendicular from *O* to *XZ*.

2. Form an equation in *x* for each of the following and solve the equation.

(a)

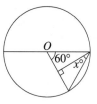

(b)

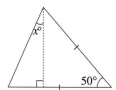

3. Find the angles marked *x*.

(a)

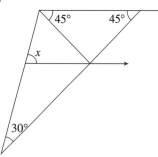

(b)

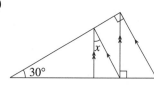

4. Form an equation in *x* for each of the following and solve the equation.

(a)

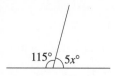

(b)

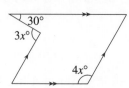

5. Find the value of x in each case.

(a)

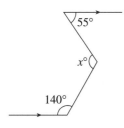

(b)

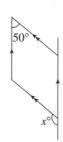

6. In each case, form an equation in x and solve the equation.

(a)

(b)

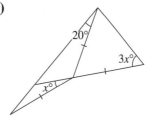

7. Copy the figures, then draw lines of symmetry or mark O as the centre of rotational symmetry where possible.

(a)

(b)

(c)

(d)

8. A manufacturer allows a retailer a discount of 40% on the list price. What is the list price of an item for which the retailer pays $72?

9. A shopkeeper makes a profit of 12% if he sells an article for $84.
   (a) Find the cost price of the article.
   (b) If 5% discount is allowed for cash payment, find the cash price of the article.

10. Find the values of x and y.

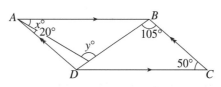

11. Find the values of x and y.

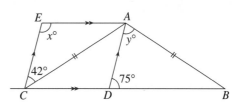

Revision 3E   (answers on p 435.)

1. Draw a triangle *XYZ* such that *XY* > *YZ*. Produce *XY* and *XZ* to *A* and *B* respectively. Construct the bisectors of $X\hat{Y}Z$, $X\hat{Z}Y$, $A\hat{Y}Z$ and $B\hat{Z}Y$ to meet at *P* and *Q*. Does the line joining *P* and *Q* pass through the vertex *X*? Is this line the bisector of $\hat{X}$? (Answer these questions by measurement.)

2. How many sides are there in a polygon if the sum of the interior angles is
   (a) equal to the sum of the exterior angles,
   (b) double the sum of the exterior angles,
   (c) five times the sum of the exterior angles?

3. Form an equation in *x* for each of the following and solve the equation.
   (a)

   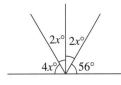

   (b)

   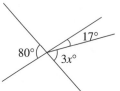

   (c)

   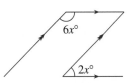

4. Find the value of *x* in each case.
   (a)

   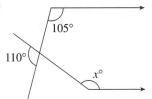

   (b)

   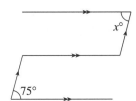

5. The rate of exchange between Singapore dollars (S$) and US dollars (US$) is S$1.40 to US$1. Find
   (a) the cost, in S$, of a holiday in America which costs US$2 500,
   (b) the cost, in US$, of an airfare to Singapore which costs S$2 310.

6. A discount of 15% was given for an article. Calculate the discount if it was sold for $510.

7. Which of the symmetrical figures have
   (a) line symmetry,   (b) rotational symmetry?
   (i)

   (ii)

   (iii)

   (iv)

8. A man borrowed a sum of $1 750. Find the amount he had to pay back at the end of 2 years if the simple interest was charged at 6% per annum.

9. Each figure has a rotational symmetry about O. What is the order of symmetry?
    (a) 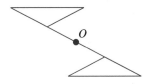   **(b)**

10. A shopkeeper sold an article for $420.
    (a) If he made a profit of 20%, what was his cost price?
    (b) If he incurred a loss of 20%, what was his cost price?

11. The list price of an article is $2 500.
    (a) If the discount for cash payment is 20%, how much does the buyer have to pay?
    (b) If the buyer pays a down payment of 10% of the list price and then $105 per month for 24 months, how much does he pay for the article?

MISCELLANEOUS EXERCISE 3

(answers on p. 436)

1.

$$2, 7, 12, 17, 22, \ldots$$

(a) Write down the 6th term in the sequence.

(b) Write down the 10th term in the sequence.

(c) Find a formula for the *n*th term in the sequence.

2. The list price of a set of furniture was $1 280.

(a) Mr Li paid cash for the furniture and was given a $7\frac{1}{2}$% discount of the list price. How much did he actually pay?

(b) Mr Hwang bought the furniture on hire purchase terms. He paid a down payment which was equal to $\frac{1}{5}$ of the list price. He paid the rest in 10 monthly instalments of $106.40. How much did he pay altogether?

(c) How many percent more did Mr Hwang pay than Mr Li? Give your answer correct to one decimal place.

3. In the figure, $A\hat{O}B = B\hat{O}C = 20°$. $B\hat{O}C$ and $A\hat{O}D$ are supplementary angles. Find $C\hat{O}D$.

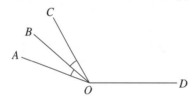

4. *AB* is produced to *C* such that *BC* = 2*AB*. *D* is the midpoint of *AB*. *E* and *F* are points on *BC* such that *EF* = 3*BE* and *FC* = 2*EF*. Find *DF* if *AB* = 20 cm.

5. The difference between $\hat{A}$ and $\hat{B}$ is 20°. If $\hat{A}$ and $\hat{B}$ are complementary angles, find the difference between the supplementary angles of $\hat{A}$ and that of $\hat{B}$.

6. The difference between 2 supplementary angles *A* and *B* is 24°. If $\hat{A} > \hat{B}$, find the complementary angle of $\hat{B}$.

7. When the clockface shows the time quarter past one, find the angle between the minute hand and the hour hand.

8. The two arms of $\hat{A}$ and the two arms of $\hat{B}$ are parallel and $\hat{A}$ is 20° less than 3 times of $\hat{B}$. Find $\hat{A}$ and $\hat{B}$.

9. John walks in the north direction for 2 m. Then, he turns 36° clockwise and walks for another 2 m. Then, he again turns 36° clockwise and walks for another 2 m and so on. Find the total distance he must walk before returning to the starting point.

10. (a) Find the sum of angles A, B, C, D and E.
  (b) If $2\hat{A} = \hat{B} = \hat{C} = \hat{D} = \hat{E}$, find $\hat{A}$.

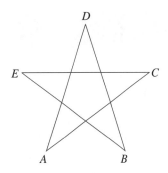

11. In the figure, BM and CN are bisectors of $\hat{B}$ and $\hat{C}$.
  (a) Find $\hat{p} + \hat{q}$ if $\hat{A} = 80°$.
  (b) Find $\hat{A}$ if $B\hat{N}C = 96°$ and $B\hat{M}C = 84°$.

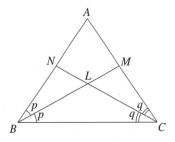

12. In $\triangle ABC$, BL and CL are bisectors of $\hat{B}$ and $\hat{C}$. If $B\hat{L}C = 130°$, find
  (a) $L\hat{C}B$,
  (b) $\hat{A}$.

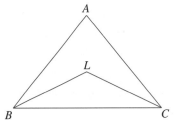

13. In the figure, $ACEG$ and $ABDF$ are straight lines such that $AB = BC = CD = DE = EF = FG$. If GF is perpendicular to AF, find $\hat{A}$.

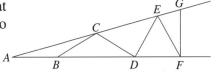

14. In the figure, $AB = AC$. D and E are points on AB and AC such that $CB = CD$ and $DA = DE = CE$. Find $\hat{A}$.

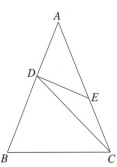

15. In the figure, XYZ is an isosceles triangle such that $XY = XZ$. If $\hat{a} = 2\hat{b} = 4\hat{c}$ and $\hat{d} = 90°$, find $\hat{a}$.

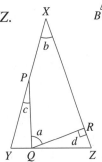

INVESTIGATION 3

1. **(a)** Verify

   (i) $\dfrac{15}{6} - \dfrac{15}{21} = \dfrac{15}{6} \times \dfrac{15}{21}$,

   (ii) $\dfrac{4}{7} - \dfrac{4}{11} = \dfrac{4}{7} \times \dfrac{4}{11}$,

   (iii) $\dfrac{5}{9} - \dfrac{5}{14} = \dfrac{5}{9} \times \dfrac{5}{14}$.

   (b) Write down two interesting examples such as those given in (a).
   Is there a rule for finding such examples? Investigate.

2. 3 and 5, 5 and 7, 11 and 13, 17 and 19, . . . are called 'twin primes' because they are prime numbers which differ by 2. Find the next 4 sets of twin primes. Can you find more sets of twin primes? Investigate.

3. A mathematics teacher had to answer an urgent telephone call. Before he left the class, he gave his students the following problems so that they can have some practice in using the calculator.
   Find the exact value of each of the following.

   (i) $2^3 \div 3$ **(ii)** $3^3 \div 8$

   (iii) $4^3 \div 15$ **(iv)** $5^3 \div 24$

   (v) $6^3 \div 35$ **(vi)** $7^3 \div 48$

   (vii) $8^3 \div 63$ **(viii)** $9^3 \div 80$

   Menghui wrote down the answers straightaway.

   (i) $2\dfrac{2}{3}$ **(ii)** $3\dfrac{3}{8}$

   (iii) $4\dfrac{4}{15}$ **(iv)** $5\dfrac{5}{24}$

   (v) $6\dfrac{6}{35}$ **(vi)** $7\dfrac{7}{48}$

   (vii) $8\dfrac{8}{63}$ **(viii)** $9\dfrac{9}{80}$

   (a) Have you discovered the rule used by Menghui?

   (b) Can you use Menghui's rule to do the following?

   $10^3 \div 99$, $11^3 \div 120$, $12^3 \div 143$, $13^3 \div 168$

   (c) Can you use Menghui's method to do all the divisions of the form $a^3 \div b$? Investigate.

4.

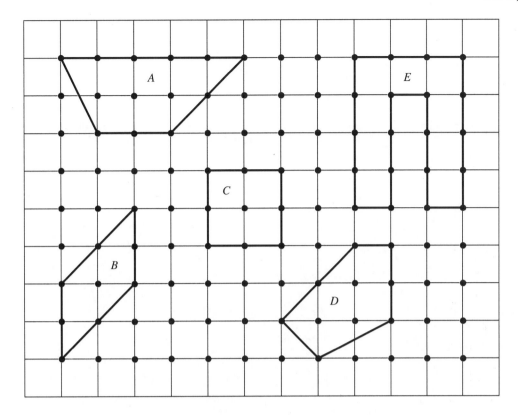

Polygons *A*, *B*, *C*, *D* and *E* are constructed on a geo board as shown. Adjacent pairs of pins on the board are 1 cm apart.

Suppose *m* = number of pins on the boundary of the figure,
       n = number of pins inside the figure,
      A = area of the figure on the geo board.

(a) Copy and complete the following table.

Figure	Area *A* (cm²)	*m*	*n*	$\left(\dfrac{m}{2} - 1\right)$
A	7	10	3	4
B				
C				
D				
E				

(b) Study the table and describe the relationship between *A*, *m* and *n*.
(c) Investigate by constructing any 5 polygons on a geo board.

Chapter 12

Area and Perimeter

Chapter Highlights

- Using formulae to find the perimeter and area of squares, rectangles, parallelograms, trapeziums, triangles and circles.
- Solving mensuration problems involving perimeter and area.

12.1 PERIMETER AND AREA OF POLYGON

Perimeter

The **perimeter** of a polygon is the total length of its boundary. For example, the perimeter of a rectangle measuring 5 cm by 3 cm is 2(5 + 3) cm. In general, we have

Perimeter is the length around a figure.

$$\text{perimeter of rectangle} = 2 \times (\text{length} + \text{breadth}).$$

Note that we usually refer to the longer side of a rectangle as its **length** and the shorter side as its **breadth** or **width**.

Area

When we compare the size of a football field to that of a tennis court, we notice that the football field is larger. We say that the football field has a larger **area** than the tennis court.

We use square regions as units for measuring area. If each side of a square is 1 centimetre in length, the unit is a **square centimetre** written as 1 cm². Fig. 12.1 shows an area of 1 cm². We can also measure area in **square metres** (m²), etc.

Fig. 12.1

MATHSTORY

Around 300 BC, Euclid wrote a book called 'Elements'. In the book, Euclid shows how the distributive property works for area. 'If one large rectangle is divided into 3 smaller ones, the area of the one is equal to the areas of the 3 smaller ones added together!'

Examples

(a) There are 10 rows of 10, i.e. 100 small squares in the big square (Fig. 12.2). If the area of the big square is 1 cm², then the area of each small square is 1 mm².

Thus, 1 cm² = 100 mm²
or   1 mm² = 0.01 cm².

Fig. 12.2

(b) Look at a rectangle with dimensions 5 cm by 3 cm.

The area of each square is 1 cm². There are 5 rows of 3 squares in the rectangle. Therefore, the area of the rectangle is (5 × 3) cm², i.e. 15 cm². Notice that the number of area units is the product of the number of units in the length and the number of units in the breadth.

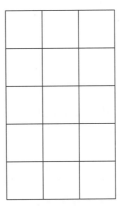

Fig. 12.3

In short, we say that

> **area of rectangle = length × breadth.**

(c) When we derive the area formula for a rectangle, we think of the number of rows and the number of square units in each row. Does the formula still work if the dimensions are not given in whole numbers?

Let us take a rectangle with dimensions 2.4 cm by 1.7 cm.

If we use the formula

$$\text{area of rectangle} = \text{length} \times \text{breadth},$$

we have

$$\text{area of rectangle} = (2.4 \times 1.7) \text{ cm}^2$$
$$= 4.08 \text{ cm}^2$$

To check whether this formula gives the correct area, we proceed as follows:

Let us write

$$2.4 \text{ cm} = 24 \text{ mm},$$
$$1.7 \text{ cm} = 17 \text{ mm}.$$

There are 24 rows of 17 squares in the rectangle. Since each square is 1 mm², we have

$$\text{area of rectangle} = (24 \times 17) \text{ mm}^2$$
$$= 408 \text{ mm}^2$$
$$= 408 \times 0.01 \text{ cm}^2$$
$$= 4.08 \text{ cm}^2$$

This is the same as before.

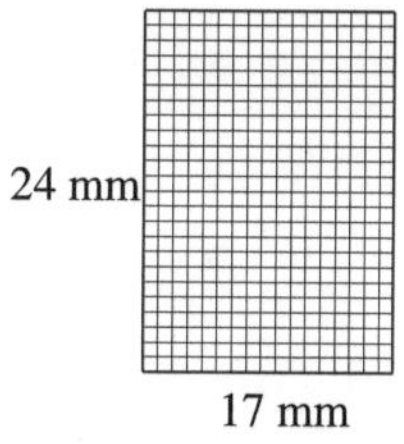

Fig. 12.4

Therefore, the formula still works even though the length and breadth are not given as whole numbers.

(d) Any side of a rectangle can be taken as a base. The perpendicular from a point on the opposite side to the base is called the **height** of the rectangle for that base.

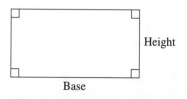

Fig. 12.5

The formula for the area of a rectangle can also be written as

> **area of rectangle = base × height.**

Class Activity

1. *ABCD* is a parallelogram. The dotted lines show how it is cut and put together to form a rectangle.

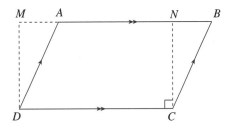

Answer the following questions.
(a) Is the parallelogram *ABCD* equal in area to the newly-formed rectangle *MDCN*?
(b) Is the area of the parallelogram *ABCD* = *NC* × *DC*?
(c) Any side of a parallelogram can be taken as a base and the perpendicular from a point on the opposite side to the base is called the height of the parallelogram for that base. Do you agree that the area of a parallelogram is base × height?

2. *ABC* is an acute-angled triangle.

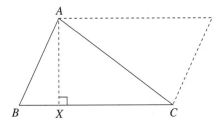

Answer the following questions.
(a) If an identical copy of △*ABC* is inverted and placed alongside △*ABC* to form a parallelogram as shown, is △*ABC* half the size of the parallelogram?
(b) Any side of a triangle can be taken as a base and the perpendicular from the opposite vertex to the base is called the height or **altitude** of the triangle for that base. If *BC* is the base of △*ABC*, then *AX* is the height. Do you agree that the area of an acute-angled triangle is

$\frac{1}{2}$ × base × height?

(c) If *ABC* is an obtuse-angled triangle as shown below, is the area equal to

$\frac{1}{2}$ × base × height?

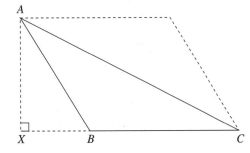

3. A trapezium is a four-sided figure which has a pair of parallel sides. *PQRS* is a trapezium with *PQ* = *a* units and *SR* = *b* units. The height of the trapezium is *h* units.

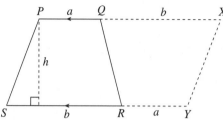

Answer the following questions.

(a) If an exact copy of the trapezium is inverted and placed alongside the original figure to form a parallelogram as shown, is *SY* a base of the parallelogram?

(b) Is *SY* = (*a* + *b*) units?

(c) Do you agree that the area of the parallelogram is (*a* + *b*) × *h* sq units?

(d) Is the trapezium *PQRS* half the size of the parallelogram?

(e) Do you agree that the area of a trapezium is $\frac{1}{2} \times h \times (a + b)$ sq units?

Remember these:

- Area of rectangle = base × height
  In symbols: $A = b \times h$

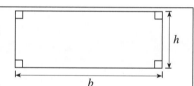

- Area of parallelogram = base × height
  In symbols: $A = b \times h$

- Area of triangle = $\frac{1}{2}$ × base × height

  In symbols: $A = \frac{1}{2} \times b \times h$

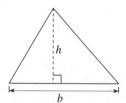

- Area of trapezium = $\frac{1}{2}$ × height × (sum of parallel sides)

  In symbols: $A = \frac{1}{2} \times h \times (a + b)$

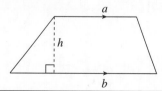

Worked Example 1
The area of a rectangle is 64 cm². If its length is 16 cm, find its perimeter.

Solution:

$$\text{Breadth of rectangle} = \frac{\text{Area of rectangle}}{\text{Length of rectangle}}$$

$$= \frac{64}{16} \text{ cm}$$

$$= 4 \text{ cm}$$

$$\text{Perimeter of rectangle} = 2 \times (l + b) \text{ cm}$$

$$= 2 \times (16 + 4) \text{ cm}$$

$$= 40 \text{ cm}$$

Worked Example 2
In the figure, AD and EC are altitudes of $\triangle ABC$. If $AD = 5$ cm, $BC = 12$ cm and $AB = 10$ cm, find CE.

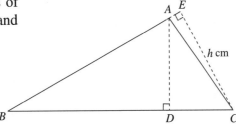

Solution:

$$\text{Area of } \triangle ABC = \frac{1}{2} \times BC \times AD$$

$$= \left(\frac{1}{2} \times 12 \times 5\right) \text{ cm}^2$$

$$= 30 \text{ cm}^2$$

Let $CE = h$ cm.

$$\text{Area of } \triangle ABC = \frac{1}{2} \times AB \times CE$$

$$= \left(\frac{1}{2} \times 10 \times h\right) \text{ cm}^2$$

$$= 5h \text{ cm}^2$$

Thus,

$$5h = 30$$

$$h = 6$$

Therefore, CE is 6 cm.

Worked Example 3
Express
(a) 5.5 cm² in m²,
(b) 1 mm² in cm²,
(c) 25 m² in km²,

(d) 15 km² in are (a), where 1 a = 100 m²,

(e) 2.2 km² in hectare (ha), where 1 ha = 100 ares.

Solution:

(a)
$$1 \text{ cm} = 0.01 \text{ m}$$
$$1 \text{ cm}^2 = (0.01)^2 \text{ m}^2$$
$$= 0.000\ 1 \text{ m}^2$$
$$\therefore \ 5.5 \text{ cm}^2 = (5.5 \times 0.000\ 1) \text{ m}^2$$
$$= 0.000\ 55 \text{ m}^2$$

(b)
$$1 \text{ mm} = 0.1 \text{ cm}$$
$$\therefore \ 1 \text{ mm}^2 = (0.1)^2 \text{ cm}^2$$
$$= 0.01 \text{ cm}^2$$

(c)
$$1 \text{ m} = 0.001 \text{ km}$$
$$1 \text{ m}^2 = (0.001)^2 \text{ km}^2$$
$$= 0.000\ 001 \text{ km}^2$$
$$\therefore \ 25 \text{ m}^2 = (25 \times 0.000\ 001) \text{ km}^2$$
$$= 0.000\ 025 \text{ km}^2$$

(d)
$$1 \text{ km} = 1\ 000 \text{ m}$$
$$1 \text{ km}^2 = (1\ 000)^2 \text{ m}^2$$
$$= 1\ 000\ 000 \text{ m}^2$$
$$15 \text{ km}^2 = (15 \times 1\ 000\ 000) \text{ m}^2$$
$$= 15\ 000\ 000 \text{ m}^2$$
$$\text{But } 100 \text{ m}^2 = 1 \text{ a}$$
$$\therefore \ 15 \text{ km}^2 = 150\ 000 \text{ a}$$

(e)
$$1 \text{ km} = 1\ 000 \text{ m}$$
$$1 \text{ km}^2 = (1\ 000)^2 \text{ m}^2$$
$$= 1\ 000\ 000 \text{ m}^2$$
$$= 10\ 000 \text{ a}$$
$$= 100 \text{ ha}$$
$$\therefore \ 2.2 \text{ km}^2 = (2.2 \times 100) \text{ ha}$$
$$= 220 \text{ ha}$$

Exercise 12.1

answers on p 436

1. Which of the following figures has a greater area, and how much greater?

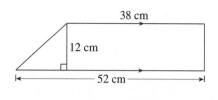

Fig. a

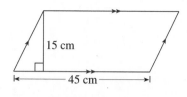

Fig. b

2. Find the difference in area between a rectangle measuring 35 cm by 12 cm and a triangle whose base and height are 22 cm and 32 cm respectively.

3. Find the area of triangle *ABC* in each case.

(a)

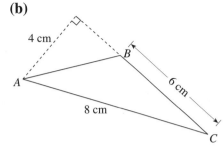

(b)

4. The figure *ABCD* is a rectangle. If *AB* = 6 cm, *AD* = 11 cm and *AE* = *FC* = 5 cm, find the area of the parallelogram *BFDE*.

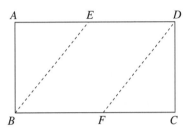

5. The figure *ABCD* on the right is a rectangle. If *AB* = 7 cm, *AD* = 15 cm, *AE* = 6 cm and *FC* = 3 cm, find the area of *EBFD*.

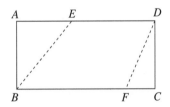

6. Find the perimeter and area of each of the following trapeziums.

(a)

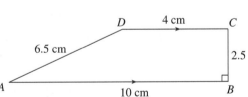

(b)

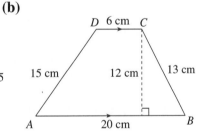

7. A farmer has three pieces of land as shown below. These lands are exchanged for a new piece of land of area 134 000 m². Find his gain or loss in land area.

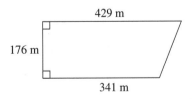
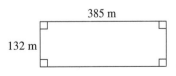

8. A triangle has an area of 35 cm² and a base of 7 cm. Find the height that corresponds to the base.

9. A triangle has an area of 46 square units and a height of 10 units. What is the length of the corresponding base?

10. The area of a rectangle is 40 cm². If the length of the rectangle is 8 cm, find its perimeter.

11. The area of a rectangle is 35 cm². If its breadth is 5 cm, find its perimeter.

12. The area of a parallelogram is 25 square units. The base is 4 units. Find the corresponding height.

13. The area of a parallelogram is 72 cm². If one of its sides is 8 cm and one of its heights is 6 cm, find the other height and the perimeter.

14. In the figure on the right, CR and QB are altitudes of $\triangle PQR$. If PQ = 12 cm, PR = 6 cm and CR = 4 cm, find QB.

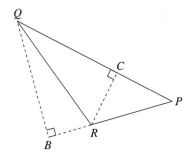

15. In the figure shown, BE and CF are altitudes of $\triangle ABC$. If AB = 9 cm, AC = 6 cm and CF = 4 cm, find BE.

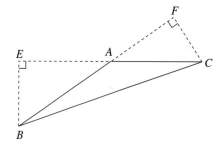

16. Find the perimeters of the following triangles whose areas are given.
    (a)   (b)

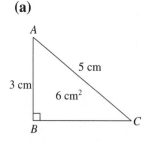
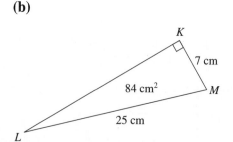

17. Express
    (a) 6.5 cm² in m²,   (b) 1.5 mm² in cm²,   (c) 5.2 m² in cm²,
    (d) 44.2 cm² in mm²,   (e) 33.3 km² in a,   (f) 3.1 a in m²,
    (g) 62.7 m² in km²,   (h) 1.1 a in cm²,   (i) 3 246.7 km² in a,
    (j) 73 150 cm² in km²,   (k) 3.4 ha in km²,   (l) 46.2 a in ha.

18. Find the lengths of the sides of the following squares whose areas are

    (a) 100 mm²,   **(b)** 81 cm²,   **(c)** 225 cm²,

    (d) 169 m²,   **(e)** 441 km²,   **(f)** 1 296 m².

12.2 CIRCUMFERENCE AND AREA OF CIRCLE

Fig. 12.6 shows a circle with centre O. The line segment AB, passing through O, is a **diameter** of the circle. OA (or OB) is called the **radius** of the circle. Notice that AB divides the circle into halves and each half is known as a **semicircle**

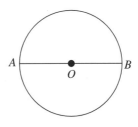

Fig. 12.6

The perimeter of a circle is called its **circumference**. If you measure the diameter and circumference of any circular object as in Fig. 12.7, you will find that the quotient, $\dfrac{\text{circumference}}{\text{diameter}}$ is about 3.

The length around a circle is called its circumference.

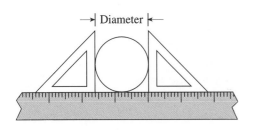 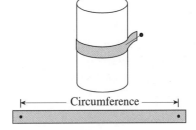

Fig. 12.7

Mathematicians find that it is not possible to find the exact value of this quotient and use the Greek letter 'π' which is read as 'pi' to represent this quotient.

Some calculators give the approximate value of π as 3.141 592 6. In practice, 3.14, 3.142 and $\dfrac{22}{7}$ are usually taken as approximations of the values of π.

If we denote the circumference and the radius of a circle by C units and r units respectively, we may write

$$\pi = \frac{C}{2r}.$$

Thus, the formula for the circumference, C units, of a circle of radius r units is

$$C = 2\pi r.$$

Fig. 12.8 shows that if we divide a circle of radius r into sixteen equal parts and rearrange them as shown, the new figure obtained will look like a parallelogram.

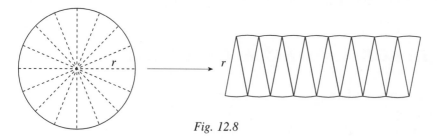

Fig. 12.8

If we now divide the circle into thirty-two equal parts, the new figure formed will look more like a rectangle as shown in Fig. 12.9. If we repeat this by dividing the circle into more and more equal parts, the figure formed will be more and more like a rectangle. The length of the rectangle will be closer and closer to half the circumference and the breadth to the radius of the circle.

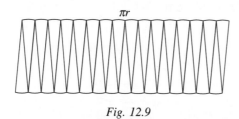

Fig. 12.9

We note that the area of the rectangle is $r \times \pi r$ sq units or πr^2 sq units. This rectangle also has the same area as the circle. Thus, the formula for the area, A sq units, of a circle of radius r units is

$$A = \pi r^2.$$

Worked Example 4

Using 3.14 for π, find the circumference and the area of a circle with radius 5.4 cm. Give your answers correct to one decimal place.

Solution:

$$C = 2\pi r$$
$$= 2 \times 3.14 \times 5.4$$
$$= 33.912$$

Thus, the circumference is 33.9 cm (correct to 1 decimal place).

Also,
$$A = \pi r^2$$
$$= 3.14 \times 5.4^2$$
$$= 91.562\,4$$

Thus, the area is 91.6 cm² (correct to 1 decimal place).

Worked Example 5

Find the radius of a circle

(a) if its circumference is 176 units,

(b) if its area is 2 464 square units.

$\left(\text{Take } \pi = \dfrac{22}{7}.\right)$

Solution:

(a) $2\pi r = 176$

$\therefore r = \dfrac{88}{\pi}$

$= \left(88 \times \dfrac{7}{22}\right)$

$= 28$

Thus, the radius is 28 units.

(b) $\pi r^2 = 2\ 464$

$r^2 = \left(2\ 464 \times \dfrac{7}{22}\right)$

$= 784$

$\therefore r = \sqrt{784}$

$= 28$

Thus, the radius is 28 units.

Worked Example 6

The radius of a wheel of a bicycle is 25.5 cm. How many revolutions must it make to cover a distance of 40 m. Give your answer correct to the nearest whole number. (Take $\pi = 3.142$.)

Solution:

Circumference of the wheel $= 2\pi r$ cm

$= (2 \times 3.142 \times 25.5)$ cm

$= 160.242$ cm

The distance to be covered is 40 m or 4 000 cm.

$\therefore$ the number of revolutions required $= \dfrac{4\ 000}{160.242}$

$= 25$ (correct to the nearest whole number)

Thus, the wheel has to make 25 revolutions.

Exercise 12.2

answers on p. 436

For the following problems, take $\pi = \dfrac{22}{7}$ unless otherwise stated.

1. Find the circumference and area of a circle if its radius is
   - **(a)** 7 cm,
   - **(b)** 14 cm,
   - **(c)** 16.8 cm,
   - **(d)** 25.2 cm,
   - **(e)** 28 cm,
   - **(f)** 63 cm.

2. Find the perimeter and area of a semicircle if its diameter is
   - **(a)** 35 cm,
   - **(b)** 21 cm,
   - **(c)** 14 cm,
   - **(d)** 8.4 cm.

3. Find the radius of a circle whose circumference is
   (a) 11 cm,   (b) 21 cm,
   (c) 30 cm,   (d) 1 m.

4. Find the area of a circle whose circumference is
   (a) $29\frac{1}{3}$ cm,   (b) 44 cm,   (c) 132 cm.

5. Find the radius of a circle whose area is
   (a) 154 cm²,   (b) 616 cm²,   (c) 1 386 cm².

6. Find the circumference of a circle whose area is
   (a) 2 464 cm²,   (b) 3 850 cm²,   (c) 5 544 cm².

7. The minute hand of a clock is 5 cm long. What distance will the tip of the hand move in 45 minutes? Give your answer correct to 1 decimal place. (Take $\pi = 3.142$.)

8. The minute hand of a clock is 9 cm long and the hour hand is two-thirds as long. How much more distance will the tip of the minute hand move than the hour hand in one hour? Give your answer correct to 1 decimal place. (Take $\pi = 3.142$.)

9. The diameter of a bicycle wheel is 60 cm. How far will the bicycle travel in 140 turns of the wheel? Give your answer correct to the nearest metre. (Take $\pi = 3.142$.)

10. How many revolutions will a car wheel make if its radius is 20 cm and the distance covered is 1.1 km? Give your answer correct to the nearest whole number. (Take $\pi = 3.142$.)

11. A satellite is circling around the earth. Its circular path has a diameter of 20 000 km. Taking π to be (a) 3.142, and (b) 3.141 6, find the distance the satellite covers if it completes 100 orbits. Give the difference of the results obtained in (a) and (b).

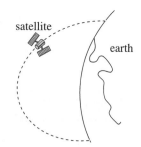

12.3 MORE PROBLEMS ON AREA AND PERIMETER

Worked Example 7

The diagram represents a field with a circular pond of diameter 14 m. *AFD* and *BEC* are semicircles, and *ABCD* is a rectangle in which *AB* = 112 m and *BC* = 56 m. Find
(a) the distance around the field,

(b) the area of the field excluding the pond.

$\left(\text{Take } \pi = \dfrac{22}{7}.\right)$

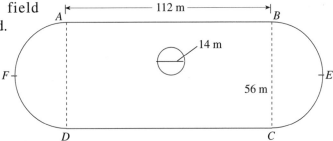

Solution:

(a) The distance around the field $= 2\left(112 + \dfrac{56}{2}\pi\right)$ m

$$= (224 + 56\pi) \text{ m}$$

$$= \left(224 + 56 \times \dfrac{22}{7}\right) \text{ m}$$

$$= (224 + 176) \text{ m}$$

$$= 400 \text{ m}$$

(b) Area of the field excluding the pond

$$= \left[\dfrac{\pi(28)^2}{2} + 112 \times 56 + \dfrac{\pi(28)^2}{2} - \pi(7)^2\right] \text{ m}^2$$

$$= [\pi(28)^2 + 112 \times 56 - 49\pi] \text{ m}^2$$

$$= \left[\dfrac{22}{7} \times (28)^2 + 112 \times 56 - 49 \times \dfrac{22}{7}\right] \text{ m}^2$$

$$= [22 \times 112 + 112 \times 56 - 7 \times 22] \text{ m}^2$$

$$= [112(22 + 56) - 154] \text{ m}^2$$

$$= 8\,582 \text{ m}^2$$

Worked Example 8

The length of a rectangle is 10 cm greater than its width. Its perimeter is 70 cm. Find

(a) its width, **(b)** its length.

Solution:

(a) Let x cm be the width.

Then, the length is $(x + 10)$ cm.

Perimeter $= 2[x + (x + 10)]$ cm

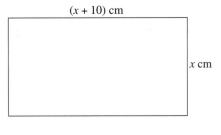

Since its perimeter is given as 70 cm,

$2[x + (x + 10)] = 70$

$4x + 20 = 70$

$4x = 70 - 20$

$4x = 50$

$x = 12\dfrac{1}{2}$

$\therefore$ the width is $12\dfrac{1}{2}$ cm.

(b) The length is $\left(12\frac{1}{2} + 10\right)$ cm = $22\frac{1}{2}$ cm.

Exercise 12.3

answers on p. 436

1. Find the area of the shaded part of each of the following figures. (All angles at the corners are right angles.)

   (a)

   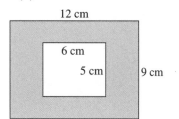

   (b)

   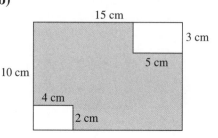

2. A carpet, 10 m long and 8 m wide, is laid in a square room of side 12 m. Find the area of the floor left uncovered.

3. A path, 2 m wide, surrounds a rectangular garden, 30 m long and 16 m wide. Find the area of the path.

4. A man wants to tile a terrace measuring 8 m by 12 m. Each tile is a 20-cm square. How many tiles are needed? How many tiles does he need if each tile is a 10-cm square?

5. A gravel path, 1 m wide, runs round a grass lawn, 18 m by 10 m. There are four ornamental bushes in the lawn, each growing on a square of side $1\frac{1}{2}$ m.

   A garden shed, 5 m by 3 m, stands in the middle of the lawn.
   (a) Find the area of the path in m².
   (b) Find the area of the space covered with grass in m² (i.e. the shaded area).
   (c) What fraction of the lawn is not covered with grass?

   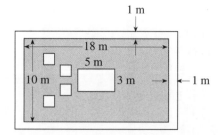

6. The floor dimensions of a room are 6 m by 5 m. It is 3 m high. There are two windows, each 2 m by $1\frac{1}{2}$ m, and a door, 2 m by 1 m. A painter wants to paint the walls and ceiling. Each can of paint can cover an area of 11 m². How many cans of paint must he buy?

7. The diagram represents a field. *LMN* and *PQR* are semicircles, and *LNRP* is a rectangle in which *LP* = 124 m and *PR* = 63 m. There is a circular pond of diameter 21 m in the centre of the field. Find
   (a) the distance around the field,
   (b) the area of the field excluding the pond.

$\left(\text{Take } \pi = \dfrac{22}{7}.\right)$

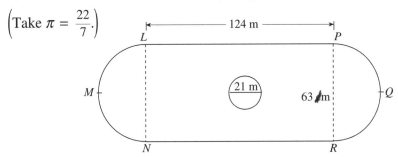

8. A square metal plate of sides 5 cm each, has four semicircles and four quadrants (quarter-circles), each of radius 1 cm, cut from its sides and corners. What is the perimeter of the ornamental plate formed?

$\left(\text{Take } \pi = \dfrac{22}{7}.\right)$

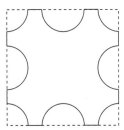

9. Find the area of the shaded region between two concentric circles with radii 4 cm and 6 cm. Compare this area with the area of the smaller circle.

$\left(\text{Take } \pi = \dfrac{22}{7}.\right)$

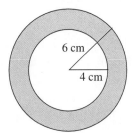

10. A carpet priced at $15 per m² is used to cover a room, 20 m by 18 m, leaving a margin of 1.5 m all round. Find the cost of the carpet.

11. Planks of wood, 1.5 m long and 0.2 m wide, are placed vertically edge to edge to form a paling round a plot of land, 45 m long and 35 m wide. Find the total length of the planks used.

12. A rectangle is six times as long as it is wide. Its perimeter is 154 cm. How wide is the rectangle?

13. The length of a rectangle is 4 cm greater than its width. The perimeter is 100 cm. Find the width.

14. The width of a rectangle is 10 cm less than the length. If the perimeter is 140 cm, find the width.

15. A rectangle has a length 3 cm greater than the width. If the perimeter is 34 cm, find the width and the length.

16. The height of a trapezium is 11 cm. Find the sum of its two parallel sides if its area is 264 cm². If the longer side is twice the shorter side, what is the length of the longer side?

17. The diagram shows a square of side 7 cm with two quadrants drawn inside. Find the area of the shaded region.

$\left(\text{Take } \pi = \dfrac{22}{7}.\right)$

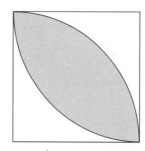

18. The diagram shows a square of side 14 cm with four quadrants drawn inside. Find the area of the shaded region.

$\left(\text{Take } \pi = \dfrac{22}{7}.\right)$

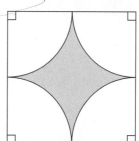

*19. The diagram shows that region X is bounded by three semicircular arcs whose lengths are in the ratio $1 : 2 : 3$, and region Y is also bounded by three semicircular arcs. Find the ratio of the area of region X to that of region Y.

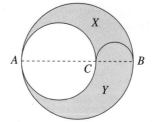

*20. The shaded shape is bounded by two line segments of length 7 cm each and two quarter circles of radius 7 cm each. Find the area of the shaded shape.

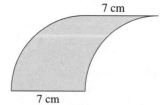

*21. $ABCD$ is a parallelogram. $AD = 15$ cm, $DE = 10$ cm and $DF = 12$ cm. Find
(a) the area,
(b) the perimeter of the parallelogram.

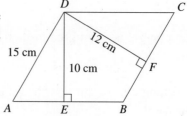

*22. In the figure, *ABEG* is a rectangle and *E* and *G* are the centres of the circles. If *BE* = 7 cm and the areas of the shaded part *ABC* and the shaded part *CDF* are equal, find *GE*.

$\left(\text{Take } \pi = \dfrac{22}{7}.\right)$

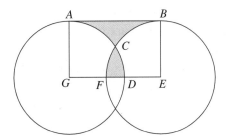

*23. In the figure, *AC* is an arc of a circle, centre *O*. *BDA* is a semicircle, centre *M*. If *OA* is perpendicular to *BA* and *OA* = *BA* = 14 cm, find the total area of the shaded parts.

$\left(\text{Take } \pi = \dfrac{22}{7}.\right)$

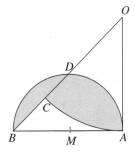

*24. *OAB* is a quadrant of radius 7 cm. Find the total area of the shaded parts.

$\left(\text{Take } \pi = \dfrac{22}{7}.\right)$

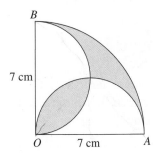

Chapter Review

1. Perimeter
- Perimeter of a rectangle = 2 × (length + breadth)
- The circumference, *C* units, of a circle of radius *r* units is given by
$$C = 2\pi r$$

2. Area
- Area of a rectangle = length × breadth

  or

  base × height

  = *l* × *b* sq. units

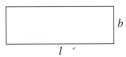

- Area of a triangle $= \dfrac{1}{2} \times$ base $\times$ height

  $= \dfrac{1}{2} \times b \times h$ sq. units

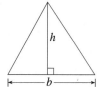

- Area of a trapezium

  $= \dfrac{1}{2} \times$ height $\times$ (sum of parallel sides)

  $= \dfrac{1}{2} \times h \times (a + b)$ sq. units

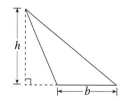

- The area, A, of a circle of radius r is given by $A = \pi r^2$.

CHALLENGER 12

1. If the rectangle is 3 times as large as $\triangle CDX$ and 4 times as large as $\triangle BCY$, what fraction of the rectangle is shaded?

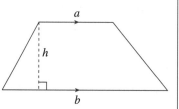

2. In the figure, ABC is an isosceles triangle, $\hat{A} = 90°$ and $PQRS$ is a square of side 1 cm. Find the area of $\triangle ABC$.

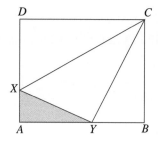

3. The diagonals of a rhombus are in the ratio 3 : 5. If one diagonal is 4 cm longer than the other, find the area of the rhombus.

4. In the figure, $ABCD$ is a parallelogram. M and N are the midpoints of AD and BC respectively.
   (a) Does the figure have rotational symmetry?
   (b) What fraction of the parallelogram is the shaded area?
   (c) If the shaded area is a rectangle, find $AB : BC$.

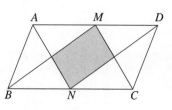

5. *ABCD* is a rhombus. *E* and *F* are the mid-points of *AD* and *CD* respectively.

(a) Does the figure have rotational symmetry?

(b) Does the figure have line symmetry?

(c) What fraction of the rhombus is the shaded area?

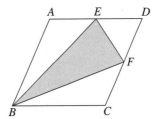

6. *ABCD* is a rhombus and $\hat{A} = 30°$. If its area is x cm² and its perimeter is x cm, find the value of x.

Problem Solving 12

Changing Shape

It is given that the perimeter of a quadrilateral *ABCD* is 51 cm. You can change the figure *ABCD* into a rhombus if you add 5 cm to *AB*, subtract 4 cm from *BC*, multiply *CD* by 3 and divide *DA* by 2. Find the longest side of the original figure.

The strategies to use are **use tabulation**, **work backwards** and **use equations**. Suppose each side of the rhombus is x cm, we have

	AB	**BC**	**CD**	**DA**
Quadrilateral	$x - 5$	$x + 4$	$\dfrac{x}{3}$	$2x$
	↑ -5	↑ $+4$	↑ $\div 3$	↑ $\times 2$
Rhombus	x	x	x	x

So,

$$x - 5 + x + 4 + \frac{x}{3} + 2x = 51$$

$$4x + \frac{x}{3} = 52$$
$$12x + x = 52 \times 3$$
$$13x = 52 \times 3$$
$$x = 4 \times 3$$
$$= 12$$

∴ the longest side, $DA = (2 \times 12)$ cm $= 24$ cm.

After you have checked your answer, think of an alternative method. Find out whether it would be easier to work forward using algebra.

Problems...

1. **Colour Beads**   A box contained 19 beads of four different colours. If 2 red beads were added in, 3 blue beads were taken out, the number of green beads was doubled and the number of yellow beads was halved, the box would contain the same number of beads for each colour. How many red beads were in the box originally?

2. **From Quadrilateral to Parallelogram**   The perimeter of a quadrilateral *ABCD* is 18 cm. If *AB* is lengthened by 2 cm, *BC* is shortened by 2 cm, *CD* is doubled and *DA* is halved, the quadrilateral will become a parallelogram *ABCD* with the perimeter unchanged. Find the longest side of the given quadrilateral.

3. **Fair Division**   The figure shows 7 circles of the same size.

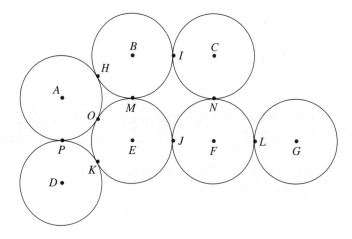

    (a) Describe how you would draw a straight line through at least two of the points *A*, *B*, . . ., *P* to divide the total area of the circles in halves. Name the line.

    (b) If you have more than one answer, give the other answer (or answers).

4. **Finding the Remainder**   When a number is divided by 5, the remainder is 2. What is the remainder when the number is multiplied by 8 and then divided by 5?

Volume, Surface Area and Density

Chapter Highlights

- Using formulae to find the volume and surface area of cubes, cuboids, prisms and cylinders.
- Finding the density, volume and mass of a substance using the formula

$$\text{density} = \frac{\text{mass}}{\text{volume}}$$

  given the other two quantities.
- Solving mensuration problems involving volume, surface area and density.

13.1 VOLUME AND SURFACE AREA OF PRISM AND CYLINDER

Prism

Bonaventura Cavalieri (1598–1647), an Italian mathematician and disciple of Galileo, contributed to the development of geometry, trigonometry, and algebra in the Renaissance. He became a Jesuit at an early age and later, after reading Euclid's 'Elements', was inspired to study mathematics. In 1629, Cavalieri became a professor at Bologna and held that post until his death. Cavalieri is best known for his principle concerning the volumes of solids.

Fig 13.1 and Fig. 13.2 show two solids. Which one of them occupies more space?

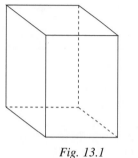

Fig. 13.1

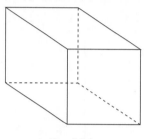

Fig. 13.2

It is difficult to answer unless you have made some measurements.

If two solids occupy the same amount of space, we say that the solids have the same **volume**.

To measure volume we must have a volume unit.

We may choose a unit which is a cube of edge 1 cm as shown in Fig. 13.3. We call this unit one **cubic centimetre**, written as 1 cm³. We can also measure volume in **cubic metres** (m³).

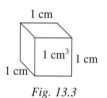

Fig. 13.3

Example

The volume of a box with dimensions 3 cm by 2 cm by 4 cm is 24 cm³ because you need 24 of the unit cubes to fill up the box.

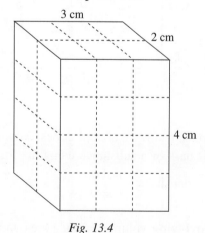

Fig. 13.4

Notice that the volume 24 cm³ can be obtained by the product of the length, width and height, i.e. $(3 \times 2 \times 4)$ cm³.

Notice also that length × breadth is the area of the rectangular base. So, the formula for volume of a cuboid can be written as

> **volume of cuboid = length × breadth × height**
> **or volume of cuboid = area of base × height.**

Volume describes how much space a three-dimensional figure occupies.

The solid shown in Fig. 13.5 is a **prism**. If any cut is made through it horizontally, the surface exposed to view is always of the same size and shape. This surface is called the **cross-section** of the solid, and the solid is said to be of uniform cross-section. Notice that the area of the cross-section is the same as the area of the base. In this case, the base is a trapezium.

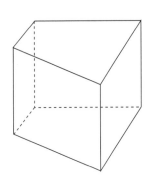

Fig. 13.5

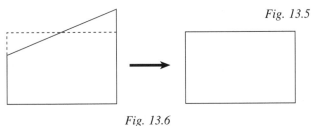

Fig. 13.6

The base area can be cut and rearranged to form a rectangle as shown in Fig. 13.6. We see that the prism can be cut and rearranged to form a cuboid. Therefore, the volume of the prism is equal to the volume of the cuboid formed.

Thus, the formula for volume of a prism can be written as

> **volume of prism = area of base × height**
> **or volume of prism = area of cross-section × height.**

The formula applies to various types of prisms.

Here are some examples of prisms.

(i) 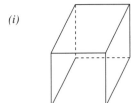   *(ii)* 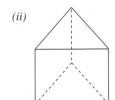   *(iii)*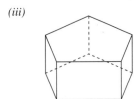

(iv)   *(v)*

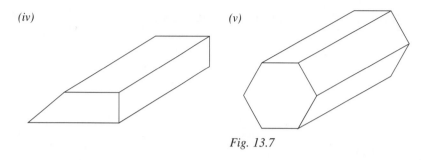

Fig. 13.7

Notice that Fig. 13.7(i) is a cuboid. It is also known as a rectangular prism. Fig. 13.7(ii) is known as a triangular prism.

The total surface area of any prism is the sum of the areas of all the faces.

Note: When we use the term prism in this chapter, we always refer to right prism because oblique prisms are excluded. In a right prism, the centre of the top face is directly above the centre of the base.

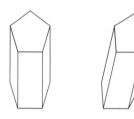

A right prism   An oblique prism

Fig. 13.8

Cylinder

Fig. 13.9

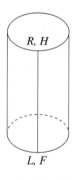

Fig. 13.10

If you bend a rectangular sheet of paper (as shown in Fig. 13.9) to bring a pair of opposite edges together, you will get an open tube like the one in Fig. 13.10.

This is called an **open cylinder**. The surface area of this open cylinder is the area of its curved surface given by the product of the distance round the rim and the height. If the two ends of the cylinder are covered, it is called a **closed cylinder**. So, we have

> **surface area of closed cylinder = area of curved surface + twice the base area.**

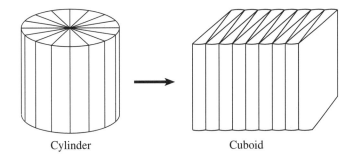

Cylinder   Cuboid

Fig. 13.11

A cylinder can be divided into many parts and rearranged to form a cuboid as shown in Fig. 13.11 above. It is reasonable to assume that

volume of cylinder = area of base × height.

In general, for a solid cylinder with radius r units and height h units (see Fig. 13.12), we have

$$\text{surface area} = 2\pi r \times h + 2 \times \pi r^2$$
$$= 2\pi r(h + r)$$
$$\text{and} \quad \text{volume} = \pi r^2 h.$$

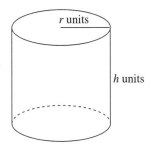

Fig. 13.12

Worked Example 1

The volume of a rectangular solid is 576 cm³. It is 12 cm long and 6 cm wide. Find its height.

Solution:

$$\text{The area of the base} = (12 \times 6) \text{ cm}^2$$
$$= 72 \text{ cm}^2$$
$$\therefore \text{ the height of the solid} = \text{Volume} \div \text{Area of base}$$
$$= (576 \div 72) \text{ cm}$$
$$= 8 \text{ cm}$$

Worked Example 2

The figure shows a rectangular prism whose length, breadth and height are given. Find the surface area of the figure.

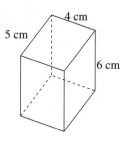

Solution:

The surface area = $[(5 \times 6) + (4 \times 6) + (5 \times 6) + (4 \times 6) + (5 \times 4) + (5 \times 4)]$ cm^2
= $(30 + 24 + 30 + 24 + 20 + 20)$ cm^2
= 148 cm^2

Alternative solution:

The surface area = $[(5 + 4 + 5 + 4) \times 6 + 2 \times (5 \times 4)]$ cm^2
= $(18 \times 6 + 40)$ cm^2
= $(108 + 40)$ cm^2
= 148 cm^2

Worked Example 3

Express
(a) 106.5 cm^3 in m^3,
(b) 3.6 m^3 in cm^3,
(c) 12 780 mm^3 in cm^3.

Solution:

(a)
1 cm = 0.01 m
1 cm^3 = $(0.01)^3$ m^3
= $0.000\ 001$ m^3
$\therefore$ 106.5 cm^3 = $(106.5 \times 0.000\ 001)$ m^3
= $0.000\ 106\ 5$ m^3

(b)
1 m = 100 cm
1 m^3 = $(100)^3$ cm^3
= $1\ 000\ 000$ cm^3
$\therefore$ 3.6 m^3 = $3\ 600\ 000$ cm^3

(c)
1 mm = 0.1 cm
1 mm^3 = $(0.1)^3$ cm^3
= 0.001 cm^3
$\therefore$ $12\ 780$ mm^3 = $(12\ 780 \times 0.001)$ cm^3
= 12.78 cm^3

Worked Example 4

A solid cylinder has an altitude of 15 cm and a base of radius 7 cm. Find
(a) the volume,
(b) the total surface area,
of the cylinder.

$$\left(\text{Take } \pi = \frac{22}{7}.\right)$$

Solution:

(a) Volume of the cylinder $= \pi r^2 h$ cm³

$$= \left(\frac{22}{7} \times 7^2 \times 15\right) \text{ cm}^3$$

$$= 2\,310 \text{ cm}^3$$

(b) Total surface area $= (2\pi rh + 2\pi r^2)$ cm²
$$= 2\pi r(h + r) \text{ cm}^2$$

$$= \left[2 \times \frac{22}{7} \times 7 \times (15 + 7)\right] \text{ cm}^2$$

$$= 968 \text{ cm}^2$$

Exercise 13.1

answers on p. 436

In the following problems, take $\pi = \frac{22}{7}$.

1. Find the volume of a rectangular box when
   (a) $L = 2$ cm, $W = 3$ cm, $H = 5$ cm,
   (b) $L = 3$ cm, $W = 5$ cm, $H = \frac{1}{2}$ cm,

   where L is the length, W the width and H the height of the box.

2. Find the width of a rectangular box if the volume is 30 cm³, length is 5 cm and height is 2 cm.

3. Calculate the volume and surface area of each of the following solids.
   (a)   **(b)**

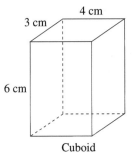

Cuboid

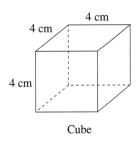

Cube

4. Find the volume of each of the following solids. (Assume that all the angles at the corners are right angles.)

(a)

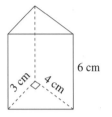

(b)

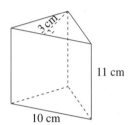

5. Find the volume of each of the following prisms.

(a)

(b)

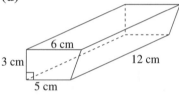

(c)

(d)

6. Find the total surface area of a cube whose volume is 27 cm³.

7. The altitude of a rectangular prism is 4 units and the width and length of its base are 3 units and 2 units respectively. Find the total surface area of the prism.

8. Express
   (a) 11 034 cm³ in m³,   **(b)** 11.5 m³ in cm³,
   (c) 34 567 mm³ in cm³,   **(d)** 5 699 cm³ in m³,
   (e) 691 250 mm³ in m³.

9. The radius of the base of a solid cylinder is 2 units and its altitude is 3 units. Find
   (a) the volume,
   (b) the area of the curved surface,
   (c) the total surface area,
   of the cylinder.

10. A solid cylinder has an altitude of 14 cm and a base of diameter 8 cm. Find
    (a) the volume,
    (b) the total surface area,
    of the cylinder.

11. Eight litres of water are poured into an empty cylindrical jug of internal diameter 20 cm. Find the height of the water level, correct to the nearest cm.

12. A horizontal drinking trough for cattle has a triangular cross-section whose measurements are shown in the diagram. How much water (in cm³) can it hold when full?

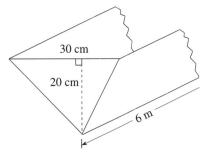

30 cm

20 cm

6 m

13. The circumference of a base of a solid cylinder is 44 cm and its height is 8 cm. Find
    (a) the curved surface area,
    (b) the total surface area,
    of the cylinder.

14. The curved surface area of a solid cylinder is 880 cm² and its height is 10 cm. Find the circumference and area of a base of the cylinder.

13.2 DENSITY

The **density** of a substance is its mass per unit volume.

$$\textbf{Density} = \frac{\textbf{Mass}}{\textbf{Volume}}$$

Worked Example 5
A rectangular solid block, 3 cm by 5 cm by 10 cm, weighs 1 200 g. Calculate
(a) its volume,   (b) its density.

Solution:
(a)   Volume = Length × Breadth × Height
                   = $(3 \times 5 \times 10)$ cm³
                   = 150 cm³

Thus, the volume of the object is 150 cm³.

(b)   Density = $\dfrac{\text{Mass}}{\text{Volume}}$

                   = $\dfrac{1\ 200\ \text{g}}{150\ \text{cm}^3}$

                   = 8 g/cm³

Thus, the density of the object is 8 g/cm³.

Note: We read 'g/cm³' as 'grams per cubic centimetre'.

Worked Example 6

A piece of square metal plate whose density is 7.2 g/cm³ weighs 828 g.
(a) Calculate the volume of the plate.
(b) If this plate has an area of 100 cm², find its thickness.

Solution:

(a)
$$\text{Volume} = \frac{\text{Mass}}{\text{Density}}$$
$$= \frac{828}{7.2} \text{ cm}^3$$
$$= 115 \text{ cm}^3$$

Thus, the volume of the metal plate is 115 cm³.

(b)
$$\text{Thickness} = \frac{\text{Volume}}{\text{Area}}$$
$$= \frac{115}{100} \text{ cm}$$
$$= 1.15 \text{ cm}$$

Thus, the thickness of the metal plate is 1.15 cm.

Exercise 13.2

answers on p. 437

1. Calculate the densities of the following.
    (a) 150 cm³ of a lump of metal that weighs 1 200 g
    (b) 85 cm³ of a liquid whose mass is 51 g
    (c) 0.22 m³ of a substance that weighs 198 kg

2. Calculate the masses of the following.
    (a) 350 cm³ of a metal whose density is 2.2 g/cm³
    (b) 560 cm³ of a liquid whose density is 0.9 g/cm³
    (c) 400 cm³ of a substance whose density is 0.7 g/cm³

3. Calculate the volumes of the following.
    (a) A metal rod of mass 265.2 g and density 10.4 g/cm³
    (b) A liquid of mass 28.8 g and density 0.8 g/cm³
    (c) A substance of mass 42.6 g and density 1.1 g/cm³

4. A piece of wire with radius 1.5 mm is 10 m long and weighs 423.9 g. Taking $\pi = 3.14$, find
    (a) the volume of the wire, in cm³,
    (b) the density (in g/cm³) of the metal.

5. A rectangular solid block, 20 cm by 35 cm by 5 cm, has a density of 2.2 g/cm^3. Find
   (a) its volume,
   (b) its mass.

6. An object whose mass is 500 g has a density of 3.2 g/cm^3. Find the volume of the object.

7. The figure shows a metal girder with the dimensions given. (All angles at the corners are right angles.) If the density of the metal is 7.6 g/cm^3, find
   (a) its volume,
   (b) its mass.

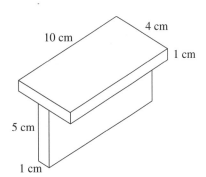

8. The diameter of a rod is 4 cm. If the material weighs 9.42 kg and has a density of 6 g/cm^3, find the length of the rod. (Take $\pi = 3.14$.)

9. A rectangular piece of metal, 2 cm thick, weighs 520 g. If the density of the metal is 6.5 g/cm^3, find the length of the metal if it is 5 cm wide.

13.3 MORE PROBLEMS ON VOLUME AND SURFACE AREA

Worked Example 7
The height of a solid pentagonal prism is 5 cm. The lengths of the edges of its base are given as shown in the diagram. Find
(a) the volume of the solid,
(b) the total surface area of the solid.

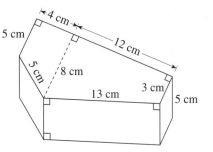

The sum of the areas of the surfaces of a three-dimensional figure is the surface area of the figure.

Solution:

(a) $\qquad$ Base area $= \left[\dfrac{1}{2} \times 4 \times (5 + 8) + \dfrac{1}{2} \times 12 \times (8 + 3)\right]$ cm^2

$\qquad\qquad\qquad\quad = 92$ cm^2

$\therefore$ volume of prism $= (92 \times 5)$ cm^3

$\qquad\qquad\qquad\qquad = 460$ cm^3

(b) Total surface area $= [(5 + 5 + 4 + 12 + 3 + 13) \times 5 + 92 \times 2]$

$\qquad\qquad\qquad\quad = 394$ cm^2

Worked Example 8

A cylindrical pipe of length 42 cm has an outer diameter of 12 cm and a thickness of 2 cm. Find

(a) the outer curved surface area,

(b) the inner curved surface area.

$\left(\text{Take } \pi = \dfrac{22}{7}.\right)$

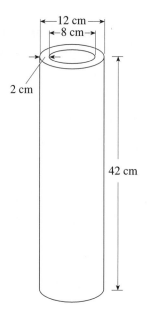

Solution:

(a) Outer curved surface area

$= 2\pi rh \text{ cm}^2$

$= \left(2 \times \dfrac{22}{7} \times 6 \times 42\right) \text{ cm}^2$

$= 1\ 584 \text{ cm}^2$

(b) Inner curved surface area

$= 2\pi rh \text{ cm}^2$

$= \left(2 \times \dfrac{22}{7} \times 4 \times 42\right) \text{ cm}^2$

$= 1\ 056 \text{ cm}^2$

Worked Example 9

A solid cylinder of radius 14 cm and height 20 cm stands on a horizontal floor. A slice of it is removed by cutting vertically downwards through the radii *OM* and *ON* as shown in the diagram. If the slice is

$\dfrac{1}{5}$ of the whole volume, find

(a) the volume of the remaining solid,

(b) its total surface area.

$\left(\text{Take } \pi = \dfrac{22}{7}.\right)$

Solution:

(a) Volume of the cylinder $= \pi r^2 h$

$= \left(\dfrac{22}{7} \times 14^2 \times 20\right) \text{ cm}^3$

$= 12\ 320 \text{ cm}^3$

$\therefore$ volume of the remaining solid $= \left(12\ 320 - \dfrac{12\ 320}{5}\right) \text{ cm}^3$

$= 9\ 856 \text{ cm}^3$

(b) Curved surface area of the remaining solid

$$= \frac{4}{5} \times 2\pi rh$$

$$= \left(\frac{4}{5} \times 2 \times \frac{22}{7} \times 14 \times 20\right) \text{cm}^2$$

$$= 1\ 408 \text{ cm}^2$$

$\therefore$ the total surface area

$$= \left(1\ 408 + 14 \times 20 \times 2 + 2 \times \frac{4}{5} \times \frac{22}{7} \times 14^2\right) \text{cm}^2$$

$$= (1\ 408 + 560 + 985.6) \text{ cm}^2$$

$$= 2\ 953.6 \text{ cm}^2$$

Worked Example 10

Water flows at 4 m per second through a pipe of internal diameter 7 cm. Find, correct to the nearest minute, the time taken to fill 90% of a tank, 3 m by 4 m by 5 m. $\left(\text{Take } \pi = \frac{22}{7}.\right)$

Solution:

Volume of water flowing out per second $= \left[\frac{22}{7} \times (3.5)^2 \times 400\right] \text{cm}^3$

$$= 15\ 400 \text{ cm}^3$$

$$= 0.015\ 4 \text{ m}^3$$

Time taken to fill the tank $= \dfrac{3 \times 4 \times 5 \times 0.9}{0.015\ 4}$ s

$$= \dfrac{3 \times 4 \times 5 \times 0.9}{0.015\ 4 \times 60} \text{ min}$$

$$= 58 \text{ min}$$

Exercise 13.3 ✍ *answers on p. 437*

1. A cylindrical pipe of outer diameter 10 cm and thickness 2 cm is 70 cm long. Find
   (a) the diameter of the hollow,
   (b) the inner curved surface area,
   (c) the outer curved surface area.

2. The figure represents a two-tier cylindrical cake. Each is 3 cm thick. The diameters of the upper and bottom tiers are 20 cm and 30 cm respectively. Find the volume of the cake. (Take $\pi = 3.14$.)

3. Two 3-cm thick wooden wheels, each with radius 5 cm, are attached to a cylindrical wooden rod. The diameter and length of this rod are 2 cm and 4 cm respectively. Find the volume of this object. (Take $\pi = 3.14$.)

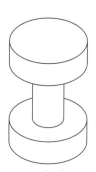

4. A cylindrical piece of cheese of radius 6 cm and thickness 4 cm stands on a horizontal table top. $\frac{1}{4}$ of the whole piece is removed by cutting vertically downwards through the radii OX and OY as shown in the diagram. Find
   (a) the volume of the remaining piece of cheese,
   (b) its total surface area.
   (Take $\pi = 3.14$.)

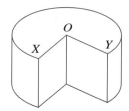

5. The figure shows how 20 1-cm cubes are glued together to form a solid. Find the surface area of the solid.

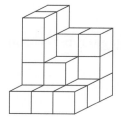

6. A trough whose cross-section is given on the right is 10 m long. If AB and ED are vertical, and AE is horizontal, find the amount of water it can hold when full.

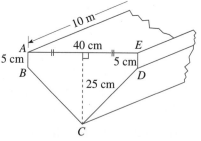

7. A rectangular tank, 3 m long, 2 m broad and 1 m deep, is filled with water to a depth of $\frac{3}{4}$ m. How many bricks measuring $\frac{1}{5}$ m by $\frac{1}{8}$ m by $\frac{1}{10}$ m can be put into it before the water overflows?

8. The external dimensions of a closed metallic rectangular box are 16 cm by 28 cm by 40 cm. If the metal is 2 cm thick, what are the internal measurements of the box? Find the volume of the metal used in making the box.

9. A piece of stone is submerged in a rectangular water tank whose base is 25 cm by 50 cm, raising the level of the water by 1 cm. What is the volume of the stone?

10. A rectangular hole, 3 cm by 4 cm, is cut through a cylinder whose base radius is 10 cm and whose height is 12 cm. Find the volume of the remaining solid.

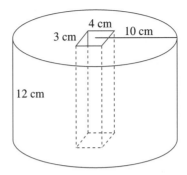

11. A swimming pool, 50 m long and 25 m wide, is 5.5 m deep at one end and 1.5 m deep at the other. The floor of the pool slopes uniformly. Find the volume of water when it is filled.

12. The height of a solid pentagonal prism is 12 cm. The lengths of the edges of its base are given as shown in the diagram. Find
    (a) the volume,
    (b) the total surface area,
    of the solid.

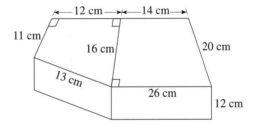

13. Find the amount of water, in litres, discharged in 5 min from a pipe, 3 cm in diameter measured internally, if the water flows a speed of 70 cm per second. $\left(\text{Take } \pi = \dfrac{22}{7}.\right)$

14. Water flows at 3.5 m per second through a pipe, 3 cm in diameter measured internally. The water is collected in an empty cylindrical tank of internal diameter 30 cm. Find the height of the water level in the tank after 1 min.

15. Water flows at 2 m per second through a pipe of internal diameter 7 cm. Find, correct to the nearest minute, the time required to fill a tank, 2 m by 2 m by 1 m.
    $\left(\text{Take } \pi = \dfrac{22}{7}.\right)$

*16. A solid metal bar of circular cross-section 6 cm in diameter is melted down and recast into a pipe of external diameter 6 cm. If the length of the pipe is 80% longer than the original metal bar, find the thickness of the pipe.

*17. A cylindrical container with diameter 28 cm is partly filled with water. A piece of metal weighing 91 kg is put into the container and is completely covered by water. If the density of the metal is 6.3 g/cm³, calculate the rise in water level. Give your answer correct to the nearest cm. (Take $\pi = 3.14$)

*18. An open box with internal dimensions 20 cm by 20 cm by 20 cm contains a solid cylinder of diameter 20 cm and height 20 cm. If 1 717 m*l* of water is required to fill all the space in the box, calculate the value of π correct to (a) 4 significant figures, and (b) 3 significant figures.

*19. The figure shows a machine part. All the corners are square corners, and the cross-section of the curved surface is a semicircle of diameter 18 cm. Find the volume of the machine part correct to the nearest cm³.

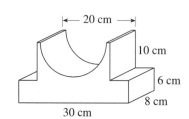

*20. The figure shows the cross-sectional area of a machine part of thickness 4 mm. *EDC* is a semicircle. Find the total mass of 2 000 pieces of this part if the density is 7.2 g/cm³. Give your answer in kilogram, correct to 1 decimal place. (Take $\pi = 3.14$)

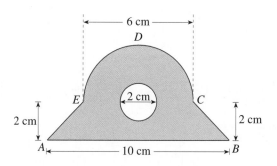

Chapter Review

1. **Volume**
   • Volume of cuboid = length × breadth × height

   or

   area of base × height

   $= l \times b \times h$ cu. units

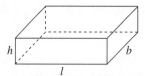

   • Volume of prism = area of base × height

   or

   area of cross-section × height

- Volume of a cylinder = area of base × height
  = $\pi r^2 h$ cu units

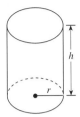

2. **Surface Area**
   - Total surface area of any prism is the sum of areas of all faces.

   - The surface area of a closed cylinder is the area of the curved surface plus twice the base area.
     Surface area = $(2\pi rh + 2\pi r^2)$ sq units or $2\pi r (h + r)$ sq units

3. **Density**
   - The formula for finding density is given by density = $\dfrac{\text{mass}}{\text{volume}}$.

CHALLENGER 13

1. A reservoir has a horizontal rectangular base which measures 120 m by 6 m. The end-faces are formed by two vertical wall 120 m apart and the side-faces are inclined outwards at 45° with the vertical. Find the volume of water in litres when the depth is 8 m.

2. A rectangular solid block of volume 162 cm³ is divided with one cutting into two parts. If one of the parts is a cube of volume $91\dfrac{1}{8}$ cm³, find the total surface area of the original block.

3. Solid C is made up of cuboids A and B such that it has the least total surface area. If the dimensions of cuboids A and B are 7 cm by 7 cm by 6 cm and 5 cm by 8 cm by 10 cm respectively, find the total surface area of solid C.

4. A solid cube whose edge is 1 m long has 3 square holes of sides 30 cm made through the central part of the cube as shown. Find the total surface area of the remaining solid.

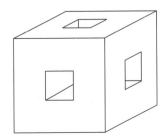

5. A cuboid made of 12 1-cm cubes is divided into two parts A and B. Part A which is made up of 6 cubes is shown in the diagram. Find the total surface area of part B.

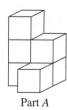

Part A

6. If you are given a bottle which is about a quarter filled with water, a marker pen and a ruler, can you make a mark on the bottle so that it can be used to measure half a bottle of water? Explain how you do it.

Problem Solving 13

Apples and Pears

Ali bought a total of 70 apples and pears. He paid $12 for the apples and $18 for the pears. If a pear cost twice as much as an apple, how many pears and how many apples did he buy?

If we use the usual algebraic method and let x be the number of pears and $(70 - x)$ be the number of apples, we may have to solve fractional equations such as

$$\frac{18}{x} = 2\left(\frac{12}{70 - x}\right).$$

Since fractional equations will be taught in book 2, we shall use a different approach to solve the problem.

Suppose he paid $18 for $3x$ pears. Then, he would pay $12 for $2x$ pears and hence $12 for $4x$ apples.

From the above, $$7x = 70$$
$$x = 10$$
$$\therefore \text{ Number of pears} = 3 \times 10 = 30$$
$$\text{Number of apples} = 4 \times 10 = 40$$

Notice that we have skilfully represented the number of pears by $3x$ to avoid using fractions. The strategy used is **make connection** between this problem and the concepts of ratio and proportion.

Alternatively, we can use the strategy **make supposition**

Suppose Ali exchanged the $12 worth of apples for the same number of pears which would cost $24.

Then, he would have 70 pears. So,

Cost of 70 pears = $18 + $24 = $42
Cost of 1 pear = ($42 ÷ 70) = $0.60
Therefore, original number of pears = 18 ÷ 0.6
                                   = 30
and the original number of apples = 70 – 30
                                   = 40

Problems...

1. **Overtime**   A man worked a total of 70 hours to complete a job. He was paid $160 for his normal work and $240 for working overtime. If the hourly pay for overtime work was doubled that of his normal work, how many hours did he work overtime?

2. **Apples and Oranges**   John bought 63 apples and oranges altogether. He paid 3 times as much for the oranges than for the apples. But the price for each apple was twice that for each orange. How many apples and how many oranges did he buy?

3. **Sharing Sweets**   Each of the girls in a class brought 6 sweets to a party. The sweets were shared equally among the 26 boys of the class and no sweet was left. How many sweets altogether did the girls bring to the party if the class has fewer than 43 pupils?

4. **Salty Solution**   A solution was prepared by adding salt to water. A man found that the solution was too strong and he diluted 1 350 g of it with 750 g of water. The new solution was then too diluted and he added 1.2 g of salt into the new solution and obtained a solution containing 0.9% salt. Find the percentage of salt in the original solution.

Chapter 14

Similarity and Congruence

Chapter Highlights

- Recognising similar and congruent figures and using their properties to find unknown sides and angles.
- Using similar and congruent figures to make designs and tessellations and determining whether a given figure can tessellate.
- Recording and making scale drawings.
- Solving simple map problems given map scales or representative fractions.

14.1 SIMILAR AND CONGRUENT FIGURES

Examples

(a)

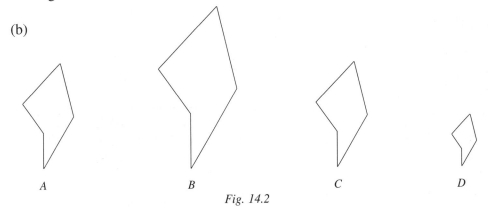

Fig. 14.1

In Fig. 14.1, *B* is an enlarged copy of *A* and *C* is a reduced copy of *A*. These three figures have the same **shape**. *D*, however, is a distorted copy of *A*. It is drawn out of proportion. It does not have the same shape as the other figures.

(b)

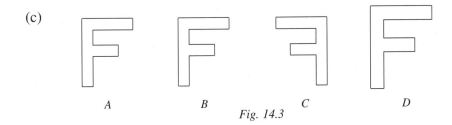

Fig. 14.2

Figures having the same shape are said to be **similar** figures. Thus, *A*, *B*, *C* and *D* are similar figures. Notice that *A* and *C* have the same shape and also the same size. We say that they are **congruent** figures.

(c)

F F ꟻ F
A B C D

Fig. 14.3

In Fig. 14.3, *A* and *B* are congruent figures. They fit exactly if one is placed on top of the other. *C* is a mirror image of *A* (and of *B*). If it is 'flipped over', it can also fit onto *A* exactly. These two figures are also said to be congruent figures. Similarly *C* and *B* are also congruent figures. *D* has the same shape as *A* and *B*. We also say that it has the same shape as *C*. Thus, *A*, *B*, *C* and *D* are similar figures.

Class Activity 1

1. Identify the pairs of similar figures and also the pairs of congruent figures among the following.

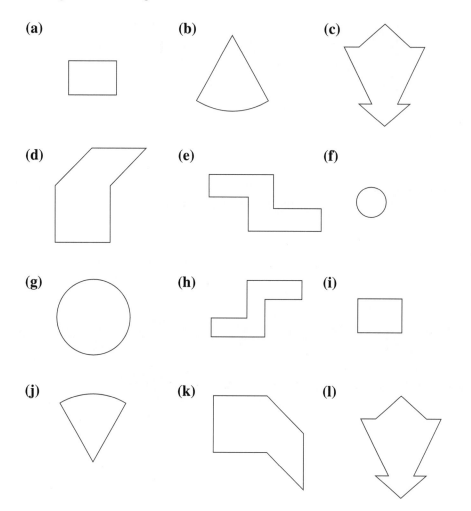

(a)

(b)

(c)

(d)

(e)

(f)

(g)

(h)

(i)

(j)

(k)

(l)

2. Copy the figures onto graph paper. For each part of the question, the figure on the left is made of two similar figures. Complete the rest of the figures to show these similar figures separately.

(a)

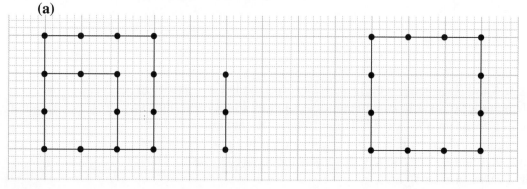

(b)

(c)

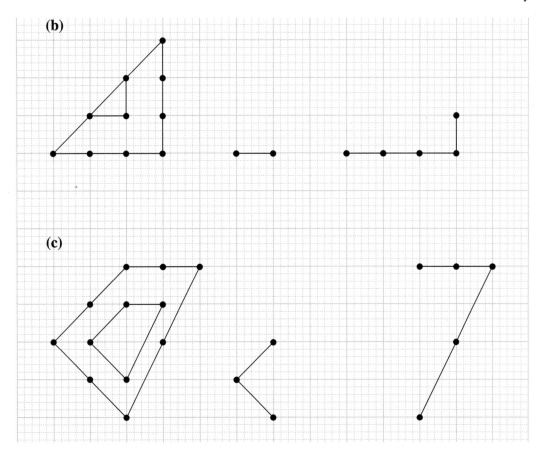

3. Copy the figures onto graph paper. For each part of the question, complete
    the figures on the right to make the two figures similar.

    (a)

    (b)

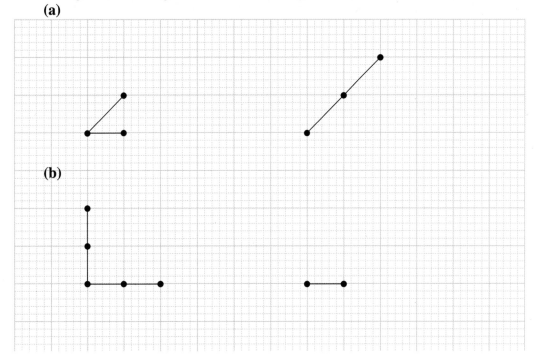

(c)

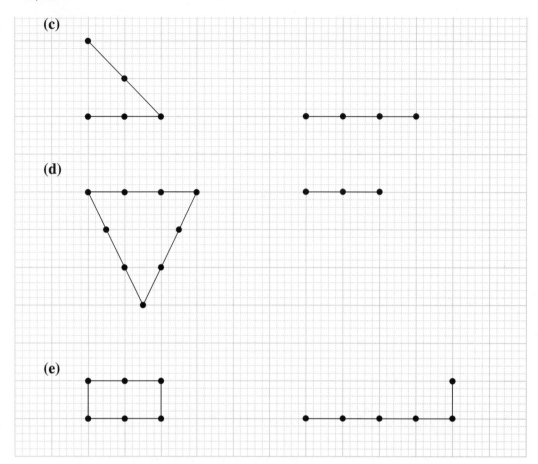

(d)

(e)

4. Copy the figures onto graph paper. For each part of the question, draw, by the side of the given figure, a similar figure according to the given ratio of its corresponding sides.

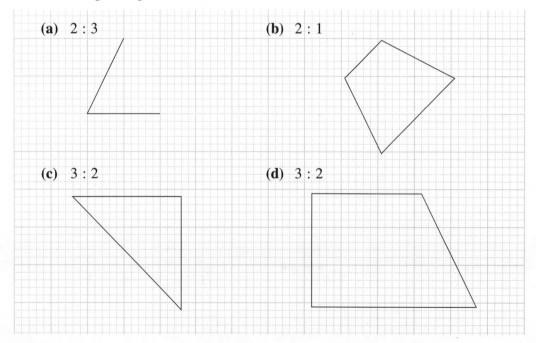

(a) 2 : 3

(b) 2 : 1

(c) 3 : 2

(d) 3 : 2

(e) $1 : 2$

(f) $1 : 1\frac{1}{2}$

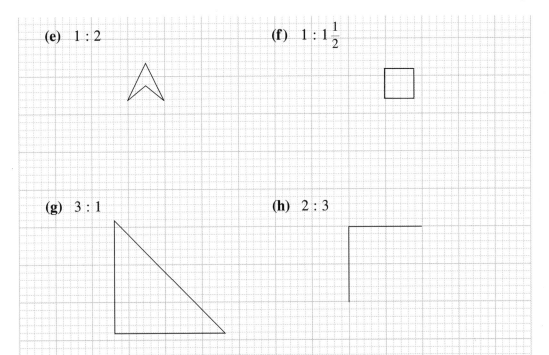

(g) $3 : 1$

(h) $2 : 3$

5. For each part of the question, the two figures are similar. State whether the following statements are true or false. Make measurements when necessary.

(a)

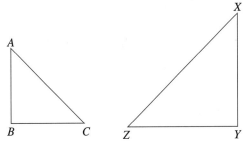

(i) $\hat{A} = \hat{X}$

(ii) $\hat{B} = \hat{Y}$

(iii) $\hat{C} = \hat{Z}$

(iv) $AB : XY = 2 : 3$

(v) $BC : YZ = 2 : 3$

(vi) $AC : XZ = 2 : 3$

(b)

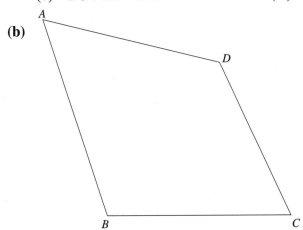

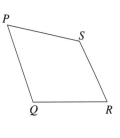

(i) $\hat{A} = \hat{P}$ (ii) $\hat{B} = \hat{Q}$

(iii) $\hat{C} = \hat{R}$ (iv) $\hat{D} = \hat{S}$

(v) $AB : PQ = 5 : 2$ (vi) $BC : QR = 5 : 2$

(vii) $CD : RS = 5 : 2$ (viii) $DA : SP = 5 : 2$

6.   For each part of the question, the two figures are congruent. State whether the following statements are true or false. Make measurements when necessary.

(a)

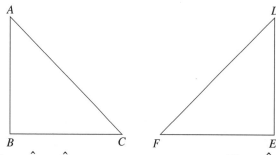

(i) $\hat{A} = \hat{D}$ (ii) $\hat{B} = \hat{E}$

(iii) $\hat{C} = \hat{F}$ (iv) $AB = DE$

(v) $BC = EF$ (vi) $AC = DF$

(b)

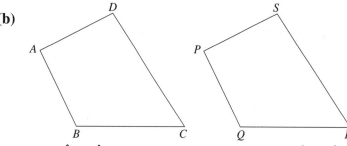

(i) $\hat{A} = \hat{P}$ (ii) $\hat{B} = \hat{Q}$

(iii) $\hat{C} = \hat{R}$ (iv) $\hat{D} = \hat{S}$

(v) $AB = PQ$ (vi) $BC = QR$

(vii) $AD = PS$ (viii) $CD = RS$

From the above class activity, we have observed that

- **the corresponding sides of two similar figures are proportional,**
- **the corresponding angles of two similar figures are equal,**
- **the corresponding sides or angles of two congruent figures are equal.**

Note that when making statements about similar (or congruent) figures such as 'polygon *ABCD* is similar (or congruent) to polygon *PQRS*', make sure that the letters *A*, *B*, *C* and *D* match the letters *P*, *Q*, *R* and *S* in the correct correspondence.

A simple way to remember the correspondence is by a 'matching diagram'.

Polygon *ABCD* is similar (or congruent) to polygon *PQRS*.

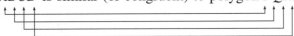

We often show equal line segments and angles by putting the same small marks on them.

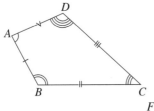 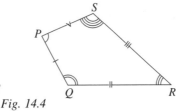

Fig. 14.4

In Fig. 14.4, the marks show that

$\hat{A} = \hat{P}$, $\hat{B} = \hat{Q}$, $\hat{C} = \hat{R}$, $\hat{D} = \hat{S}$,

$AB = PQ$, $BC = QR$, $CD = RS$ and $AD = PS$.

Exercise 14.1 ✐

answers on p. 437

1.

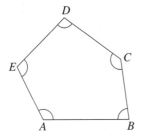 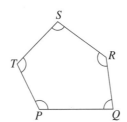

The figures are two similar polygons in which $\hat{A}$, $\hat{B}$, $\hat{C}$, $\hat{D}$ and $\hat{E}$ are equal to $\hat{P}$, $\hat{Q}$, $\hat{R}$, $\hat{S}$ and $\hat{T}$ respectively. Which of the following are correct statements?

(a) Polygon *ABCDE* is similar to polygon *PQRST*.
(b) Polygon *AEDCB* is similar to polygon *PTSRQ*.
(c) Polygon *BCDEA* is similar to polygon *RSTPQ*.
(d) Polygon *ACDEB* is similar to polygon *PRSTQ*.
(e) Polygon *TSRQP* is similar to polygon *EDCBA*.
(f) Polygons *CDEAB* and *RSTPQ* are similar.

2. Copy and complete the following.
    (a) It is given that $\triangle ABC$ and $\triangle XYZ$ are congruent.
        (i) *AB* and _____ are corresponding sides.
        (ii) *BC* and _____ are corresponding sides.
        (iii) *CA* and _____ are corresponding sides.
        (iv) $\hat{A}$ and _____ are corresponding angles.
        (v) $\hat{B}$ and _____ are corresponding angles.

      (vi) $\hat{C}$ and ____ are corresponding angles.

  (b) It is given that $\triangle PQR$ and $\triangle UST$ are similar.

      (i) *PQ* and ____ are corresponding sides.

      (ii) *QR* and ____ are corresponding sides.

      (iii) *RP* and ____ are corresponding sides.

      (iv) $\hat{P}$ and ____ are corresponding angles.

      (v) $\hat{Q}$ and ____ are corresponding angles.

      (vi) $\hat{R}$ and ____ are corresponding angles.

  (c) It is given that polygon *WXYZ* and polygon *GHEF* are congruent.

      (i) *WX* and ____ are corresponding sides.

      (ii) *XY* and ____ are corresponding sides.

      (iii) *YZ* and ____ are corresponding sides.

      (iv) *ZW* and ____ are corresponding sides.

      (v) $\hat{W}$ and ____ are corresponding angles.

      (vi) $\hat{X}$ and ____ are corresponding angles.

      (vii) $\hat{Y}$ and ____ are corresponding angles.

      (viii) $\hat{Z}$ and ____ are corresponding angles.

3. For each part of the question, the two figures are similar. Find the unknown sides.

  (a)

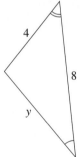

  (b)

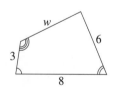 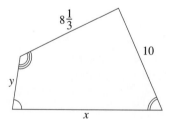

  (c)

 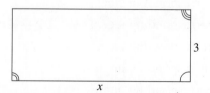

(d)

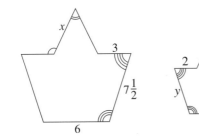

4. **(a)** *ABCD* and *PQRS* are similar.
   (i) Name the pairs of corresponding angles.
   (ii) Find $\hat{x}$ and $\hat{y}$.

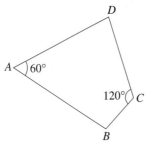 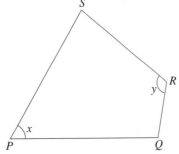

   (b) *WXYZ* and *EFGH* are similar.
   (i) Name the pairs of corresponding angles.
   (ii) Find $\hat{a}$ and $\hat{b}$.

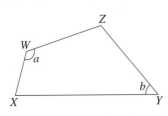 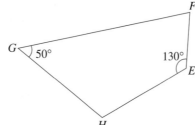

   (c) $\triangle ABC$ and $\triangle XYZ$ are similar.
   (i) Name the pairs of corresponding angles.
   (ii) Find $\hat{p}$ and $\hat{q}$.

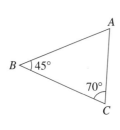 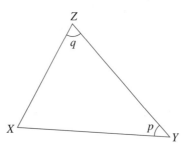

5. For each part of the question, the two figures are congruent. Find the
   unknown sides.
   (a)

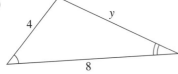 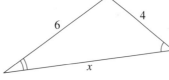

(b)

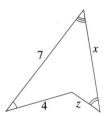 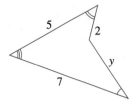

(c)

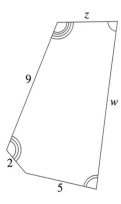 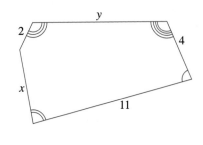

(d)

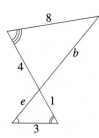 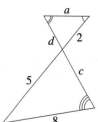

6. For each part of the question, the two figures are congruent. Find the unknown angles.

(a)

 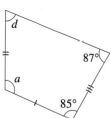

(b)

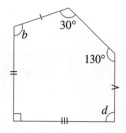 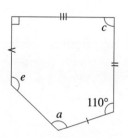

(c)

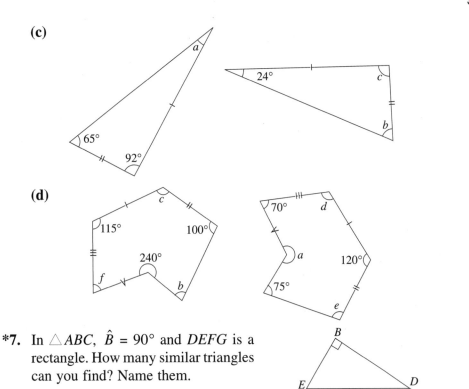

(d)

*7. In $\triangle ABC$, $\hat{B} = 90°$ and *DEFG* is a rectangle. How many similar triangles can you find? Name them.

*8. *ABC* is an equilateral triangle in which $AF = BD = CE$. There are several sets of 3 triangles that are congruent. How many sets are there? Name the triangles in each set.

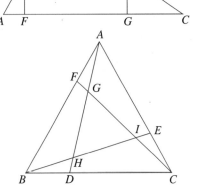

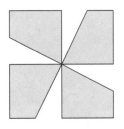

14.2 DESIGNS AND TESSELLATIONS

Designs

Many designs are made of congruent and similar figures.

Examples

(a) The pattern on the right is made of four congruent shapes. We can use this pattern as a **basic unit** to make a design like the one on the next page simply by repeating this unit.

Designs with hexagons are fixed (think of a piece of honeycomb) because there is only one set way to tessellate them.

Fig. 14.5

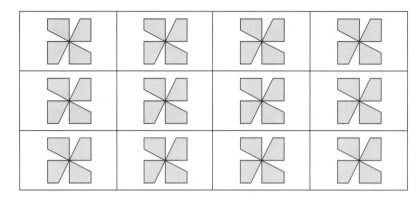

Fig. 14.6

(b) The pattern on the right is made of four similar rhombuses. Using this pattern as a basic unit repeatedly, we can make the following design.

Fig. 14.7

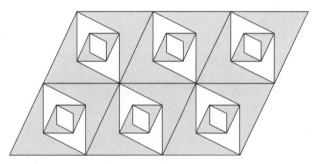

Fig. 14.8

Class Activity 2

1. Make a design by using each of the following basic units repeatedly. Use your choice of colours to colour your designs.

(a)   (b)   (c)   (d)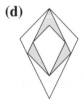

2. Make a design by using basic units of your choice repeatedly.

Tessellation

In tiling, we often fit a set of congruent tiles together to cover a surface completely without gaps. We call the pattern formed a **tessellation**, provided it can be extended as far as we like in any direction.

MATHSTORY

The Alhambra (from an Arabic word meaning red) is an ancient palace and fortress in Spain. It has many brightly-coloured, tile-covered walls, floors, halls and courtyards with many of the designs being tessellations. It is one of the finest examples of Moorish art in Europe. The Moors restricted their art to designs of an abstract geometrical type and in the 13th century, the Arabs demonstrated, in the Alhambra, the principle that there are only 17 different symmetry groups in which a basic pattern can be repeated endlessly in two dimensions. It was not until 1891 that a Russian crystallographer named E. S. Fedorov proved this theory to be true.

The word 'tessellation' comes from the Latin word 'tessallare'. It means to pave with tiles.

Examples

(a)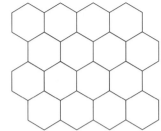

(b)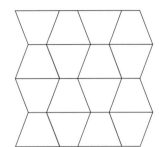

Class Activity 3

1. The figure on the right shows a pattern of four congruent shapes. Any one of these shapes can be taken as the basic unit of the pattern.
    (a) Make a copy of the pattern and extend the four units to ten units.
    (b) Do you think these shapes tessellate?

2. Using each of the figures below as a basic unit, make a pattern by fitting twelve units together without gaps. Do you think the pattern formed is a tessellation?
    (a)  (b)  (c)

3. Using each of the figures below as a basic unit, make a pattern by fitting four units together without gaps.
    (a) 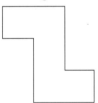 (b)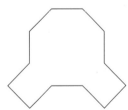

    Which of the above figures does not tessellate?

4. Using each of the figures below as a basic unit, make a pattern by fitting eight units together without gaps.
    (a)   (b)  (c)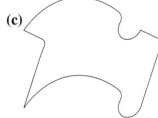

    Do you think each of the figures tessellate?

5. A square is a basic unit that can tessellate. It can be transformed into an 'irregular' figure like this:

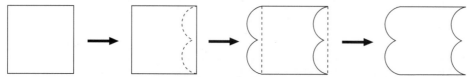

Does the resulting 'irregular' figure tessellate? If it does, give an example using 10 repeated figures to illustrate your answer.

6. We can repeatedly place a given equilateral triangle round a point P so that the sum of their angles that meet at P is $360°$ as shown below.

For each of the following, can you repeatedly place the given figure round a point P so that the sum of their angles that meet at P is $360°$?

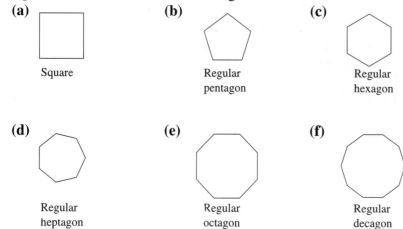

(a) Square

(b) Regular pentagon

(c) Regular hexagon

(d) Regular heptagon

(e) Regular octagon

(f) Regular decagon

Give reasons for your answers.

Exercise 14.2

answers on p. 437

1. Which of the following shapes can tessellate? Illustrate your answers with sketches.

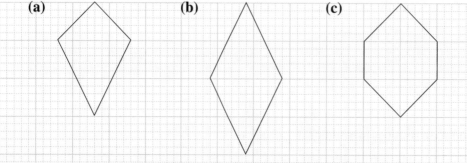

(a)

(b)

(c)

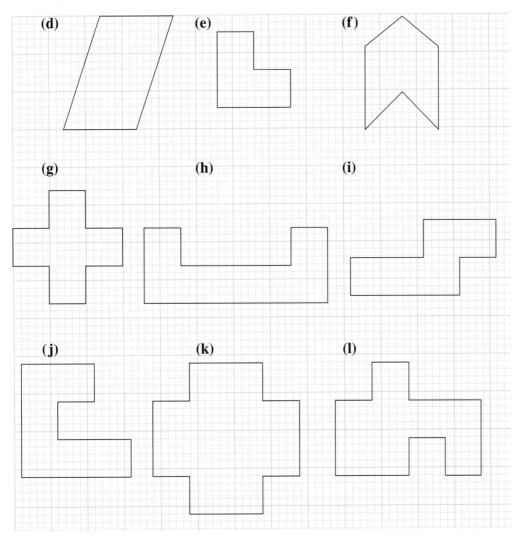

(d)   **(e)**   **(f)**

(g)   **(h)**   **(i)**

(j)   **(k)**   **(l)**

2. Which of the following regular polygons do you think can tessellate? Give reasons for your answers.
   (a) An octagon   **(b)** A pentagon
   (c) A hexagon   **(d)** A square
   (e) A nonagon   **(f)** A decagon

3. Which of the following can be used as a basic unit to tessellate? Give reasons for your answers.
   (a)    **(b)** 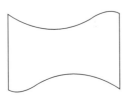   **(c)**

4. Find **(a)** an octagon, **(b)** a nonagon which can tessellate.

5. Tessellations can also be made using a combination of shapes, for example, squares and regular octagons as shown below.

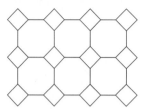

Can you use a combination of the following shapes to tessellate? Illustrate your answers with sketches.
    (a) Equilateral triangles and regular hexagons.
    (b) Rhombuses and regular pentagons.
    (c) Rhombuses and squares.
*(d) Equilateral triangles, squares and regular hexagons.
 *(e) Squares, regular hexagons and regular 12-sided polygons.

6. Design some 'irregular' shapes that can be used to tessellate. (Produce these as posters for your school bulletin board.)

14.3 SCALE DRAWING

When you look at a map of a piece of land, you will notice that it is drawn many times smaller than the original land. In other words, a **map** is a drawing of an area, usually a piece of land, that has been drawn to a certain scale. For instance, the map of the Republic of Singapore in Fig. 14.9 is drawn to a scale of 1 cm representing 3 km. Sometimes, this scale is expressed in the form of a ratio such as 1 : 300 000. We call this the **scale** of a map. The scale 1 : 300 000 means that 1 cm on the map represents 300 000 cm on the ground.

A scale is a ratio that compares a length on a model to the actual length.

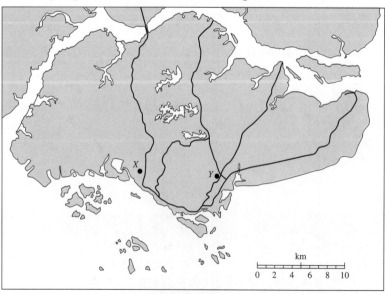

Fig. 14.9

If you measure the distance between *X* and *Y* in Fig. 14.9 and compare it with the scale provided, you will find that the actual distance between the two places is 9 km.

An architect has to make an outline drawing of a house using a certain scale before it can be built.

The scale drawing on the right showing the view from the top is a **plan** of a house. The dimensions shown are in metres.

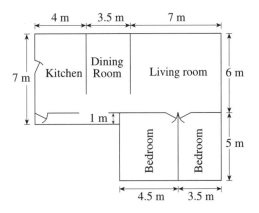

Fig. 14.10

We can also draw the plan of a school field by showing its boundary. If the school field is a quadrilateral with angles 80°, 90°, 80° and 110°, then the plan also has these angles as shown in Fig. 14.11.

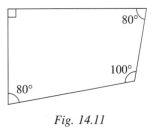

Fig. 14.11

We may say that in scale drawing, distances are drawn proportionately while angles remain the same.

In fact, a scale drawing of any figure can be thought of as a picture having the same shape as the original. They are similar figures.

The scale of a map is usually given as 1 : *n*. Sometimes, the ratio 1 : *n* is written in the form of a fraction $\frac{1}{n}$. This $\frac{1}{n}$ is called the **representative fraction** (or RF).

$$RF = \frac{\textbf{Distance on the map}}{\textbf{Actual distance on the ground}} = \frac{1}{n}$$

Example

A certain school field is a quadrilateral. The lengths of the four sides are 50 m, 65 m, 55 m and 78 m (in this order, counterclockwise). The angle between the first two sides is a right angle. Let us draw the plan of the field using 1 mm to represent 1 m, and then find the length of the two diagonals in metres.

1. Draw a line segment *AB* of length 50 mm.

2. From *B*, which is the point at the right end of the segment, construct a perpendicular segment *BC* of length 65 mm.

3. With a pair of compasses and with *C* as centre, draw an arc whose radius is 55 mm.

4. Again with *A* as centre, draw another arc whose radius is 78 mm to intersect the first arc at *D*.

5. Draw *CD* and *AD*. We have thus obtained a quadrilateral *ABCD* which is the plan of the field.

6. With a pair of dividers and ruler, we find that *AC* and *BD* are 82 mm and 94 mm respectively. Hence, the length of the diagonals of the school field are 82 m and 94 m.

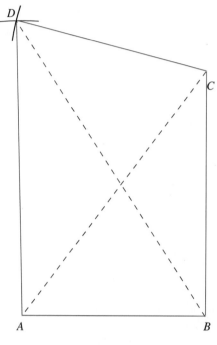

Fig. 14.12

Class Activity 4

1. A ladder $2\frac{1}{2}$ m long leans against a vertical wall. The point at which the ladder meets the ground is $1\frac{1}{2}$ m from the wall. Use a scale drawing to find how high up the wall the ladder reaches.

2. The length and width of a rectangular field on the map of a certain town are 10 cm and 8 cm respectively. The representative fraction (RF) is $\frac{1}{800}$.
   (a) What is the actual length of the field?
   (b) What is the actual width of the field?
   (c) Find the area of the field in square metres.

3. The following are plots of land (not drawn to scale) whose boundaries have shapes and dimensions as given. For each, draw a plan on your paper with the scale required. Also, with the use of a pair of dividers, ruler and protractor, find the measurements of the unspecified sides and angles from your plans.

(a)

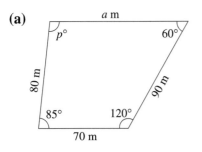

Scale: 1 cm to 10 m

(b)

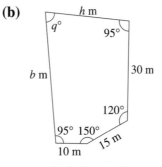

Scale: 1 cm to 5 m

(c)

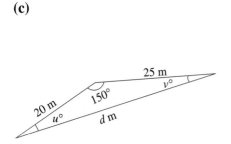

Scale: 1 cm to 5 m

(d)

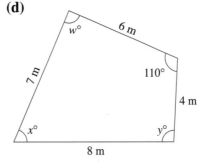

Scale: 1 cm to 1 m

4. Suppose you are given a quadrilateral $ABCD$. Can you draw the plan **(a)** if you know AB, BC, CD, $A\hat{B}C$ and $B\hat{C}D$, **(b)** if you know AB, BC, CD, $B\hat{C}D$ and $C\hat{D}A$? If you can, give an example to illustrate your answer for **(b)**.

5. Make actual measurements of a flat, a house, a basketball court or a hall, etc. and draw a plan of it stating the scale you have used.

Worked Example 1

The scale of a map is 4 cm to 1 km. Express the ratio in the form of $1 : n$.

Solution:

$$\frac{4 \text{ cm}}{1 \text{ km}} = \frac{4 \text{ cm}}{(1 \times 1\ 000 \times 100) \text{ cm}}$$

$$= \frac{4}{100\ 000}$$

$$= \frac{1}{25\ 000}$$

Therefore, the scale of the map is $1 : 25\ 000$.

Worked Example 2

The RF of a plan is $\dfrac{1}{2\ 000}$. Find the dimensions, in metres, of a field which measures $6\dfrac{1}{2}$ cm by 5 cm on the plan.

Solution:

1 cm on the plan represents 2 000 cm or 20 m on the ground.

Therefore, $6\dfrac{1}{2}$ represents $\left(6\dfrac{1}{2} \times 20\right)$ m or 130 m on the ground and 5 cm represents (5×20) m or 100 m on the ground.

Therefore, the field is 130 m by 100 m.

Exercise 14.3

answers on p. 438

1. The scale of a map is 1 : 20 000. Find, in km, the length of a railway line which is 5.2 cm long on the map.

2. A ground plan of a house is drawn on a scale of 1 cm to 2 m. Express the scale of the plan in the form of 1 : n. Find also the length and breadth of the plan of a room, 2.5 m by 1.5 m.

3. On a map whose scale is 5 cm to 1 km, the distance between two road junctions is 4 cm. What would be the distance between the two road junctions on another map whose scale is 3 cm to 1 km?

4. Two towns, A and B, are 20 km apart. What is this distance on a map which has a scale of 2.5 cm to 1 km? What would be the distance, in cm, between A and B on another map which has a scale of 1 : 15 000?

5. Two towns are 120 km apart. Find, to the nearest mm, the distance between these two towns on a map with an RF of $\dfrac{1}{200\ 000}$.

6. The distance between town X and town Y on a map with a scale of 1 : 500 000 is 14 cm. Find the actual distance on the ground, in km, between the two towns.

7. What is the distance, in cm, on a map between two points which are 45 km 520 m apart if the RF is $\dfrac{1}{100\ 000}$. If the length of a stream is 4.3 cm on the map, what is its actual length in km?

8. The map below has a graduated scale shown at the corner. Use the scale to find out the approximate distance between Muar and Batu Pahat in kilometres.

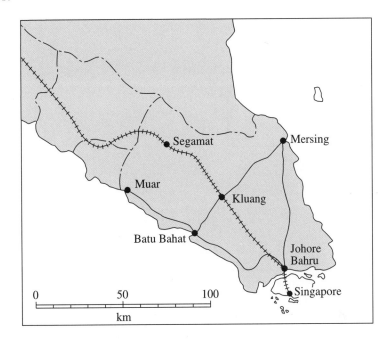

9. The diagram on the right represents a design. The dimensions are given in m. Use a scale of 1 cm : 1 m to draw the plan of the design. (All angles at the corners are right angles.)

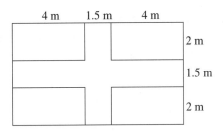

10. Using a scale of 1 cm to 10 cm, draw the plans of the following figures.

(a)

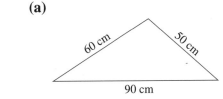

(b)

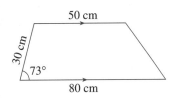

(c)

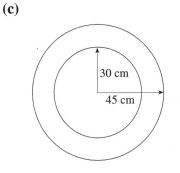

(d)

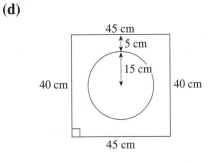

11. The diagram below shows a rectangular wooden frame, 2 m by 4 m. The width of the frame is $\frac{1}{2}$ m. Using a scale of 2 cm : 1 m, draw the plan of the frame.

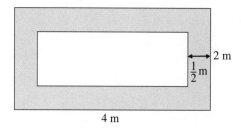

12.

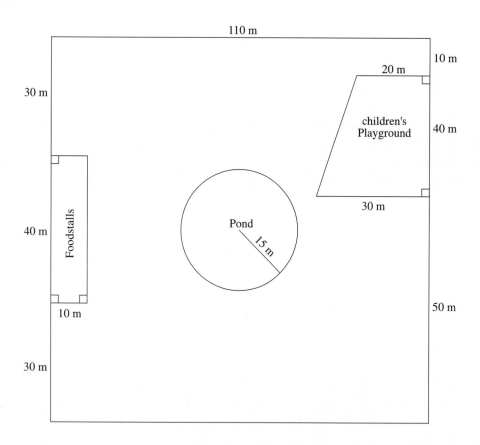

The above diagram (not drawn to scale) shows a rectangular park, 110 m by 100 m. There is a circular pond right at the centre of the park, with foodstalls and a children's playground on either side. Using a scale of 1 cm to 10 m, draw the plan of the park.

Chapter Review

1. **Similar triangles.**

 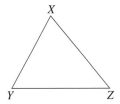

If △s *ABC* and *XYZ* are similar, then

(a) their corresponding sides are proportional;

Example: $\dfrac{AB}{XY} = \dfrac{BC}{YZ} = \dfrac{AC}{XZ}$

(b) their corresponding angles are equal.

Example: $\hat{A} = \hat{X}, \ \hat{B} = \hat{Y}, \ \hat{C} = \hat{Z}$

2. **Congruent triangles**

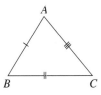 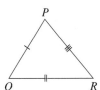

If △s *ABC* and *PQR* are congruent, then they are equal in all respects.

Examples: $AB = PQ, \ BC = QR, \ AC = PR.$

$\hat{A} = \hat{P}, \ \hat{B} = \hat{Q}, \ \hat{C} = \hat{R}$

Area of △*ABC* = Area of △*PQR*

3. **Tessellation**

   • A tiling consisting of congruent figures to cover an area completely is called a tessellation.

4. **Scaling**

   • The scale of a map in the form of a fraction $\dfrac{1}{n}$ is called the representative fraction (RF).

   • RF = $\dfrac{\text{Distance on the map}}{\text{Actual distance on the ground}} = \dfrac{1}{n}$

CHALLENGER 14

1. Do you think what Menghui, Fatimah and Samy say below are possible? Give examples to illustrate your answers.

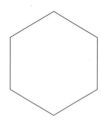

   (a) Menghui says: 'I can divide a regular hexagon into 6 congruent equilateral triangles.'

   (b) Fatimah says: 'I can divide a regular hexagon into 6 congruent isosceles triangles (each of her isosceles triangles has only two equal sides).'

   (c) Samy says: 'I can divide a regular hexagon into 6 congruent parallelograms.'

2. Can you divide a regular hexagon into 6 congruent trapeziums?
   If you can, give an example to illustrate your answer.

3. John says: 'I can divide a regular hexagon into 12 congruent triangles.'
   Mary says: 'I can get as many as 36 congruent triangles.'
   Mary explains her method through the telephone as follows:

   • A hexagon has 6 vertices. Line segments joining pairs of adjacent vertices are called the sides of the hexagon.

   • Line segments joining pairs of vertices which are not adjacent pairs are called diagonals of the hexagon.

   • To divide a regular hexagon into 36 congruent triangles, first draw all the diagonals of the given hexagon. The diagonals drawn include 3 lines of symmetry of the hexagon. Next, draw the remaining 3 lines of symmetry to complete the construction.

   Is Mary's description clear? If so, follow her instruction to divide a regular hexagon into 36 congruent triangles.

4. Meili says she can divide a regular hexagon into many more congruent triangles than what Mary can (refer to question 3), and can in fact go on to have more and more.
   Do you think what Meili says is possible?
   If so, give an example to show how this can be done.

5. The term 'pentomino' is used to name shapes obtained when five squares are joined together.
   For example, these are pentominoes.

These are not pentominoes.

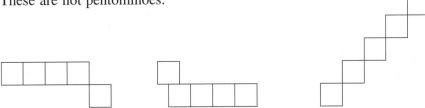

How would you describe a pentomino to your friend through the telephone?

6. Pentominoes which can fit each other (with or without flipping) are taken to be of the same type. There are twelve types of pentominoes.
   (a) Draw the twelve types of pentominoes.
   (b) Make three tessellations using pentominoes.
      (Use about 20 congruent pentominoes to show each tessellations.)

Problem Solving 14

Oily Move

A, B and C are 3 containers and each of them contains a certain amount of oil.

If $\frac{1}{3}$ of oil in A is poured into B, $\frac{1}{3}$ of oil in B is poured into C and $\frac{1}{3}$ of oil in C is poured into A, they will have 4 l of oil each. Find the amount of oil in each container at first.

We use a table like the one shown below, where a, . . . , i, x, y and z denote the amount of oil. x, y and z are given, i.e. $x = y = z = 4\ l$.

We work backwards to find the amounts a to i.

	A	**B**	**C**
Start	$a = 3\ l$	$b = 5\ l$	$c = 4\ l$
Step 1: $\frac{1}{3}$ of oil in A to B	$d = 2\ l$	$e = 6\ l$	$f = 4\ l$
Step 2: $\frac{1}{3}$ of oil in B to C	$g = 2\ l$	$h = 4\ l$	$i = 6\ l$
Step 3: $\frac{1}{3}$ of oil in C to A	$x = 4\ l$	$y = 4\ l$	$z = 4\ l$

Therefore, at the beginning, A has 3 l, B has 5 l and C has 4 l.

The strategies involved are **use tabulation**, **work backwards** and **use before-after concept**.

Explanation of the *thinking process* involved.

Working backwards, we find the amounts *a* to *i* as follows:

After step 3:   (1) $z = \dfrac{2}{3}$ of *i*

Before step 3: (1) $i = \dfrac{3}{2}$ of $z = \dfrac{3}{2} \times 4\,l = 6\,l$

(2) $g = x - $ (amount from *C*)
$= x - (i - z)$
$= 4\,l - (6\,l - 4\,l)$
$= 2\,l$

(3) $h = y = 4\,l$ (since *B* is not affected by step 3)

After step 2:   (1) $h = \dfrac{2}{3}$ of *e*

Before step 2: (1) $e = \dfrac{3}{2}$ of $h = \dfrac{3}{2} \times 4\,l = 6\,l$

(2) $f = i - $ (amount from *B*)
$= i - (e - h)$
$= 6\,l - (6\,l - 4\,l)$
$= 4\,l$

(3) $d = g = 2\,l$ (since *A* is not affected by step 2)

After step 1:   (1) $d = \dfrac{2}{3}$ of *a*

Before step 1: (1) $a = \dfrac{3}{2}$ of $d = \dfrac{3}{2} \times 2\,l = 3\,l$

(2) $b = e - $ (amount from *A*)
$= e - (a - d)$
$= 6\,l - (3\,l - 2\,l)$
$= 5\,l$

(3) $c = f = 4\,l$ (since *C* is not affected by step 1)

Communication skill:
You are probably not required to present these steps in written form. However, you may be asked to explain your thinking process orally to improve your communication skill.

Problems...

1. **Pails of Water**   Each of the 3 pails *A*, *B* and *C* contains a certain amount of water. If $\frac{1}{4}$ of water in *A* is poured into *B*, $\frac{1}{4}$ of water in *B* is poured into *C* and $\frac{1}{4}$ of water in *C* is poured into *A*, they will all have 9 *l* of water each. Find the amount of water in each pail at first.

2. **How Much Detergent?**   Each of the three containers *A*, *B* and *C* contains a certain amount of detergent. If 300 m*l* of detergent in *A* is poured into *B*, then *B* will have twice the amount in *A*. After this, if 300 m*l* of detergent in *B* is poured into *C*, then *C* will have twice the amount in *B*. After this, if 300 m*l* of detergent in *C* is poured into *A*, then *C* and *A* will have the same amount of detergent. Find the amount of detergent each container has at the beginning.

3. **No Wastage**   How many squares of the largest possible size can you cut from a vanguard sheet of dimensions 48 cm by 32 cm, if there is no wastage of material?

4. **Tiling**   At least how many tiles of dimensions 21 cm × 12 cm are needed to form a square?

REVISION EXERCISE 4

Revision 4A   *(answers on p. 438)*

1. The area of a circle is $\dfrac{77}{2}$ cm². Calculate its diameter. $\left(\text{Take } \pi = \dfrac{22}{7}.\right)$

2. Find the volume of each of the prisms below.

(a)

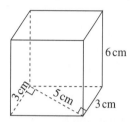

6 cm

3 cm   5 cm   3 cm

(b)

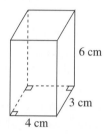

6 cm

3 cm

4 cm

3. A solid cylinder has radius r cm and height h cm.
   (a) Write down an expression for its total surface area including the two ends.
   (b) If r and h are integers and this total surface area is 112π cm², find one possible pair of values of r and h.

4. This is a $4 \times 3 \times 2$ block made from small cubes. Henry painted the outside of the block green. Then he took it apart piece by piece.
   (a) How many cubes with 3 faces green did he find?
   (b) How many cubes with only 2 faces green did he find?
   (c) How many cubes with only 1 face green did he find?

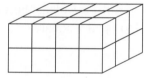

5. When π is taken to be $\dfrac{22}{7}$, the circumference of a circle is found to be 88 cm. Find its radius.

6. Find the area of the following figures.

(a)

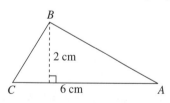

B

2 cm

C   6 cm   A

(b)

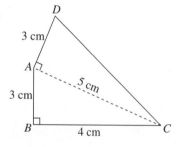

D

3 cm

A

3 cm

B   4 cm   C

5 cm

7. Find the volume of the rectangular solid, given that the area of the hole is 4 cm².

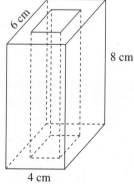

6 cm

8 cm

4 cm

8. There are five cylindrical wooden posts each 10 cm in diameter and 8 m high. The curved surface and the top end of each post need to be painted. If the cost of painting is \$4.50/m², find the cost of painting all the posts to the nearest dollar. (Take $\pi = 3.142$.)

9. Can you tessellate using pentagons as the basic units? If so, give an example using 12 pentagons to illustrate your answer.

10. It is given that $\triangle APQ$ and $\triangle AXY$ are similar.
    (a) Explain why PQ is parallel to XY.
    (b) If $XY = 4$ cm, $PQ = 6$ cm and the height AZ of $\triangle AXY$ is 5 cm, find the height AR of $\triangle APQ$.
    (c) Find also the area of quadrilateral $XYQP$.

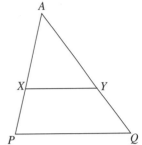

Revision 4B *(answers on p. 438)*

1. A piece of glass measuring 30 cm by 15 cm is 1.35 cm thick. Find its mass to the nearest gram if the density of glass is 2.5 g/cm³.

2. Find the area of the following figures.
   (a)

   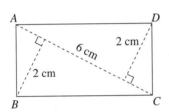

   (b)

   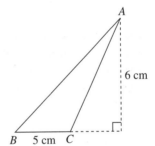

3. A water tank, 24.5 m long and 13.5 m wide, is filled with water. If it contains 135 000 *l* of water when full, how deep is the tank?

4. (a) The area of a square is 400 cm². Find the length of a side.
   (b) If the length is now decreased by 20%, find the area of the new square.

5. An archway is constructed with two vertical walls surmounted by an arch of semicircular cross-section. If the vertical walls are 2 m high and $3\frac{1}{2}$ m apart, find the internal surface area of the archway if it is 8 m long. (Take $\pi = 3.14$.)

6. (a) Calculate the actual length of the boat in metres, if the length of the model is 30 cm.
   (b) Calculate the length of the mast of the model in cm, if the actual length of the mast is 7 m.

Model: Scale 1 to 20

7. Find the perimeter of the figure.
(All angles at the corners are right angles.)

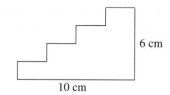

6 cm

10 cm

8. The four walls of a room, each measuring 4.7 m long and 2.1 m high, need painting. Allowing 2.7 m² for doors and windows, find the labour cost if the cost of painting is $0.50 for 500 cm².

9. Can you tessellate using octagons as the basic units? If so, give an example using 10 octagons to illustrate your answer.

10. It is given that △ABC and △ADE are similar and △FGE and △ADE are congruent. If BC = 5 cm, FE : ED = 3 : 2, find the length of AC.

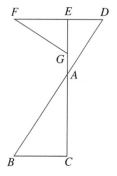

Revision 4C *(answers on p. 438)*

1. Find the area of the following figures.
   (a)

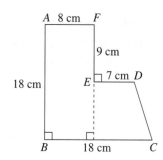

   (b)

   A 8 cm F

   9 cm

   18 cm   E 7 cm D

   B   18 cm   C

2. A tank, $2\frac{1}{2}$ m long and 100 cm wide, contains liquid to a depth of 70 cm. The liquid is poured into an empty tank measuring 3 m long and $1\frac{1}{2}$ m wide. Find the depth of the water in the new tank. Give your answer in cm, correct to 1 decimal place.

3. A 3-cm thick hollow cylindrical pipe with external radius 10 cm is cast from cement. If the length of the pipe is $1\frac{1}{2}$ m long, how much cement (by volume) is needed? (Take $\pi = 3.14$.)

4. The diameter of cake A is 24 cm. Cake B which is of the same variety has a diameter of 32 cm. If they are of the same thickness, which one of them is a better buy? (Show your calculation.)

$5.50

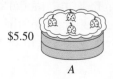

$9

A

B

5. Find the number of tiles, each measuring 21 cm by 20 cm, that are required to cover a floor, 4.8 m long and 4.2 m wide.

6. Find the area of the following figures. In (b) *ABEF* and *CDGH* are rectangles.

   (a)
   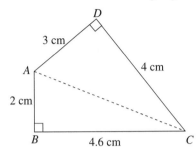

   (b)
   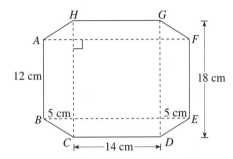

7. A swimming pool is 25 m long and 15 m wide. How many litres of water must be added to it to raise the water level by 60 cm?

8. A cylindrical water pipe discharges 7 850 *l* of water in 1 minute. How long does it take to fill a tank, 30 m by 20 m by 5 m? Give your answer to the nearest hour.

9. The diagram shows a tile whose shape is a rhombus. How many such tiles are needed to cover a rectangular floor of area 12 m by 8 m?

   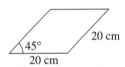

10. *R* and *S* bisect *AB* and *AE* respectively. Pentagons *ABCDE* and *PQRST* are similar. Also △*ARS* and △*PQT* are congruent. What type of quadrilateral is *BESR*?

    Find the value of $\dfrac{\text{area of } \triangle PQT}{\text{area of quadrilateral } BESR}$.

    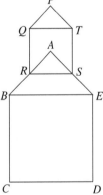

MISCELLANEOUS EXERCISE 4

(answers on p. 438)

1. **(a)** Write down the next term in the sequence.

$$\frac{1}{2}, \frac{2}{3}, \frac{3}{4}, \frac{4}{5}, \frac{5}{6}, \underline{\qquad}$$

   (b) Arrange the following numbers in descending order. Do these numbers form a pattern? If they do, write down the next term.

$$7, 3.5, 28, 14, 1.75$$

2. A, B, C and D are 4 points on a plane such that 3 of these points lie on a straight line. Join the points. How many line segments can you get? Name them.

3. If the complementary angle of an acute angle A is $\frac{1}{4}$ the supplementary angle of angle A, find angle A.

4. The supplementary angle of $\hat{A}$ is $20°$ more than twice the complementary angle of $\hat{A}$. Find $\hat{A}$.

5. The length of a rectangle is thrice its width. If the length is reduced by 5 cm and the width is increased by 3 cm, the length will only be twice the width. Find the length and breadth of the original rectangle.

6. The figure shows a rectangular piece of cardboard. A square is cut off from each corner as shown.
   (a) Find the area of the shaded part.
   (b) The shaded part of the card is folded to make an open box. Find the volume of this box.

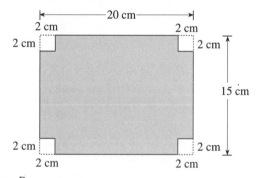

7. $ABCD$ is a rectangle. Find
   (a) the value of x and y,
   (b) the area of $\triangle EBF$.

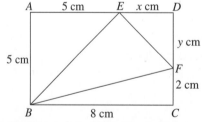

8. A cylindrical pipe of length 35 cm has an outer diameter of 14 cm and a thickness of 1 cm. Find
   (a) the outer curved surface area,
   (b) the inner curved surface area.

$$\left(\text{Take } \pi = \frac{22}{7}.\right)$$

9. The diagram shows an open-top container of negligible thickness. The cross-section *ABCD* is a trapezium. The horizontal base is a rectangle measuring 30 cm by 960 cm. The vertical height of the container is 45 cm. The edge *DC* is 60 cm. Calculate
   (a) the area of the cross-section *ABCD*,
   (b) the capacity, in litres, of the container.

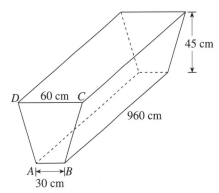

10. A circular swimming pool of radius 4 m is surrounded by a path 1 m wide. Find in terms of π in their simplest form, expressions for
    (a) the circumference of the circle forming the outer edge of the path,
    (b) the area of the path.

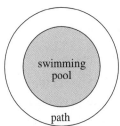

11. The diagram shows a flower bed formed by four quarter circles, each of radius *r* cm.
    (a) Express the perimeter of the flower bed in terms of *r*.
    (b) Show that the area, A cm², of the flower bed is given by $A = (4 - \pi)r^2$.
    (c) Given that *r* = 7 m, calculate the value of A.

    $\left(\text{Take } \pi = \dfrac{22}{7}.\right)$

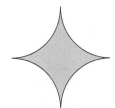

12. A closed storage container consists of a cuboid *ABDEPQST* to which a quadrant of a cylinder *BCDQRS* is attached as shown in the diagram. *AE* = 20 cm, *ED* = 30 cm, *DC* = 20 cm and *CR* = 70 cm.
    Taking π to be 3.142 and giving each answer correct to 3 significant figures, calculate
    (a) the area of the face *ABCDE*,
    (b) the volume of the container,
    (c) the length of the circular arc *BC*,
    (d) the area of the curved surface *BQRC*,
    (e) the total surface area of the outside of the container.

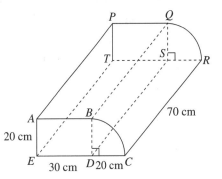

13. (a) In the figure, *ABCD* is a trapezium, *AD* = *DC* = *CB* = 60 cm and *AN* = 30 cm.
    Calculate
    (i) the base *AB*,
    (ii) the area of the trapezium, correct to the nearest cm².

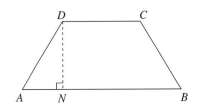

(b) The figure in part (a) represents the top of a table. Six such tables are put together as shown.

Find, in the form $n : 1$, the ratio of the total area of the six table tops to the area of the shaded region in the middle.

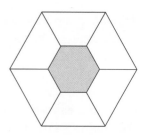

(c) *PQRSTU* is a table top in the shape of a regular hexagon with each side equal to 120 cm. Calculate the area of the table top, correct to the nearest cm².

14. The diagram shows a driveway. The angles at *D*, *E*, *H* and *A* are right angles. The two curved parts are each a quarter circle of radius 1 m. $AB = 9$ m, $DC = 7$ m, $DE = 3$ m, $EF = 4$ m, $GH = 6$ m and $HA = 3$ m.

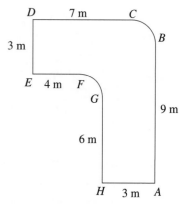

(a) Calculate the total area of the driveway.

(b) The driveway is made of concrete with a thickness of 15 cm. Calculate the volume of concrete used.

(c) The concrete consists of one part of cement, $2\dfrac{1}{4}$ parts of sand and 3 parts of gravel. Calculate the volume of cement used.

(d) If 1 m³ of cement weighs 226.6 kg, calculate the mass of cement used.

15. If *F* is taken to be 4, what digit does each letter stand for so that the multiplication is correct? (*Note:* Different letters do not represent the same number.)

$$
\begin{array}{r}
A\,B\,C\,D\,E \\
\times \qquad\quad F \\
\hline
E\,D\,C\,B\,A
\end{array}
$$

1. A cube has 6 faces. If 3 cubes are glued to form a 'suitcase' as shown, it will have 14 exposed faces.

    (a) If 6 cubes are glued as shown, how many exposed faces are there?

    (b) If the tallest column of the 'staircase' has n cubes, how many cubes are there in the 'staircase'?
    Express the number of exposed faces in terms of n.

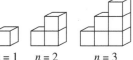

$n = 1$ $n = 2$ $n = 3$

2. (a) Verify

    (i) $4\dfrac{1}{2} \times 1\dfrac{2}{7} = 4\dfrac{1}{2} + 1\dfrac{2}{7}$,

    (ii) $2\dfrac{2}{3} \times 1\dfrac{3}{5} = 2\dfrac{2}{3} + 1\dfrac{3}{5}$,

    (iii) $1\dfrac{5}{6} \times 2\dfrac{1}{5} = 1\dfrac{5}{6} + 2\dfrac{1}{5}$.

    (b) Is there a rule for finding interesting examples such as those given in (a)? Investigate.

3. Copy and complete the following table.

n	1	2	3	4	5	6	7	8	9	10
$n^2 - n + 41$	41	43	47	53						

Study the table.
    (a) What do you notice?
    (b) Extend the table to $n = 11, 12, \ldots, 20$. What do you observe?
    (c) What conclusion can you draw? Investigate further.

4. (a) Copy and complete the following. (Use calculator to help you investigate.)

    $1^3 + 2^3 = 9$
    $1^3 + 2^3 + 3^3 = 36$
    $1^3 + 2^3 + 3^3 + 4^3 = \underline{\hphantom{000}}$
    $1^3 + 2^3 + 3^3 + 4^3 + 5^3 = \underline{\hphantom{000}}$
    $1^3 + 2^3 + 3^3 + 4^3 + 5^3 + 6^3 = \underline{\hphantom{000}}$
    $1^3 + 2^3 + 3^3 + 4^3 + 5^3 + 6^3 + 7^3 = \underline{\hphantom{000}}$
    $1^3 + 2^3 + 3^3 + 4^3 + 5^3 + 6^3 + 7^3 + 8^3 = \underline{\hphantom{000}}$
    $1^3 + 2^3 + 3^3 + 4^3 + 5^3 + 6^3 + 7^3 + 8^3 + 9^3 = \underline{\hphantom{000}}$
    $1^3 + 2^3 + 3^3 + 4^3 + 5^3 + 6^3 + 7^3 + 8^3 + 9^3 + 10^3 = \underline{\hphantom{000}}$

    (b) What is the value of $1^3 + 2^3 + \ldots + 20^3$?

5. A number that is equal to the sum of all its factors excluding the number itself is known as a perfect number. For example, 6 is a perfect number because 6 = 1 + 2 + 3, and 1, 2 and 3 are factors of 6.

Find another perfect number.

Can you find one more perfect number?

Investigate. (*Hint:* Try numbers between 490 and 500.)

ASSESSMENT 1

Paper I *(answers on p. 439)*   **50 marks**   **1 h**

Answer all the questions without using the calculator.

1. Express
   (a) 45% as a fraction,
   (b) 120% as a mixed number,
   (c) $\frac{1}{4}$% as a fraction.   [3]

2. In the figure, triangles *PQR* and *PMN* are similar. *PM* = *QR* = 9 cm and
   MN = *NR* = 5 cm. Find
   (a) *PQ*,
   (b) *PR*.

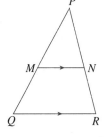
        [3]

3. *BCD* is a straight line. Form an equation in *x* and solve the equation.

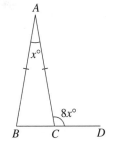
        [3]

4. A man bought 150 magazines for $450. He sold half of them at a profit of 20%, 50 of them at a
   profit of 10% and the rest at a loss of 4%.
   (a) How much did he receive from the sales?
   (b) Find his gain percent, correct to the nearest percent.   [3]

5. A man started work on the first day of January 1995 and was paid $125 per week for 25 weeks.
   He was given a raise of $15 per week for the rest of the year. How much did he earn for that year?
   (Take 1 year = 52 weeks.)   [3]

6. The HCF and LCM of 2 numbers are 8 and 408 respectively. If one of the unknown numbers is
   136, find the other unknown number.   [3]

7. (a) A piece of alloy weighs 22 kg. If it is made up of 55% copper and 45% tin, find the weight
       of each metal in the alloy.   [2]

   (b) The yearly interest at $4\frac{1}{2}$% on a certain sum of money was $36. Find the value of the yearly

       interest on the same amount at $6\frac{1}{4}$%.   [2]

8. (a) A cylindrical container whose base area is 616 cm² is filled with water. If 3 080 cm³ of water is drawn from it, what is the drop in the water level? [1]

 (b) Find the mass in grams of a rectangular piece of copper sheet, 13 cm long, 4.5 cm wide and 2 mm thick, if the density is taken to be 8.9 g/cm³. [2]

9. (a) Triangles *ABC* and *LMN* are similar.
 Copy and complete the following.

 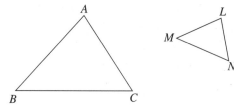

 $\hat{A}$ = ＿＿＿

 $\dfrac{AB}{AC}$ = ＿＿＿ [2]

 (b) If *ABCD* is a rectangle, find $\hat{x}$, $\hat{y}$ and $\hat{z}$.

 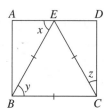

 [2]

10. (a) A man cycled *d* km at 16 km/h and then walked for three-quarters of an hour. Altogether, he took $3\frac{1}{2}$ hours. Find *d*. [2]

 (b) The full fare for an adult on a holiday trip was $245. Find the cost of the tickets for a family of 6 of which 4 were children who travelled at half-fare. [2]

11. (a) If *x* = 5, *y* = 3, find the value of *w* in $w = \dfrac{xy}{x + y}$. [2]

 (b) A number is divisible by 3. When this number is divided by 3 and 5 is subtracted from the quotient, the result is 4. What is the number? [3]

12. (a) Solve the equation $5x - 7 = 13 - x$ [1]

 (b) The price of an article was increased in the ratio 5 : 3. Find the new price if the previous price was $12. [1]

 (c) 6 men working together, could complete a job in $2\frac{1}{3}$ hours. How long would 7 men take to complete the same job? [2]

13. The figure shows two containers, one cylindrical and the other rectangular. If all the water in the cylindrical container is poured into the empty rectangular one, find the water level of the rectangular container, correct to the nearest cm.

 $\left(\text{Take } \pi = \dfrac{22}{7}.\right)$

 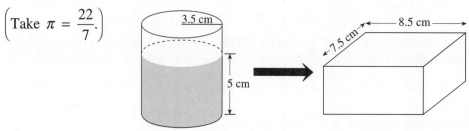

 [4]

14. The figure shows a rectangular plot of land, $4x$ m long and $2x$ m wide. There is a border round a rectangular garden.

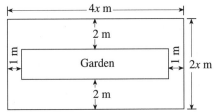

(a) Write an expression in terms of x for
   (i) the perimeter of the garden,
   (ii) the area of the border round the garden.   [2]
(b) If $x = 15$, find
   (i) the area,
   (ii) the perimeter
   of the garden.   [2]

Paper II   (answers on p. 438)   **50 marks**   **1 h 15 min**

Answer all the questions. You may use the calculator.

Section A (22 marks)

1. (a) Factorise completely $3ab - 12bc + 9abc$.   [2]

   (b) Find $1\dfrac{1}{5} + \dfrac{1}{\dfrac{1}{2} + \dfrac{1}{1 + \dfrac{1}{3}}}$.   [3]

2. (a) Complete the following sequences.

   (i) $\dfrac{1}{4}, \dfrac{1}{2}, \dfrac{3}{4}, 1, \underline{\qquad}$ [1]
   (ii) $-1, 0, 2, 5, \underline{\qquad}$ [1]

   (b) (i) Copy the diagram and fill in the numbers 1, 2, 3, 4, 5, 6, 7 and 8 in the spaces on the diagram so that the numbers along each side of the triangle add up to 21. (You may use each number only once.)   [2]
      (ii) Give another answer.   [1]

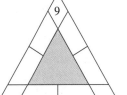

3. The 2 560 people who watched a badminton game are shown in the table below.

Men	x
Women	262
Boys	1 424
Girls	362

(a) Find the value of x. [2]

(b) Express the number of adults as a percentage of the total number of boys and girls. [2]

(c) Some of the boys who were present did not wear uniform. The ratio of the number of boys wearing uniform to the number of boys not wearing uniform was 5 : 3. How many boys did not wear uniform? [2]

4. In the figure, $QT = TP = PR$. If $S\hat{P}R = 110°$ and $P\hat{R}T = x°$,
   (a) find $T\hat{P}R$ in terms of x, [1]
   (b) find $P\hat{Q}T$ in terms of x, [1]
   (c) form an equation in x, [2]
   (d) solve the equation. [2]

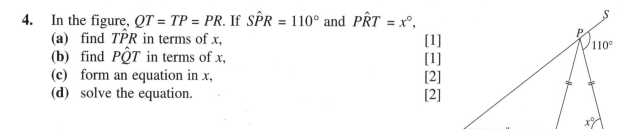

Section B (28 marks)

5. The workers of a firm are given an increase in salary according to 2 schemes.

Scheme A	Scheme B
Increase of 8% of the present monthly salary.	Increase of 6% of the present monthly salary plus an extra $39 per month.

   (a) Peter earns $1 850 a month at present. Calculate his monthly increase
      (i) under scheme A, [1]
      (ii) under scheme B. [1]
   (b) Express his increase under scheme B as a percentage of his present salary. Give your answer to the nearest percent. [2]
   (c) Paul's new salary would be the same under either scheme. Find his present salary. [3]

6. (a) (i) The volume of a cube is 216 cm³. Find the length of one of its edges. [1]
      (ii) A student, when using his calculator, finds that a number when multiplied by itself gives 23.04. What is the number? [1]
   (b) In this question, take π to be 3.142. A firm sells 250-g packs of butter in the form of a rectangular block measuring 6 cm by 8 cm by 10.5 cm. The firm also sells 500-g packs of butter in the form of a cylinder with radius 3.9 cm.
      (i) Calculate
         (a) the volume of the rectangular block of butter, [1]
         (b) the height of the cylindrical block of butter. [2]
      (ii) If the firm decides to sell 250-g packs of butter in the form of a cylinder with a height of 13.2 cm, calculate the radius of the cylinder. [2]

7. (a) If $0 < n < 1$, arrange the following in ascending order.

$$n, n^2, \frac{1}{n}$$

[2]

(b) *ABCDE* is a regular pentagon.

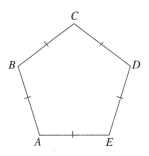

(i) Calculate the size of one of the exterior angles of the pentagon. [1]

(ii) The sides *BA* and *DE* are produced to meet at *X*.

  (a) Calculate $A\hat{X}E$. [2]

  (b) What type of quadrilateral is *BCDX*? [1]

  (c) Describe fully the symmetry of the quadrilateral *BCDX*. [1]

8. A spring is 80 cm long when unstretched. For every 500 g hung at the end of the spring, its length increases by 3 cm.

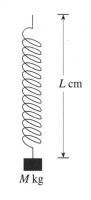

(a) Write down a formula connecting the extended length of the spring, *L* cm, with the mass, *M* kg. [2]

(b) If $M = 2$, find *L*. [1]

(c) If $L = 92$, find *M*. [1]

(d) If the unstretched length of the spring increases by $x\%$ when a mass y g is hung at its end, express y in terms of x. [3]

ASSESSMENT 2

Paper I *(answers on p. 439)*   **50 marks**   **1 h**

Answer all the questions without using the calculator.

1. **(a)** Find the HCF of the following set of numbers.

                28, 42, 98   [1]

   (b) Express the first quantity as a percentage of the second in each of the following.

      (i) $3\frac{1}{4}$, 6.5

      (ii)   95 cm, 1 km   [2]

2. **(a)** A sum of $2 700 is shared by 3 brothers in the ratio 2 : 3 : 4. How much is the biggest share?   [1]

   (b) 5 similar pumps, all working together, could fill a tank with water in 12 hours. How long would it take to fill the tank if 2 pumps were not working?   [2]

3. A piece of wood, 1.2 m long, 15 cm wide and 3 mm thick, weighs 340 g. Find the density of the wood. Give your answer correct to 2 decimal places.   [3]

4. The perimeter of a rectangle is 30 cm. If the length is $1\frac{1}{2}$ times as long as the breadth, find the area of the rectangle.   [3]

5. Find the angle marked x.

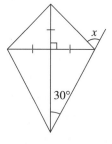

     [3]

6. A hole with a diameter of 3 cm is drilled through a square copper nut as shown in the diagram. Find the volume of the copper nut, correct to the nearest cm^3.

   $\left(\text{Take } \pi = \dfrac{22}{7}.\right)$

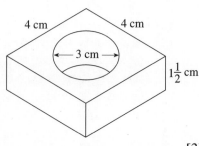

     [3]

7. **(a)** *ABCD* is a rectangle, and *CDP* and *BQP* are straight lines.

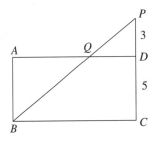

   (i) △*ABQ* and △*DPQ* are similar. Copy and complete the following.

   $$\frac{AQ}{QD} = \frac{\quad}{3}$$

   (ii) △*PQD* and △*PBC* are similar. Copy and complete the following.

   $$\frac{QD}{BC} = \frac{3}{\quad}$$

   (b) In the figure, △*ABC* and △*AML* are similar. Find

   (i) $A\hat{L}M$,

   (ii) *AB*.

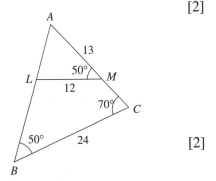

[2]

[2]

8. **(a)** The sum of three consecutive even numbers is 162. Find the numbers. [2]

   (b) Solve the following equation. Give your answer correct to 4 significant figures.

   $$3a + 5 = 32(3 - 2a)$$ [2]

9. **(a)** If $5\frac{1}{2}$% discount on a certain price was $22, what would be $3\frac{1}{2}$% discount on the same price? [2]

   (b) A car costs $55 000 when new and depreciates by 20% at the end of the first year.

   (i) What is the value of the car at the end of the first year?

   (ii) In the second year, it depreciates by a further 20%. What is the value of the car at the end of two years? [2]

10. **(a)** If $k = 9$ and $x = 6$, find the value of y in $y = kx^2$. [1]

   (b) The figure shows a rectangle whose length is $(3x - 1)$ cm and breadth $(x + 3)$ cm. If $x = 4$, find

   (i) the length and breadth of the rectangle,

   (ii) the perimeter of the rectangle,

   (iii) the area of the rectangle. [3]

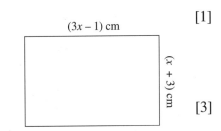

11. **(a)** Express 126 as a product of its prime factors. [1]

   (b) The shaded part shows the uniform cross-section of a solid made up of 2 rectangular blocks. Find

   (i) the total surface area, [2]

   (ii) the volume [1]

   of the solid.

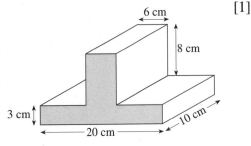

12. **(a)** Draw a triangle ABC such that $AB = 6$ cm, $BC = 7$ cm and $AC = 8$ cm. [1]
    (b) Mark a point X on BC such that $BX = 5$ cm. [1]
    (c) From X, construct a line perpendicular to BC to cut AC at Y. [1]
    (d) Measure $B\hat{Y}X$. [1]

13. A man drove to town X and back. He made the following entries in his diary.
    • Distance from home to town X is 318 km.
    • On the average the car travels 12 km on 1 litre of petrol.
    The price of petrol was $1.20 per litre. Find
    (a) the least number of litres of petrol he should put in the tank, allowing an extra 10 litres for emergency. [2]
    (b) the cost of petrol used by the car for the whole journey. [2]

14. A company made 30% profit on its capital. The profit amounted to $72 000. This profit included an increase of 20% of the previous years' profit.
    (a) What was the capital of the company? [1]
    (b) Find the profit of the previous year. [2]
    (c) What was the percentage profit of the previous year? (Assume that the capital remained the same.) [1]

Paper II   *(answers on p. 440)*   **50 marks**   **1 h 15 min**

Answer all the questions. You may use the calculator.

Section A (22 marks)

1. **(a)** Solve the equation $\frac{1}{2}(2x + 1) + \frac{1}{4}(x + 5) = 2\frac{3}{8}$. [2]

    (b) Given that $x = \frac{1}{4}$, $y = 6$, $z = -\frac{1}{2}$ and $w = 0$, find the value of

$$\frac{1}{x + y} + \frac{1}{y - zw}.$$ [3]

2. In the diagram, the straight line ABC is parallel to WX and BY is parallel to CX. $A\hat{B}Y = 57°$, $X\hat{W}Y = 132°$ and $B\hat{X}C = 63°$. Calculate
    (a) $B\hat{C}X$, [1]
    (b) $B\hat{X}W$, [2]
    (c) $B\hat{Y}W$. [2]

3. The following is part of a sequence of dot patterns.

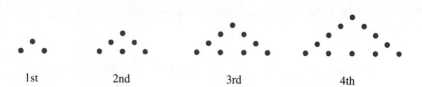

1st   2nd   3rd   4th

(a) How many dots are there in the 5th pattern? [1]
(b) How many dots are there in the 10th pattern? [2]
(c) Write down an expression for the nth pattern. [3]

4. Peter, Paul and Henry each decided to buy a similar television set whose list price was $640.

(a) Peter paid cash for his set and was given a discount of $7\frac{1}{2}$%. How much did he actually pay?

[1]

(b) Paul bought his set on hire purchase. He paid a deposit which was $\frac{1}{4}$ of the list price and the rest in 12 monthly instalments. If he paid $688 altogether, how much was his monthly instalment? [3]

(c) Henry bought his set with 24 monthly payments. He was charged 20% interest on the list price. How much did he pay monthly? [2]

Section B (28 marks)

5. **(a)** **(i)** The diagram shows the dials on the electricity meter at Bala's house on the day before it was replaced by a digital meter.

What reading is shown by the dials? [1]

(ii) A digital meter showed a reading of 45.2 units when it was installed on 31st March. The diagram below shows its reading on 30th August.

0	0	9	0	7	3
10 000	1 000	100	10	1	$\frac{1}{10}$

How much electricity did Bala's family use between 31st March and 30th August?

[2]

(iii) What was his average monthly electricity consumption? [1]

(b) In the figure, $2AB = BC$, $2BC = CD$ and $AD = 14$ cm. If X and Y are points on AD such that $AB = 2XB$ and $CD = 4YC$, find the possible lengths of XY.

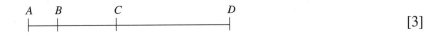

[3]

6. Mr Wu's basic salary is $210 for working a 40-hour week.

   (a) What is his hourly rate of pay? [1]

   (b) If he works overtime, he is paid 60% more. Calculate his hourly overtime rate of pay. [1]

   (c) Find how much he will earn if he works 50 hours a week. [2]

   (d) He spends $\frac{3}{5}$ of his basic salary each week and saves the rest. If he works 45 hours a week, how much does he save? [3]

7. In this question, take π to be 3.142.

The figure is a segment of a circle, centre O. The radius OA is 48 cm and $A\hat{O}B = 90°$.

The figure represents a formica top of a table with the edge AB fixed to the wall. A thin metal strip is fixed to the circular part of the table top.

   (a) Calculate, to two decimal places,

      (i) the length of the metal strip, [2]

      (ii) the area of the table top. [2]

   (b) If the table top was cut from a rectangular sheet of formica measuring 96 cm by 104 cm, what percentage of formica is wasted? [3]

8. **(a)** In the triangle ABC, $AC = CB$ and $A\hat{C}B = 35°$. The point M lies on AC such that $BM = MC$. Calculate

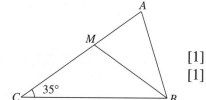

      (i) $B\hat{A}C$, [1]

      (ii) $B\hat{M}C$. [1]

   (b) $ABCDE$ is a regular pentagon. Calculate

      (i) $A\hat{B}C$ [2]

      (ii) $B\hat{C}E$ [2]

      (iii) What type of quadrilateral is $ABCE$? [1]

ANSWERS

Chapter 1

Exercise 1.1 *(p. 3)*

1. **(a)**
$$
\begin{array}{r}
567 \\
+\ 238 \\
\hline
805
\end{array}
$$
(b)
$$
\begin{array}{r}
1\ 063 \\
-\ 329 \\
\hline
734
\end{array}
$$
(c)
$$
\begin{array}{r}
70\ 089 \\
+\ 9\ 947 \\
\hline
80\ 036
\end{array}
$$

(d)
$$
\begin{array}{r}
2\ 302 \\
-2\ 169 \\
\hline
133
\end{array}
$$
(e)
$$
\begin{array}{r}
31\ 116 \\
-\ 28\ 974 \\
\hline
2\ 142
\end{array}
$$
(f)
$$
\begin{array}{r}
714 \\
+\ 189 \\
\hline
903
\end{array}
$$

2. **(a)**
$$
\begin{array}{r}
25 \\
\times\ 19 \\
\hline
225 \\
25\ \ \\
\hline
475
\end{array}
$$
(b)
$$
\begin{array}{r}
728 \\
\times\ 54 \\
\hline
2\ 912 \\
36\ 40\ \ \\
\hline
39\ 312
\end{array}
$$
(c)
$$
\begin{array}{r}
62 \\
12\,\overline{)744} \\
72 \\
\hline
24 \\
24 \\
\hline
\end{array}
$$

(d)
$$
\begin{array}{r}
55 \\
15\,\overline{)825} \\
75 \\
\hline
75 \\
75 \\
\hline
\end{array}
$$
(e)
$$
\begin{array}{r}
654 \\
32\,\overline{)20928} \\
192 \\
\hline
172 \\
160 \\
\hline
128 \\
128 \\
\hline
\end{array}
$$
(f)
$$
\begin{array}{r}
131 \\
\times\ 69 \\
\hline
1\ 179 \\
7\ 86\ \ \\
\hline
9\ 039
\end{array}
$$

3. **(a)**
$$
\begin{array}{r}
97\ 531 \\
+\ 86\ 420 \\
\hline
183\ 951
\end{array}
$$
(b)
$$
\begin{array}{r}
10\ 468 \\
+\ 23\ 579 \\
\hline
34\ 047
\end{array}
$$
Other answers are also possible.

4. **(a)**
$$
\begin{array}{r}
98\ 765 \\
-\ 10\ 234 \\
\hline
88\ 531
\end{array}
$$
(b)
$$
\begin{array}{r}
50\ 123 \\
-\ 49\ 876 \\
\hline
247
\end{array}
$$

Exercise 1.2 *(p. 6)*

1. **(a)** 23   **(b)** 16   **(c)** 10
   (d) 58   **(e)** 111   **(f)** 64

2. **(a)** 48   **(b)** 3   **(c)** 245
   (d) 15

3. **(a)** 1   **(b)** 18   **(c)** 13
   (d) 23

4. **(a)** 880   **(b)** 12   **(c)** 418
   (d) 13

5. **(a)** 176   **(b)** 1 071   **(c)** 273
   (d) 0

6. **(a)** 17 332   **(b)** 137   **(c)** 9
   (d) 270

7. **(a)** ÷   **(b)** ×   **(c)** ×, +
   (d) ÷, ÷

8. **(a)** $10 + 15 \times (5 + 15) \div 5 = 70$
   or $10 + 15 \times [(5 + 15) \div 5] = 70$
   (b) $38 + (21 - 7) \times 15 = 248$
   (c) $(32 - 13) \times (16 - 5) = 209$
   (d) $18 \div [(12 - 9) \times 2] = 3$

Exercise 1.3 *(p. 10)*

1. **(a)** 1, 3, 5, 15   **(b)** 1, 2, 4, 7, 14, 28
   (c) 1, 2, 3, 6, 7, 14, 21, 42
   (d) 1, 2, 3, 6, 13, 26, 39, 78
   (e) 1, 3, 7, 9, 21, 63
   (f) 1, 2, 3, 4, 5, 6, 8, 10, 12, 15, 20, 24, 30, 40, 60, 120

2. **(a)** 3, 6, 9, 12, 15, 18, 21, 24, 27, 30
   (b) 5, 10, 15, 20, 25, 30, 35, 40, 45, 50
   (c) 6, 12, 18, 24, 30, 36, 42, 48, 54, 60
   (d) 9, 18, 27, 36, 45, 54, 63, 72, 81, 90
   (e) 15, 30, 45, 60, 75, 90, 105, 120, 135, 150
   (f) 19, 38, 57, 76, 95, 114, 133, 152, 171, 190

3. **(a)** 1, 2, 3, 4, 5, 6, 10, 12, 15, 20, 30, 60
   (b) 1, 2, 3, 4, 6, 8, 12, 16, 24, 32, 48, 96
   C. F: 1, 2, 3, 4, 6, 12

4. **(a)** 12, 24, 36, 48, 60, 72, 84, 96, 108, 120, 132, 144
   (b) 18, 36, 54, 72, 90, 108, 126, 144, 162, 180, 198, 216
   C. M.: 36, 72, 108, 144

5. **(a)** 98   **(b)** 196   **(c)** 497
   (d) 994

Exercise 1.4 *(p. 13)*

1. **(a)** 5^2 **(b)** 3^3 **(c)** 17^3
   (d) $2^2 \times 7^3$ **(e)** $3^3 \times 5^2 \times 11^2$
   (f) $7^2 \times 13 \times 17^2 \times 71$

2. **(a)** 2×5 **(b)** 3×5 **(c)** 2^4

Answers

(d) 2×3^2 **(e)** $2^2 \times 5$ **(f)** $2^2 \times 3^2$
(g) $2^4 \times 3$ **(h)** $2^3 \times 3^2$ **(i)** $2^4 \times 3^2$
(j) 2^8

3. **(a)** 3×3 **(b)** $2 \times 2 \times 3$
 (c) 3×7 **(d)** $2 \times 2 \times 2 \times 3$
 (e) $2 \times 3 \times 5$ **(f)** $2 \times 3 \times 7$
 (g) $2 \times 2 \times 3 \times 3 \times 3$ **(h)** $5 \times 5 \times 5$
 (i) $2 \times 2 \times 2 \times 3 \times 3 \times 3$
 (j) $2 \times 2 \times 2 \times 3 \times 3 \times 3 \times 3$

4. **(a)** 97 **(b)** 119 **(c)** 149
 (d) 199

Exercise 1.5 *(p. 15)*

1. **(a)** 1 **(b)** 1 **(c)** 6
 (d) 1 **(e)** 3 **(f)** 3
 (g) 15 **(h)** 3 **(i)** 8
 (j) 9 **(k)** 1 **(l)** 1
 (m) 24 **(n)** 12 **(o)** 2
 (p) 18 **(q)** 9 **(r)** 6
 (s) 21 **(t)** 3 **(u)** 12
 (v) 12 **(w)** 12 **(x)** 33
 (y) 25 **(z)** 39

2. **(a)** 1 **(b)** 6 **(c)** 8
 (d) 35 **(e)** 1 **(f)** 1
 (g) 12 **(h)** 3 **(i)** 8

3. 12, 60

4. 8, 64; 16, 56; 32, 40

Exercise 1.6 *(p. 17)*

1. **(a)** 34 **(b)** 15 **(c)** 36
 (d) 60 **(e)** 18 **(f)** 12
 (g) 30 **(h)** 24 **(i)** 36
 (j) 60 **(k)** 42 **(l)** 45
 (m) 60 **(n)** 80 **(o)** 144
 (p) 18 **(q)** 72 **(r)** 100
 (s) 2 184 **(t)** 2 025 **(u)** 1 188
 (v) 2 310 **(w)** 8 190 **(x)** 1 080
 (y) 5 208 **(z)** 28 700

2. **(a)** 72 **(b)** 1 440 **(c)** 72
 (d) 80 **(e)** 180 **(f)** 72
 (g) 61 425 **(h)** 1 540 **(i)** 6 300

3. **(a) (i)** 7 **(ii)** 28 **(iii)** 196
 (b) (i) 6 **(ii)** 36 **(iii)** 216
 (c) (i) 1 **(ii)** 420 **(iii)** 420

(d) (i) 24 **(ii)** 480 **(iii)** 11 520
The product of the HCF and LCM of each pair of numbers is equal to the product of the respective pair of numbers.

4. 8 5. 7, 13 or 1, 91

Exercise 1.7 *(p. 20)*

1. **(a)** 25, 36 **(b)** 15, 21 **(c)** 13, 16
 (d) 32, 64 **(e)** 29, 35 **(f)** 125, 216

2. **(a)** 27, 32; Beginning with 2, each term is 5 more than the previous term.
 (b) 243, 729; Beginning with 1, each term is 3 times the previous term.
 (c) 56, 51; Beginning with 81, each term is 5 less than the previous term.
 (d) 15, 21; Beginning with 3, each 'odd term' is 4 more than the previous 'odd term', and beginning with 9, each 'even term' is 4 more than the previous 'even term'.
 (e) 12, 6; Beginning with 384, each term is $\frac{1}{2}$ of the previous term.
 (f) 18, 21; Beginning with 6, each term is 3 more than the previous term, or, consecutive multiples of 3 beginning with 6.

3. **(a)** 30, 45: Each term is the corresponding triangular number multiplied by 3.
 (b) 16, 25; Consecutive square numbers beginning with 1.

4. **(a)** 40, 60; Each term is the corresponding triangular number multiplied by 4.
 (b) 16, 25; Consecutive square numbers beginning with 1.

5. **(a)** For each sequence, each term is twice the previous term.
 (b) 7, 21, 35
 (c) The sum of the first three terms is seven times the first term.
 (d) 7, 14, 28

Exercise 1.8 *(p. 24)*

1. 4, 8, 10, 12, 14, 16, 18
 Press '2' once and '×' twice.
 Press input number and '=' to find output number.

2. 7, 9, 13, 15, 17, 19, 21

3. $a + 7 = b$
 Press '7' once and '+' twice.
 Press input number and '=' to find output number.

4. $q = 3p - 1$

5. **(a)** $m = n^2$ **(b)** $m = 3n - 2$ **(c)** $m = 2n$
  (d) $m = 6n - 1$ **(e)** $m = 5n - 3$ **(f)** $m = 7n$

  (g) $m = 86 - 5n$ **(h)** $m = \dfrac{384}{2^{n-1}}$

6. $m = 2T + 1$

7. $D = 2S + 2$

Exercise 1.9 *(p. 27)*

1. **(a)** Commutative law of addition
  (b) Associative law of addition
  (c) Associative law of addition
  (d) Commutative law of multiplication
  (e) Associative law of multiplication
  (f) Associative law of multiplication

2. **(a)** $(3 \times 4) + (3 \times 5)$ **(b)** $(3 \times 7) + (3 \times 2)$
  (c) $(3 \times 8) + (3 \times 4)$ **(d)** $(5 \times 4) + (2 \times 4)$
  (e) $(3 \times 7) + (1 \times 7)$ **(f)** $(7 \times 11) + (4 \times 11)$

3. **(a)** 7   **(b)** 7   **(c)** 6
  (d) 2   **(e)** 20   **(f)** 5

4. **(a)** True, $a \times 1 = 1 \times a = a$
  (b) True, $a + 0 = 0 + a = a$

5. (b) is equal to (iv) by the commutative property of addition.
  (c) is equal to (vii) by the distributive property.
  (d) is equal to (iii) by the commutative property of multiplication.
  (e) is equal to (ii) by the commutative property of addition.
  (f) is equal to (viii) by the associative property of multiplication.
  (g) is equal to (v) by the distributive property.
  (h) is equal to (vi) by the associative property of multiplication.
  (i) is equal to (ix) by the commutative property of addition.
  (j) is equal to (x) by the associative property of addition.

Chapter 2

Exercise 2.1 *(p. 37)*

1. **(a)** $\dfrac{5}{6}$ **(b)** $\dfrac{1}{4}$ **(c)** $\dfrac{3}{5}$

  (d) $\dfrac{3}{8}$ **(e)** $\dfrac{1}{3}$ **(f)** $\dfrac{1}{4}$

2. **(a)** **(i)** $\dfrac{1}{4}$ **(ii)** $\dfrac{3}{4}$

  (b) **(i)** $\dfrac{2}{5}$ **(ii)** $\dfrac{4}{5}$

3. **(a)** 24, 49   **(b)** 24, 65   **(c)** 99, 51
  (d) 91, 135   **(e)** 143, 144   **(f)** 105, 72

4. **(a)** $2\dfrac{1}{2}$ **(b)** $2\dfrac{1}{4}$ **(c)** $7\dfrac{1}{2}$

  (d) $3\dfrac{3}{5}$ **(e)** $3\dfrac{19}{24}$ **(f)** $10\dfrac{11}{36}$

  (g) $11\dfrac{2}{11}$ **(h)** $18\dfrac{12}{13}$ **(i)** $2\dfrac{29}{40}$

5. **(a)** $\dfrac{5}{2}$ **(b)** $\dfrac{13}{3}$ **(c)** $\dfrac{102}{11}$

  (d) $\dfrac{59}{5}$ **(e)** $\dfrac{163}{13}$ **(f)** $\dfrac{277}{16}$

  (g) $\dfrac{2\,719}{42}$ **(h)** $\dfrac{1\,805}{23}$ **(i)** $\dfrac{4\,524}{121}$

6. **(a)** $\dfrac{7}{3}$ **(b)** $\dfrac{3}{5}$ **(c)** $\dfrac{3}{7}$

  (d) $\dfrac{11}{10}$ **(e)** $\dfrac{22}{8}$ **(f)** $\dfrac{21}{49}$

7. **(a)** $\dfrac{4}{5}$ **(b)** $\dfrac{1}{6}$ **(c)** $\dfrac{2}{5}$

  (d) $\dfrac{5}{6}$ **(e)** $\dfrac{3}{7}$ **(f)** $\dfrac{7}{10}$

  (g) $\dfrac{2}{3}$ **(h)** $\dfrac{9}{11}$ **(i)** $\dfrac{1}{3}$

  (j) $\dfrac{5}{18}$ **(k)** $\dfrac{15}{16}$ **(l)** $\dfrac{13}{23}$

8. **(a)** $\dfrac{7}{10}$ **(b)** $\dfrac{15}{36}$ **(c)** $\dfrac{18}{68}$

  (d) equal   **(e)** $\dfrac{14}{40}$ **(f)** $\dfrac{135}{165}$

9. **(a)** $\dfrac{3}{8}$ **(b)** $\dfrac{3}{8}$ **(c)** $\dfrac{26}{18}$

  (d) $\dfrac{36}{31}$ **(e)** $\dfrac{16}{135}$ **(f)** $\dfrac{21}{49}$

10. **(a)** $\dfrac{17}{23}, \dfrac{20}{27}, \dfrac{18}{24}$ **(b)** $\dfrac{27}{32}, \dfrac{23}{27}, \dfrac{24}{28}$ **(c)** $\dfrac{30}{27}, \dfrac{50}{44}, \dfrac{49}{43}$

  (d) $\dfrac{47}{53}, \dfrac{96}{106}, \dfrac{32}{35}$ **(e)** $\dfrac{123}{171}, \dfrac{82}{110}, \dfrac{500}{342}$ **(f)** $\dfrac{184}{234}, \dfrac{128}{158}, \dfrac{64}{78}$

Answers

Exercise 2.2 *(p. 41)*

1. (a) $\dfrac{5}{8}$ (b) $\dfrac{9}{22}$ (c) $\dfrac{47}{48}$

   (d) $\dfrac{4}{15}$ (e) $\dfrac{19}{60}$ (f) $\dfrac{19}{80}$

2. (a) $\dfrac{3}{8}$ (b) $\dfrac{1}{3}$ (c) $\dfrac{17}{30}$

   (d) $\dfrac{4}{15}$ (e) $\dfrac{13}{24}$ (f) $\dfrac{1}{2}$

3. (a) $3\dfrac{8}{15}$ (b) $3\dfrac{11}{20}$ (c) $1\dfrac{4}{15}$

   (d) $2\dfrac{1}{12}$ (e) $5\dfrac{51}{56}$ (f) $2\dfrac{8}{45}$

4. (a) $7\dfrac{4}{15}$ (b) $2\dfrac{2}{15}$ (c) $9\dfrac{31}{63}$

   (d) 7 (e) $3\dfrac{16}{75}$ (f) $4\dfrac{37}{42}$

5. (a) $3\dfrac{1}{12}$ (b) $3\dfrac{5}{8}$ (c) 5

   (d) $7\dfrac{31}{36}$ (e) $1\dfrac{7}{24}$ (f) $1\dfrac{7}{60}$

6. (a) 7 (b) 28 (c) $4\dfrac{37}{72}$

   (d) 3 (e) 9 (f) $83\dfrac{13}{20}$

Exercise 2.3 *(p. 44)*

1. (a) $11\dfrac{2}{3}$ (b) $84\dfrac{3}{10}$ (c) $\dfrac{1}{8}$

   (d) $7\dfrac{13}{41}$ (e) $\dfrac{14}{15}$ (f) $\dfrac{9}{28}$

2. (a) $\dfrac{5}{3}$ (b) $\dfrac{8}{3}$ (c) $\dfrac{8}{7}$

   (d) $\dfrac{10}{9}$ (e) $\dfrac{1}{5}$ (f) $\dfrac{1}{10}$

   (g) $\dfrac{3}{5}$ (h) 1

3. (a) $\dfrac{3}{25}$ (b) $10\dfrac{1}{2}$ (c) $2\dfrac{4}{19}$

   (d) $8\dfrac{8}{11}$ (e) $6\dfrac{3}{4}$ (f) $3\dfrac{3}{4}$

4. (a) 28 (b) 21 (c) $6\dfrac{1}{2}$

   (d) $1\dfrac{1}{2}$ (e) $\dfrac{2}{5}$ (f) $2\dfrac{19}{22}$

5. (a) $10\dfrac{5}{8}$ (b) $\dfrac{3}{7}$ (c) $4\dfrac{5}{8}$

   (d) $\dfrac{4}{27}$ (e) $\dfrac{7}{33}$ (f) $22\dfrac{1}{2}$

6. (a) $\dfrac{1}{63}$ (b) $8\dfrac{1}{3}$ (c) $\dfrac{9}{35}$

   (d) $2\dfrac{2}{7}$ (e) 83 (f) $-2\dfrac{71}{129}$

Exercise 2.4 *(p. 49)*

1. (a) 1.1, 11, 110   (b) 0.12, 1.2, 12
   (c) 80.01, 800.1, 8 001   (d) 950, 9 500, 95 000
   (e) 1 013.5, 10 135, 101 350
   (f) 56 830.53, 568 305.3, 568 305 3

2. (a) 7.1, 0.71, 0.071   (b) 10.051, 1.005 1, 0.100 51
   (c) 0.001 7, 0.000 17, 0.000 017
   (d) 0.000 84, 0.000 084, 0.000 008 4
   (e) 708.84, 70.884, 7.088 4
   (f) 452 06.325, 4 520.632 5, 452.06 325

3. (a) 30.69   (b) 43.15
   (c) 61.739   (d) 153.177

4. (a) 20.89   (b) 27.09   (c) 12.87
   (d) 20.37   (e) 27.337   (f) 57.883

5. (a) 21.83   (b) 16.29   (c) 27.583   (d) 76.46

6. (a) 36.18   (b) 284.9   (c) 20.37
   (d) 34.19   (e) 622.326   (f) 638.82

7. (a) 9.3   (b) 2.19   (c) 23
   (d) 250   (e) 0.05   (f) 300

8. (a) 60.025   (b) 5.6   (c) 1.32
   (d) 0.528   (e) 10.5   (f) 20.58

Exercise 2.5a *(p. 52)*

1. A: 4 cm, B: 4 cm

2. (a) 6 kg   (b) 5 kg

3. (a) 30 ml (b) 50 ml

4. (a) (i) 451 470   (ii) 451 500
   (iii) 451 000   (iv) 450 000
   (b) (i) 675 900   (ii) 675 900
   (iii) 676 000   (iv) 680 000
   (c) (i) 872 600   (ii) 872 600
   (iii) 873 000   (iv) 870 000

(d) (i) 965 350   **(ii)** 965 400
    (iii) 965 000   **(iv)** 970 000
(e) (i) 810 300   **(ii)** 810 300
    (iii) 810 000   **(iv)** 810 000
(f) (i) 405 000   **(ii)** 405 000
    (iii) 405 000   **(iv)** 400 000

5. (a) (i) 61   **(ii)** 61.2
    (iii) 61.24   **(iv)** 61.235
(b) (i) 30   **(ii)** 29.6
    (iii) 29.60   **(iv)** 29.595
(c) (i) 26   **(ii)** 26.0
    (iii) 26.00   **(iv)** 25.995
(d) (i) 88   **(ii)** 88.3
    (iii) 88.32   **(iv)** 88.320
(e) (i) 64   **(ii)** 63.6
    (iii) 63.64   **(iv)** 63.638
(f) (i) 58   **(ii)** 57.6
    (iii) 57.63   **(iv)** 57.628

6. (a) (i) $12.31   **(ii)** $12
(b) (i) $45.56   **(ii)** $46
(c) (i) $52.19   **(ii)** $52
(d) (i) $28.81   **(ii)** $29
(e) (i) 288.94   **(ii)** $289
(f) (i) $167.56   **(ii)** $168

7. (a) (i) 110 kg   **(ii)** 108 kg
    (iii) 108.3 kg   **(iv)** 108.33 kg
(b) (i) 120 l **(ii)** 124 l
    (iii) 124.3 l **(iv)** 124.29 l
(c) (i) 150 cm   **(ii)** 147 cm
    (iii) 146.7 cm   **(iv)** 146.67 cm
(d) (i) 130 m   **(ii)** 131 m
    (iii) 131.4 m   **(iv)** 131.43 m
(e) (i) 590 g   **(ii)** 591 g
    (iii) 590.6 g   **(iv)** 590.59 g
(f) (i) 210 km   **(ii)** 212 km
    (iii) 211.8 km   **(iv)** 211.82 km

Exercise 2.5b *(p. 56)*

1. (a) (i) 1 300 km   **(ii)** 1 320 km
(b) (i) 5 400 km   **(ii)** 5 410 km
(c) (i) 4 000 km   **(ii)** 4 010 km
(d) (i) 6 000 km   **(ii)** 6 020 km
(e) (i) 8 000 l **(ii)** 8 000 l
(f) (i) 4.5 m   **(ii)** 4.46 m
(g) (i) 15 m   **(ii)** 15.4 m
(h) (i) 21 m   **(ii)** 20.9 m
(i) (i) 50 cm   **(ii)** 50.0 cm
(j) (i) 0.023 km   **(ii)** 0.023 5 km
(k) (i) 0.000 56 km   **(ii)** 0.000 564 km
(l) (i) 0.98 km   **(ii)** 0.983 km
(m) (i) 1.0 km   **(ii)** 0.995 km
(n) (i) 64 000 kg   **(ii)** 64 100 kg
(o) (i) 74 000 kg   **(ii)** 74 000 kg

2. (a) 1   **(b)** 3   **(c)** 2
   (d) 4   **(e)** 4   **(f)** 5

3. (a) 3   **(b)** 4   **(c)** 3
   (d) 4   **(e)** 2   **(f)** 2

4. (a) 2   **(b)** 3   **(c)** 2
   (d) 2   **(e)** 4   **(f)** 5

5. (a) (i) 12   **(ii)** 12.2
(b) (i) 19   **(ii)** 18.8
(c) (i) 45   **(ii)** 44.8
(d) (i) 2 600   **(ii)** 2 560
(e) (i) 74   **(ii)** 74.3
(f) (i) 0.091   **(ii)** 0.091 4

Exercise 2.6 *(p. 61)*

1. (a) $\dfrac{3}{8}$ **(b)** $\dfrac{2}{125}$ **(c)** $3\dfrac{1}{5}$
   (d) $\dfrac{1}{10\ 000}$ **(e)** $\dfrac{1}{200}$ **(f)** $1\dfrac{1}{250}$

2. (a) 0.5   **(b)** 0.375   **(c)** 0.44
   (d) 0.2   **(e)** 0.25   **(f)** 0.72

3. (a) $0.1\dot{8}$ **(b)** $0.1\dot{6}$ **(c)** $0.\dot{1}$
   (d) $0.\dot{3}$ **(e)** $0.\dot{2}$ **(f)** $0.19\dot{6}$
   (g) $0.\dot{7}2\dot{9}$ **(h)** $0.\dot{9}80\ \dot{1}$

4. (a) 0.15, 0.154   **(b)** 0.48, 0.478   **(c)** 0.63, 0.632
   (d) 0.76, 0.765   **(e)** 0.91, 0.913   **(f)** 0.46, 0.464

5. (a) $\dfrac{2}{5}$, 0.419, $\dfrac{3}{7}$, 0.43   **(b)** $\dfrac{3}{8}$, 0.39, 0.411, $\dfrac{5}{11}$
   (c) $\dfrac{3}{8}, \dfrac{3}{7}, \dfrac{4}{9}, \dfrac{6}{13}$ **(d)** $\dfrac{9}{20}, \dfrac{7}{15}, \dfrac{11}{21}, \dfrac{5}{9}$

6. (a) 4.8 or $4\dfrac{4}{5}$ **(b)** 1.95 or $1\dfrac{19}{20}$ **(c)** 2.05 or $2\dfrac{1}{20}$
   (d) 3.75 or $3\dfrac{3}{4}$ **(e)** 32.5 or $32\dfrac{1}{2}$ **(f)** 3.85 or $3\dfrac{17}{20}$

7. (a) 0.2   **(b)** 70.9   **(c)** 12.7   **(d)** 0.2

8. (a) 0.46   **(b)** 1.70   **(c)** 2.68   **(d)** −8.64

Exercise 2.7 *(p. 63)*

1. (a) (iii)   **(b)** (iii)   **(c)** (ii)
   (d) (ii)   **(e)** (i)   **(f)** (iii)
   (g) (ii)   **(h)** (i)   **(i)** (iii)
   (j) (i)

2. **(a)** incorrect, 11.28   **(b)** correct
   (c) incorrect, 19.76   **(d)** incorrect, 77.52
   (e) correct   **(f)** incorrect, 12.88
   (g) incorrect, 19.55   **(h)** correct
   (i) incorrect, 9.12   **(j)** correct
   (k) incorrect, 18.12   **(l)** incorrect, 143.25

3. **(a)** 31.60   **(b)** 436.16   **(c)** 243.36   **(d)** 0.50
   (e) 6.71   **(f)** 1.11   **(g)** 4.36   **(h)** 0.84
   (i) 238.86   **(j)** 27.60   **(k)** 0.24   **(l)** 1.30
   (m) 6.07   **(n)** 1.23

Chapter 3

Exercise 3.1 *(p. 76)*

1. **(a)** 250 cm   **(b)** 0.01 m   **(c)** 0.076 m
   (d) 3 800 m   **(e)** 0.001 km   **(f)** 0.011 8 km
   (g) 200 000 cm   **(h)** 0.001 g   **(i)** 0.005 5 g
   (j) 0.001 kg   **(k)** 0.003 3 kg   **(l)** 8 500 000 mg
   (m) 3 500 kg   **(n)** 2.57 tonnes   **(o)** 4 500 g
   (p) 0.02 *l*   **(q)** 2 600 m*l*   **(r)** 2 100 s
   (s) 180 min   **(t)** 7 200 s   **(u)** 11.5 h

2. **(a)** 5 kg 252 g   **(b)** 4 kg 211 g   **(c)** 3 km 215 m
   (d) 1 km 268 m   **(e)** 4 m 62 cm   **(f)** 8 m 1 cm
   (g) 6 *l* 523 m*l*   **(h)** 360 min   **(i)** 3 min 35 s
   (j) 2 h 1 min   **(k)** 7 500 s   **(l)** 4 803 s
   (m) 1 h 17 min 5s
   (n) 1 h 1 min 19 s

Exercise 3.2 *(p. 77)*

1. **(a)** $2   **(b)** $60   **(c)** 15 pens

2. **(a)** $3\frac{1}{2}$ h   **(b)** $3\frac{1}{2}$ h   **(c)** 7 h
   (d) 35 h   **(e)** $280   **(f)** 4 weeks

3. **(a)** 25 yrs old   **(b)** 24 yrs old   **(c)** 31 yrs old

4. **(a)** 4 *l*   **(b)** 2 *l*   **(c)** 7 *l*
   (d) $1.50

5. **(a)** 34 workers   **(b)** $10 200
   (c) $102 000   **(d)** $1 200

6. **(a)** $4   **(b)** $360   **(c)** 18 m
   (d) 54 m   **(e)** $72

7. **(a)** 5   **(b)** 5   **(c)** 2 h 18 min
   (d) 3 h 39 min   **(e)** 16 15

8. **(a)** 8 min   **(b)** Towns *A* and *G*

(c) $2   **(d)** 08 27   **(e)** $6\frac{2}{3}$ cents/min

9. **(a)** *E*, *F*, *K*, *S*
   (b) *E*: 2 games, *F*: 2 games
     K: 3 games, *S*: 2 games
   (c) *E*: 3.5 goals, *F*: 2.5 goals
     K: 2 goals, *S*: 3.5 goals

10. **(a)** 4–1, *E*   **(b)** 6–0, *E*   **(c)** 6 games
   (d) 22 goals   **(e)** 16 goals

11. **(a)**

F	3	1	2	13	10	7
K	4	1	1	14	12	9
S	0	1	5	10	21	1

   (b) *E* and *K* (*E* entered on goal difference)
   (c) *E*   **(d)** *S*   **(e)** 12

Exercise 3.3 *(p. 83)*

1. 24.2°C   **2.** 1°C   **3.** $900
4. $35   **5.** 42 840   **6.** $0.50
7. $0.18   **8.** $9.68   **9.** $2
10. $27   **11.** 5   **12.** $12.05
13. $18, $54   **14.** 90   **15.** 60
16. $\frac{5}{18}$ **17.** $3 800   **18.** 6 h
19. $2.40   **20.** $0.30   **21.** 10 eggs
22. 3 days   **23.** $1 600   **24.** 10 55 and
     10 25

Chapter 4

Exercise 4.1 *(p. 95)*

1.

2. **(a)** >   **(b)** >   **(c)** <
   (d) >   **(e)** <   **(f)** >
   (g) >   **(h)** >   **(i)** <

3. **(a)** 5   **(b)** 7   **(c)** 0
   (d) 7   **(e)** 18   **(f)** 18

4. **(a)** 12   **(b)** −14

5. **(a)** −18   **(b)** −14

6. **(a)** 24   **(b)** −25

7. **(a)** −16   **(b)** −15

8. **(a)** −1, −2, −3   **(b)** 10, 12, 14
    (c) 0, 2, 4   **(d)** −3, 1, 2, 3
    (e) 0, 3, 9   **(f)** −3, −4, −5
    (g) −7, −9, −11   **(h)** −6, −8, −10
    (i) 2, 1, 0, −1   **(j)** −4, −5, −6, −7
    (k) 6, 3, 0, −3   **(l)** −6, −3, 0, 3

Exercise 4.2 *(p. 100)*

1. **(a)**

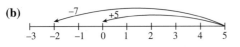

    (b)

    (c)

2. **(a)** 9   **(b)** −12   **(c)** −4   **(d)** −5
    (e) −25   **(f)** 0   **(g)** −7   **(h)** −5
    (i) −2   **(j)** −4   **(k)** −36   **(l)** −27
    (m) −5   **(n)** 43   **(o)** 13   **(p)** 0
    (q) −128   **(r)** −22

3. **(a)** 4   **(b)** −3   **(c)** −13   **(d)** −8
    (e) 11   **(f)** 12   **(g)** 2   **(h)** −4
    (i) 40   **(j)** −21   **(k)** 46   **(l)** −33
    (m) 8   **(n)** 100   **(o)** 70   **(p)** 0
    (q) −21   **(r)** −250

4. **(a)** 36   **(b)** −498   **(c)** 374   **(d)** 1 107
    (e) 1 084   **(f)** −629   **(g)** 758   **(h)** 567
    (i) 466   **(j)** 176   **(k)** −59   **(l)** 405
    (m) 461   **(n)** 170   **(o)** 160   **(p)** 0

5. 12 + 10 = 22;
    2°C, 15 + (−13) = 2;
    −3°C, 15 + (−18) = 3;
    6°C , −8 + 14 = 6;
    −9°C, −18 + 9 = −9;
    −34°C, −21 + (−13) = −34

6. 25 + (−17) = 8;
    −3, 7 + (−10) = −3;
    −7, −25 + 18 = −7;
    7, −18 + 25 = 7;
    33, 16 + 17 = 33;
    −44, −19 + (−25) = −44

7. −12 − 10 = −22;
    30, 42, 30 − (−12) = 42;
    −10, 5, −10 − (−15) = 5;
    38, 23, 38 − 15 = 23;
    −40, −22, −40 − (−18) = −22

8. **(a)** January: + \$5 000, February: +\$2 000,
    March: −\$6 000, April: +\$1 000, May: +\$4 000,
    June: −\$3 000
    (b) +\$3 000   **(c)** +\$1 000   **(d)** −\$ 4000

9. 40°C, −6.5°C

10. **(a)** [13 000 + 5 000 + (−3 000)] m
    (b) 15 000 m

Exercise 4.3 *(p. 107)*

1. **(a)** −15   **(b)** −4   **(c)** 6
    (d) 0   **(e)** 0   **(f)** 198
    (g) 98   **(h)** 42   **(i)** 60
    (j) −70   **(k)** 0   **(l)** −42
    (m) −120   **(n)** 120   **(o)** −672
    (p) 0   **(q)** −42 372   **(r)** 79 950
    (s) −72 816   **(t)** −401 250   **(u)** 39 130
    (v) −237 510   **(w)** 756   **(x)** 3 240
    (y) 9 690   **(z)** 30 000

2. **(a)** 225   **(b)** 2 025
    (c) 11 236   **(d)** 97 344

3. **(a)** +11, −11   **(b)** +16, −16
    (c) +25, −25   **(d)** +35, −35

4. **(a)** 21   **(b)** −24
    (c) −68   **(d)** 86

5. **(a)** 1 331   **(b)** −15 625
    (c) −27 000   **(d)** 74 088

6. **(a)** 5   **(b)** −12
    (c) −20   **(d)** 23

7. **(a)** 8   **(b)** −11
    (c) 21   **(d)** −25

8. Question 4:
    (a) √‾ 441 EXE or 2 ˣ√‾ 441 EXE
    (b) (−) √‾ 576 EXE or (−) 2 ˣ√‾ 576 EXE
    (c) (−) √‾ 4 624 EXE or (−) 2 ˣ√‾ 4 624 EXE
    (d) √‾ 7 396 EXE or 2 ˣ√‾ 7 396 EXE

    Question 7:
    (a) ³√‾ 512 EXE or 3 ˣ√‾ 512 EXE
    (b) ³√‾ (−) 1 331 EXE or 3 ˣ√‾ (−) 1 331 EXE
    (c) ³√‾ 9 261 EXE or 3 ˣ√‾ 9 261 EXE
    (d) ³√‾ (−) 15 625 EXE or 3 ˣ√‾ (−) 15 625 EXE

9. (a) 4 608 (b) 29 791
(c) –65 910 (d) 115 943

Exercise 4.4 *(p. 109)*

1. –2	**2.** –4	**3.** –5
4. –3	**5.** –6	**6.** 0
7. –12	**8.** 3	**9.** 4
10. 8	**11.** –41	**12.** –76
13. –56	**14.** –23	**15.** 61
16. 112	**17.** 56	**18.** –24
19. –12	**20.** 12	**21.** 23
22. –14	**23.** –10	**24.** –3
25. 4	**26.** 1	**27.** –5
28. –1	**29.** –2	**30.** –1

Exercise 4.5 *(p. 113)*

1. (a), (b), (d)

2. (a) $-\dfrac{1}{6}$ (b) $-1\dfrac{1}{4}$ (c) 0

(d) $-\dfrac{5}{12}$ (e) $-1\dfrac{46}{63}$ (f) $-2\dfrac{7}{10}$

3. (a) $\dfrac{13}{21}$ (b) 0 (c) $2\dfrac{1}{6}$

(d) $\dfrac{5}{33}$ (e) $1\dfrac{3}{10}$ (f) $-\dfrac{55}{72}$

4. (a) $\dfrac{1}{2}$ (b) $\dfrac{4}{5}$ (c) $-1\dfrac{1}{8}$

(d) $-1\dfrac{7}{8}$ (e) $2\dfrac{7}{9}$ (f) 0

5. (a) $1\dfrac{1}{6}$ (b) $-\dfrac{1}{3}$ (c) –12

(d) $6\dfrac{2}{3}$ (e) $\dfrac{1}{7}$ (f) $-12\dfrac{3}{5}$

6. (a) $-\dfrac{2}{3}$ (b) $-\dfrac{4}{5}$ (c) $-\dfrac{3}{7}$

(d) $-\dfrac{5}{16}$ (e) $\dfrac{3}{7}$ (f) $-\dfrac{4}{9}$

(g) $\dfrac{5}{24}$ (h) $-\dfrac{7}{20}$ (i) $\dfrac{9}{10}$

(j) $\dfrac{8}{15}$ (k) $\dfrac{84}{11}$ (l) $-\dfrac{678}{5}$

7. (a) > (b) < (c) <

(d) > (e) < (f) >
(g) < (h) <

8. (a) $\dfrac{1}{7}$, $\dfrac{3}{10}$, 1.2, $\sqrt{4}$, $\sqrt{\dfrac{1}{4}}$, $0.2\dot{7}$, $0.24\dot{5}$

(b) $\sqrt{3}$, $\sqrt{8}$, $\sqrt{5}$

9. (a) 1.414 (b) 1.732 (c) 2.449
(d) 2.449 (e) 4.243 (f) 2.449
(g) 1.260 (h) 1.442 (i) 1.817
(j) 1.817 (k) 2.289 (l) 1.260

Exercise 4.6 *(p. 115)*

1. 215	**2.** 29	**3.** 172
4. –1 725	**5.** 1 858	**6.** 125
7. 337	**8.** 2 189	**9.** –165
10. –1 756	**11.** –717	**12.** –173
13. 11	**14.** –30	**15.** 118

16. 429 **17.** $\dfrac{3}{32}$ **18.** $-1\dfrac{5}{16}$

19. $-2\dfrac{2}{5}$ **20.** $1\dfrac{1}{4}$

Exercise 4.7 *(p. 119)*

1. (a) $18 (b) $78 (c) $1 040
(d) 24.2 (e) 9.28 (f) 23.04

2. (a) 615 000 (b) 21 (c) 15 640
(d) 0.896 (e) 20 600 (f) 1 465

3. (a) 33 (b) 20 (c) 3
(d) 50 (e) 342 000 (f) 4 500

4. (a) 693 (b) 1 488 (c) 1 627

(d) 1 279 (e) 558 (f) $11\dfrac{1}{3}$

(g) 1 680 (h) 4

5. (a) ≈ 3 000 (b) ≈ 200 (c) ≈ 2
(d) ≈ 900 (e) ≈ 0.1 (f) ≈ 1 000

Revision Exercise 1

Revision 1A *(p. 124)*

1. (a) $2^7 \times 3$ (b) $3 \times 5 \times 37$ (c) $5 \times 11 \times 19$
(d) 2^{11}

2. (a) 60 (b) 61 (c) 62

3. Large tin because 4 tins of 125 g cost $7.20

4. **(a)** 0.014 7 kg   **(b)** 1 h 56 min

5. **(a)** −10   **(b)** −56   **(c)** 114
   (d) 45

6. **(a)** >   **(b)** <   **(c)** <
   (d) >   **(e)** >   **(f)** >
   (g) >   **(h)** >

7. **(a)** 668   **(b)** −372

8. 3, 3 000   **9.** $80   **10.** $1

Revision 1B *(p. 125)*

1. **(a)** $3 \times 5 \times 7 \times 11$ **(b)** 385

2. **(a)** 96   **(b)** 720   **(c)** 1 820
   (d) 1 050

3. **(a)** 6 112.899   **(b)** 59.713   **(c)** 7.667
   (d) 6.059

4. $12\frac{1}{16}$ m

5. **(a)**
```
  6 [4] 2 3
- 1 5 [4] 5
─────────────
  [4] 8 7 [8]
```
(b)
```
  [3] 4 [5]
+   8 7 6
───────────
  1 2 [2] 1
```

6. **(a)** $-\frac{1}{2}$ h   **(b)** +3 h   **(c)** $+11\frac{1}{2}$ h
   (d) −6 h   **(e)** $-8\frac{1}{2}$ h

7. **(a)** − 2 504   **(b)** 8 800

8. **(a)** 24 m*l*   **9.** 0.25   **10.** 3

Revision 1C *(p. 126)*

1. 48

2. **(a)** 817   **(b)** 1 271   **(c)** 773

3. **(a)** $\frac{22}{7}$ **(b)** $\frac{1}{3}$ **(c)** 0.71
   (d) $\frac{9}{13}$ **(e)** 2.23

4. $53\frac{1}{3}$ kg

5. **(a)** 8, −2, −7   **(b)** −52, −10, 18

6. +500 m, −20 m, 520 m higher

7. **(a)** $-\frac{1}{12}$ **(b)** $1\frac{23}{60}$ **(c)** $1\frac{29}{84}$
   (d) $-\frac{29}{75}$ **(e)** $-1\frac{11}{32}$

8. **(a)** 12 468   **(b)** 799   **(c)** −71

9. 126   **10.** $0.50

Revision 1D *(p. 127)*

1. (b), (c)

2. **(a)** 4   **(b)** 5   **(c)** 7
   (d) 5

3. 2   **4.** $6\frac{7}{20}$ m

5. **(a)** −6   **(b)** +6   **(c)** −5
   (d) −4   **(e)** +29

6. **(a)** $-\frac{5}{33}$ **(b)** $\frac{1}{20}$ **(c)** $-\frac{287}{892}$
   (d) $\frac{56}{75}$ **(e)** $-\frac{1}{10}$ **(f)** $6\frac{2}{3}$
   (g) $-37\frac{67}{129}$ **(h)** $\frac{27}{229}$ **(i)** $\frac{3}{28}$

7. **(a)** −302   **(b)** −1 352   **(c)** 597

8. **(a)** $8 + 5 \times (9 - 6 \div 3) = 43$
   (b) $(10 + 2 \times 3) - (8 + 16 \div 4) = 4$

9. $525   **10.** $0.70

Revision 1E *(p. 128)*

1. 4   **2.** 50   **3.** $107\frac{1}{2}$ kg

4. **(a)** +120 m   **(b)** −50 m   **(c)** +200 m
   (d) 0 m

5. **(a)** 825   **(b)** 5   **(c)** −348

6. **(a)** $45   **(b)** $20   **(c)** $30

7. 0.66

8. **(a)** 0.028   **(b)** 0.027 68

9. 50¢ **10.** 6 h

Miscellaneous Exercise 1 *(p. 130)*

1. (a) 15 **(b)** 2 h 35 min **(c)** $3 773

2. 135 **3.** 45, 82

4. 31 or 61 or 91 (i.e. 1 plus any common multiple of 2, 3 and 5)

5. 13; 4, 9 **6.** 24

7. (a) 15 yrs old **(b)** 39 yrs old
   (c) 63 yrs old **(d)** 87 yrs old

8. (a) 8 yrs old **(b)** 38 yrs old **(c)** 68 yrs old

9. 22

10. (a) False **(b)** False **(c)** True
    (d) True **(e)** True **(f)** True

11. (a) False **(b)** False **(c)** False
    (d) False **(e)** True **(f)** True

12. (a) False **(b)** False **(c)** False
    (d) False **(e)** True **(f)** True

13. (a) $1 \times 9 \div 3 + 5 - 7 = 1$
    (b) $(7 \times 5 + 1) \div 3 - 9 = 3$
    (c) $9 \div 3 \times 1 + 7 - 5 = 5$
    (d) $9 - (3 + 7) \div 5 \times 1 = 7$
    (e) $5 \times 9 \div 3 + 1 - 7 = 9$

14. (a) $(2 + 4) \div 6 \times 10 - 8 = 2$
    (b) $8 - (4 + 2 \times 10) \div 6 = 4$
    (c) $(10 + 6) \times 4 \div 8 - 2 = 6$
    (d) $8 \times 2 \div 4 + 10 - 6 = 8$
    (e) $(10 - 4) \times 2 \div 6 + 8 = 10$

15.

```
              3005028
      199 ) 598000572
            597
            1000
             995
             557
             398
            1592
            1592
               0
```

Chapter 5

Exercise 5.1 *(p. 138)*

1. $100 - x$ **2.** $7 + y$ **3.** $30 - p$

4. (a) $100s$ **(b)** $1000m$ **(c)** $100q$
   (d) $1000d$ **(e)** $1000p$ **(f)** $100s + t$
   (g) $1000p + q$

5. $2x - 5$ **6.** $2x$ **7.** $2x + 30$

8. (a) $x - 5$ **(b)** -2

9. (a) $k + 2$ **(b)** -12

10. (a) $2x + 11$ **(b)** $10\dfrac{1}{8}$

11. $x + 5$ **12.** $x - 8$ **13.** $7x$

14. $\dfrac{2}{3}x$ **15.** $\dfrac{1}{x}$ **16.** $\dfrac{1}{6}y$

Exercise 5.2 *(p. 141)*

1. (a) 14 **(b)** 2 **(c)** 21
   (d) 15 **(e)** 36 **(f)** 72
   (g) 2 **(h)** 4 **(i)** 34
   (j) 15 **(k)** $32\dfrac{6}{7}$ **(l)** $4\dfrac{4}{5}$
   (m) $\dfrac{3}{2}$ **(n)** $\dfrac{1}{6}$ **(o)** $\dfrac{30}{7}$

2. (a) $-1\dfrac{2}{3}$ **(b)** $-5\dfrac{3}{7}$ **(c)** 65
   (d) 460 **(e)** -82 **(f)** 90
   (g) -102 **(h)** $8\dfrac{1}{2}$

3. (a) LHS = RHS = $-11\dfrac{1}{2}$
   (b) LHS = RHS = $-11\dfrac{1}{2}$
   (c) LHS = RHS = $12\dfrac{1}{2}$
   (d) LHS = RHS = $12\dfrac{1}{2}$

4. (a) $2\dfrac{2}{3}$ **(b)** 7 **(c)** $240\dfrac{2}{3}$

(d) 0 **(e)** $1\dfrac{7}{8}$ **(f)** $25\dfrac{151}{225}$

(g) $-\dfrac{56}{111}$ **(h)** $23\dfrac{1}{3}$

Exercise 5.3 *(p. 143)*

1. **(a)** $8a$ **(b)** $12b$ **(c)** $-3c$
   (d) $3c$ **(e)** $-12m$ **(f)** $5x$
   (g) $4a + 3b$ **(h)** $5a + 5b$ **(i)** $5ab$
   (j) $12a^2b + 17ab^2$
   (k) $21ab^2$ **(l)** $32ab^2 - 32cb^2$

2. **(a)** $12ab$ **(b)** $-15ac$ **(c)** $12xy$
   (d) $-18xz$ **(e)** $15mn$ **(f)** $18np$
   (g) $-12pq$ **(h)** $28pr$ **(i)** $-12a^3b$
   (j) $-372a^3b^3$ **(k)** $-529x^3y$ **(l)** $-238xy^3$

3. **(a)** 8 **(b)** $-\dfrac{4a}{7}$ **(c)** $\dfrac{3}{4n}$
   (d) $-\dfrac{1}{2}$ **(e)** $\dfrac{8x}{3z}$ **(f)** $\dfrac{2x}{5z}$

4. **(a)** $10a$ **(b)** $21a^2$ **(c)** $-4b$
   (d) $-21b^2$ **(e)** $8a - 7b$ **(f)** $-105a^2b$
   (g) $2c^2 - 11c$ **(h)** $60c^4$ **(i)** $4d + 8de$
   (j) $60d^3e^2$ **(k)** $13f + 4fg$ **(l)** $144f^3g$
   (m) $-6b$ **(n)** $-\dfrac{a^2}{2}$ **(o)** $-\dfrac{1}{12y^2}$
   (p) $7ab - 21a^2$ **(q)** $-40xz$ **(r)** $\dfrac{9}{4z^2}$

Exercise 5.4 *(p. 146)*

1. **(a)** $ab - ac$ **(b)** $ac - ab$ **(c)** $ab + ac$
   (d) $-ab - ac$ **(e)** $ab - ac$ **(f)** $ab + ac$
   (g) $a + b - c$ **(h)** $a - b - c$ **(i)** $a - b + c$
   (j) $a - b - c$ **(k)** $a + b - c$ **(l)** $a + b + c$

2. **(a)** $x + 2b - c$ **(b)** $2x + 4a - 2b$
   (c) $3a - 2b + 3c$ **(d)** $2y - 3x + 2w$
   (e) $g - 4b - 3c$ **(f)** $4m - 3n - 4p$
   (g) $2n + 5t - 3u$ **(h)** $6p + 2q - 5r$
   (i) $-2x - 7y$ **(j)** $-10r - 35$
   (k) $3n - 2m$ **(l)** $7q - 6p$
   (m) $3x - 3t - 8u$ **(n)** $4r - 10s - 7t$
   (o) $6z - 3y + 5w$ **(p)** $2w - 4x + 9y$
   (q) $3y - x + 4z$ **(r)** $3b + 5c - a$

3. **(a)** $12ab - 15ac$ **(b)** $12xy - 18xz$
   (c) $15mn + 18np$ **(d)** $28pr - 12pq$
   (e) $20xz + 28yz$ **(f)** $36tv + 32uv$
   (g) $35mp - 15np$ **(h)** $42pr - 7qr$

4. **(a)** $x(4 + 3y)$ **(b)** $3(5m + 2n + 3mn)$
   (c) $2p(1 + 4q)$ **(d)** $4a(1 + 2b)$
   (e) $3x(1 + 5y)$ **(f)** $2ab(1 + 4c)$
   (g) $t(5rs + 3s - 2r)$ **(h)** $b(5a + 3c + 1)$

Exercise 5.5 *(p. 147)*

1. **(a)** $3a + b$ **(b)** $4a - 4b + c$
   (c) $4d + 5e - 4f$ **(d)** $4a^2 + a + 3b + c$
   (e) $-2b + c - c^2$ **(f)** $3a - 7b + 4b^2$
   (g) $a - a^2 + 4b + 3c$ **(h)** $-13a - 15b + c + c^2$

2. **(a)** 0 **(b)** $2b - 2a$
   (c) 0 **(d)** $2a - 2b$
   (e) 0 **(f)** $15a - 17b$
   (g) $17a + 11b$ **(h)** $17 - 48c + 3c^2$

3. **(a)** $a^2 - ab + b^2 - bc + c^2 - ac$
   (b) $a^2 - 2ab + b^2 + ac - bc$
   (c) $4a^2 - 2ab + 3c$ **(d)** $3bc^2 - 2ac^2 + cd$
   (e) $3b^2c^2 - 3a^3c$ **(f)** $2ab^2 + 3ac + 2b^2c + b$
   (g) $4xy - 4xz + 2yz$ **(h)** $3xz - xy + 2yz$

4. **(a)** $2x - 2$ **(b)** $3 - x$
   (c) $-\dfrac{3y}{10} - 3$ **(d)** $\dfrac{7x}{6} + \dfrac{1}{6}$
   (e) $\dfrac{13x}{12} + \dfrac{1}{12}$ **(f)** $\dfrac{13x}{24} - \dfrac{25}{24}$
   (g) $\dfrac{17x}{8}$ **(h)** $\dfrac{39x}{12} - \dfrac{23}{12}$

Chapter 6

Exercise 6.1 *(p. 153)*

1. **(a)** True **(b)** False **(c)** False
   (d) False **(e)** False **(f)** False

2. **(a)** 5 **(b)** 15 **(c)** $1\dfrac{1}{2}$
   (d) 1 **(e)** -7 **(f)** 3

3. **(a)** 1, 2 **(b)** 1, 2, 3 **(c)** 1
   (d) 1, 2, 3 **(e)** 1, 2, 3, 4 **(f)** 1, 2, 3, 4

4. **(a)** 3, 4, 5, 6 **(b)** 16, 17, 18, 19
   (c) 9, 10, 11, 12, 13, 14, 15
   (d) 15, 16, 17, 18, 19, 20
   (e) all natural numbers except 21
   (f) all natural numbers except 7
   (g) 1, 2, 3, . . ., 34

Answers

(h) 1, 2, 3, . . ., 12
(i) 1, 2, 3, . . ., 7
(j) 1, 2, 3, 4, 5
(k) 1, 2, 3, . . ., 8
(l) 1, 2, 3, 4, 5

5. **(a)** True **(b)** True **(c)** True
(d) True **(e)** False **(f)** True

6. **(a)** ±3 **(b)** ±2 **(c)** No solution
(d) ±5 **(e)** ±2 **(f)** No solution

Exercise 6.2 *(p. 158)*

1. **(a)** Subtract x from both sides.
Subtract 3 from both sides.
(b) Add $3x$ to both sides.
Add 4 to both sides.
(c) Divide both sides by 3.
Add 5 to both sides.
(d) Divide both sides by 3.
Add 5 to both sides.

2. **(a)** 13 **(b)** 13 **(c)** 1
(d) 1 **(e)** 3 **(f)** 12
(g) 1 **(h)** 9 **(i)** $-\frac{5}{3}=-1\frac{2}{3}$
(j) 56 **(k)** $-22\frac{1}{2}$ **(l)** $2\frac{1}{2}$
(m) $3\frac{3}{4}$ **(n)** 2 **(o)** 5
(p) 7

3. **(a)** $1\frac{3}{10}$ **(b)** $\frac{3}{8}$ **(c)** $2\frac{1}{3}$
(d) 27 **(e)** 3 **(f)** 2
(g) $1\frac{3}{10}$ **(h)** $2\frac{2}{3}$ **(i)** 26
(j) $1\frac{7}{10}$ **(k)** −26 **(l)** 30
(m) $4\frac{2}{5}$ **(n)** −2 **(o)** $-\frac{9}{5}$
(p) $-\frac{4}{3}$

4. **(a)** ±2 **(b)** ±3 **(c)** ±4
(d) ±5 **(e)** ±6 **(f)** −1, 3

Exercise 6.3 *(p. 161)*

1. 12 **2.** 1 **3.** 0

4. 1 **5.** 56 **6.** $-22\frac{1}{2}$
7. 2 **8.** 5 **9.** 7
10. −10 **11.** −70 **12.** $17\frac{1}{7}$
13. $-1\frac{2}{5}$ **14.** $12\frac{2}{5}$ **15.** $-\frac{67}{38}$
16. $-\frac{4}{11}$ **17.** 1.048 **18.** 0.681
19. 0.325 **20.** 3.768 **21.** 0.778
22. 1.25 **23.** 4.67 **24.** −1.47
25. $-\frac{1}{7}$ **26.** $\frac{19}{7}=2\frac{5}{7}$ **27.** $-\frac{10}{7}$
28. $\frac{4}{19}$ **29.** $\frac{3}{4}$ **30.** 4

Exercise 6.4 *(p. 163)*

1. $\frac{1}{2}$ **2.** 288 **3.** 950
4. 25 **5.** 3 **6.** ±6
7. $4\frac{1}{8}$ **8.** $111\frac{23}{32}$ **9.** $16\frac{2}{3}$
10. $-3\frac{4}{7}$ **11.** $\frac{3}{16}$ **12.** 33
13. ±3 **14.** $13\frac{1}{3}$

Exercise 6.5 *(p. 165)*

1. 20 **2.** 11
3. 19, 57 **4.** $4\frac{1}{4}$, 5
5. 22, 26 **6.** 12 yrs old
7. 5 weeks **8.** 26, 28
9. 103, 105 **10.** $m+2$, $m+4$, $m+6$; 5
11. $4\frac{4}{9}$ **12.** $2\frac{1}{2}$
13. −4, 6 **14.** 154
15. *A*: $34, *B*: $17, *C*: $51 **16.** 25 cents
17. Father: 64 yrs old, Son: 16 yrs old
18. 10
19. Boy: 9 yrs old, Sister: 12 yrs old
20. 40 **21.** 130
22. 12 **23.** 12

Chapter 7

Exercise 7.1 *(p. 174)*

1. **(a)** 25 **(b)** 20 **(c)** 7.5
(d) 20

2. (a) 2°C/h **(b)** 3°C/h

3. 10 km/*l*, 10 *l*/100 km

4. (a) 25 g/m² **(b)** 0.025 kg/m²

5. 1 250 m **6.** 600 s

7. (a) $833\frac{1}{3}$ **(b)** 10 **(c)** 0.25

8. 80 km/h

9. (a) 5.4 km/h **(b)** $8\frac{1}{3}$ m/s **(c)** 120 m/min

10. 96 km/h **11.** 45 km/h

12. 28 000 km/h, 672 000 km **13.** 13 06

14. 67.5 km **15.** 201.25 km **16.** 84.5 km/h

Exercise 7.2 *(p. 180)*

1. (a) 5 : 3 **(b)** 3 : 1 **(c)** 5 : 3
  (d) 8 : 3 **(e)** 2 : 3 **(f)** 49 : 16

2. (a) 1 : 5 **(b)** 100 : 7 **(c)** 2 : 25
  (d) 1 : 250 **(e)** 8 : 3 **(f)** 25 : 1

3. (a) 3 : 8 **(b)** $\frac{3}{8}$

4. 3 : 4 **5.** 20

6. (a) 1 : 40 **(b)** 2 : 5 **(c)** $\frac{1}{24}$

7. 4 : 9 **8.** 1 : 27

9. (a) $1 400 **(b)** 3 : 5

10. (a) $11 200 **(b)** 12 cm, 15 cm, 18 cm

11. (a) 10 : 7 **(b)** 3 : 10 **(c)** 3 : 7

12. (a) 3 : 4 : 6 **(b)** 15 : 12 : 2

13. 5 : 4 **14.** $18

15. (a) $20 **(b)** $1.20 **(c)** $3

16. 11.9 cm by 7.7 cm **17.** 6 : 5

18. 15 : 7 **19.** $600 **20.** 40 cm

21. 2 : 1 **22.** $1 400 **23.** $80

24. 5 : 9 : 6

Exercise 7.3 *(p. 186)*

1. 50 *l* **2.** 12.00 midnight

3. $810 **4.** $129

5. (a) 1 h **(b)** $1\frac{1}{5}$ h **(c)** 3 h

6. 1 week **7.** 2

8. $4\frac{1}{2}$ days **9.** $1 280

10. 28 **11.** 4 days

12. *A*: 40 km, *B*: 20 km **13.** 8 km/h

14. 8 *l*

15. (a) 11 h 40 min **(b)** 14 h 13$\frac{1}{3}$ min

Exercise 7.4 *(p. 190)*

1. (a) 75% **(b)** 3.2% **(c)** 100%
  (d) 250% **(e)** 110% **(f)** 2%

2. (a) 32.5% **(b)** 5% **(c)** 230%
  (d) 125% **(e)** 22.5% **(f)** 1.5%

3. (a) $\frac{1}{25}$ **(b)** $\frac{1}{20}$ **(c)** $\frac{111}{200}$
  (d) $\frac{1}{500}$ **(e)** $\frac{11}{150}$ **(f)** $\frac{9}{125}$

4. (a) 0.33 **(b)** 0.005 **(c)** 0.015
  (d) 0.125 **(e)** 2.5 **(f)** 0.75

5. (a) $3.85 **(b)** $23 **(c)** $187.57
  (d) $6.50 **(e)** $7.50 **(f)** $242

6. (a) 1% **(b)** 0.5% **(c)** 33.3%
  (d) 33.3% **(e)** 25% **(f)** 11%

Exercise 7.5 *(p. 193)*

1. (a) 115 **(b)** 5
  (c) 84 **(d)** 4

2. 12.5% **3.** 20%

4. (a) 8% **(b)** 10%

5. 522 **6.** $76

7. $20 **8.** $125

9. $300 **10.** 78.6%, 28

11. 75 marks **12.** 5 000 people

13. 6% **14.** 20%

15. 5% **16.** 1 980 g/h/worker

17. $60 **18.** 360 cm³

19. $303\frac{1}{3}$ g

20. 720 g of the first alloy and 480 g of the second alloy.

Answers

Revision Exercise 2

Revision 2A *(p. 200)*

1. $6\ 000\ l$

2. **(a)** $-8x^4 + 3x^2 + 3$
   (b) $18x^5 - 2x^4 - 7x^3 - 4x^2 - 5$

3. **(a)** True   **(b)** False   **(c)** True

4. $b = \dfrac{7}{10}$

5. **(a)** $27\ l$ **(b)** 216 km

6. $91   **7.** 23

8. 38.9% **9.** $5, -2$ **10.** 60 kg

Revision 2B *(p. 200)*

1. 500 g sweetcorn, 200 g sugar, 175 g cream, 100g water

2. **(a)** True   **(b)** False

3. **(a)** $\dfrac{lp}{c^3}$ **(b)** $\dfrac{t}{rq}$ **(c)** $\dfrac{mn^2}{a^2 p}$

4. $x = -10\dfrac{11}{16}$

5. **(a)** $F = 52$ **(b)** $-\dfrac{1}{2}$ **6.** $8.90

7. $8\ 000$ **8.** $60\ 000, $100\ 000, $140\ 000$

9. $12, 7$ **10.** $6, 22$

Revision 2C *(p. 201)*

1. 6 tonnes/man-hour, 3 men

2. **(a)** True   **(b)** False

3. 1.25

4. **(a)** $\dfrac{20}{81}$ **(b)** 3

5. **(a)** $06\ 30$ **(b)** $5.50   **6.** $324

7. 35 days   **8.** $5, 15, 17$ **9.** $179.90

10. 10 big books, 40 small books

Revision 2D *(p. 202)*

1. **(a)** $7x^2 - 2xy - y^2$ **(b)** $6ab - 4b^2$
   (c) $7a - 3b$

2. $p = 8\dfrac{1}{5}$ **3. (a)** 3 **(b)** 3

4. $117   **5.** $1\ 492$ m

6. **(a)** 14% **(b)** 74 cents/kg   **7.** 50 km

8. 10 yrs old   **9.** 33.04 kg

10. 5 Singapore stamps, 11 Malaysian stamps

Revision 2E *(p. 203)*

1. **(a)** $8 - 5b$ **(b)** $2x^2 - 3xy - y^2$
   (c) $3a^3 + a^2 + 2a$

2. $t = 5.2$ **3. (a)** $115\dfrac{1}{2}$ **(b)** -53

4. **(a)** $m^4 + 3m^3 - 55m^2 - 3m + 10$
   (b) $12t^6 + 5t^5 - t^4 + 2t^3 - 4t^2 + 2t - 4$
   (c) $\dfrac{3}{2}(a - b)$

5. 6 boys

6. **(a)** $1\ 800   **(b)** 16%

7. A: 54, B: 66 **8.** 9 yrs

9. Peter: $240, Paul: $100   **10.** Tom: $25, Jerry: $35

Miscellaneous Exercise 2 *(p. 205)*

1. **(a)**   **(b)** 16 **(c)** 31

2. $\dfrac{a(1 + c) + 2b}{c - 1}$ **3.** 10 **4.** $4 : 9$

5. $8 : 5$

6. **(a)** 21% **(b)** 17.4% **7.** $968

8. (a) $400

   (b) (i) $144   **(ii)** $24

   (c) (i) $\dfrac{50}{53}$ **(ii)** 6%

9. (a) $\dfrac{1}{40}$ **(b)** 37.5%

   (c) 40   **(d)** 8 : 5

10. (a) 36   **(b)** 36   **(c)** $28 665

11. (a) 50 *l*

   (b) (i) $1.08   **(ii)** 16 *l*

   (c) (i) 25%   **(ii)** 28 *l*

12. (a) 9 : 20   **(b)** 972 kg

   (c) $\dfrac{5}{27}$ **(d)** $288

13. 4   **14.** 72 yrs

15.

```
              97809
      124 ) 12128316
              1116
               968
               868
              1003
               992
              1116
              1116
                 0
```

Chapter 8

Exercise 8.1 *(p. 215)*

1. $2 500   **2.** $2 786.40   **3.** 15%
4. $3 000   **5.** Paul, $280   **6.** $7 800
7. $475   **8.** 14.29%   **9.** 25%
10. $150   **11.** $366.67   **12.** $9.21
13. 112%   **14.** 5 eggs   **15.** 138%
16. $3 125   **17.** $2 000   **18.** 4.5%
19. (a) $1 108   **(b)** 5.08%
20. $61   **21.** $56.25   **22.** $1 140
23. $35   **24.** $460   **25.** 5%

Exercise 8.2 *(p. 219)*

1. (a) $45   **(b)** $70.07   **(c)** $75
   (d) $56.25   **(e)** $100   **(f)** $73.50
2. 1 yr 9 mths   **3.** 3.5%   **4.** 4 yrs
5. $714.29   **6.** $675   **7.** $5.25
8. 12.5% p.a.   **9.** $300
10. $900, 7.5% p.a.

11. $9 062.50   **12.** $66 000   **13.** $210
14. $a = $32 480, $b = $36 960, $x = $28 000, $r = 8\%$
15. $945   **16.** $1 012   **17.** $3 779
18. (a) $40, $33\dfrac{1}{3}\%$ **(b)** $360, 15% **(c)** $320, $26\dfrac{2}{3}\%$

   (d) $360, $11\dfrac{1}{4}\%$ **(e)** $305, 11.73%

19. (a) $1 500   **(b)** $24 165
20. (a) $192.84   **(b)** $205.37
21. A: $287.64, B: $406.08; Shop A
22. (a) $325   **(b)** $29.25

Exercise 8.3 *(p. 224)*

1. $187.50   **2.** $326.50   **3.** $2 760.40
4. $2 697.57   **5.** $21 166.44
6. (a) $14 920   **(b)** $918.60
7. (a) 47   **(b)** 0.97   **(c)** 155
   (d) 1.23   **(e)** 636   **(f)** 249
   (g) 5.86   **(h)** 37.09   **(i)** 54, 72
   (j) 18, 1
8. (a) 2.80   **(b)** 19.35   **(c)** 7.70
   (d) 13.16   **(e)** 26.45   **(f)** 0.71
   (g) 0.47   **(h)** 0.91   **(i)** 1.79
   (j) 2.93   **(k)** 14   **(l)** 121.50
   (m) 351.85   **(n)** 134.10   **(o)** 600
9. $275   **10.** 125 000 francs
11. £1 136.36, £54.11   **12.** $15
13. (a) 0.78 kroner   **(b)** M$4.88   **(c)** 661.38 yen
   (d) S$12.42
14. $88.76

Chapter 9

Exercise 9.1 *(p. 237)*

1. Acute angles: 60°, 21°, 5°, 56°
   Obtuse angles: 115°, 150°, 160°
   Reflex angles: 195°, 245°

2. (a) 170°   **(b)** 63°   **(c)** 98°
   (d) 90°   **(e)** 15°   **(f)** 158°

   (g) 112°   **(h)** 49°   **(i)** $87\dfrac{1}{2}^\circ$

3. (a) 53°   **(b)** 42°   **(c)** 45°
   (d) 81°   **(e)** 0°   **(f)** 68°

   (g) 51°   **(h)** 3°   **(i)** $67\dfrac{1}{2}^\circ$

4. $P\hat{Q}X = 81°$, $Q\hat{X}T = 88°$, $C\hat{R}Q = 99°$, $U\hat{Y}D = 88°$
   (a) $Q\hat{X}T$ and $U\hat{Y}D$ **(b)** $P\hat{Q}X$ and $C\hat{R}Q$

6. (e) $A\hat{O}Y$ and $A\hat{O}X$, $A\hat{O}Y$ and $X\hat{O}B$, $D\hat{O}Y$ and $X\hat{O}B$,
     $D\hat{O}Y$ and $A\hat{O}X$
   (f) $D\hat{O}Y$ and $B\hat{O}Y$, $D\hat{O}A$ and $B\hat{O}A$,
     $D\hat{O}X$ and $B\hat{O}X$

Answers

Exercise 9.2 *(p. 240)*

1. **(a)** $x = 95$, $y = 20$ **(b)** $x = 55$, $y = 35$
   (c) $x = 60$, $y = 30$ **(d)** $x = 60$, $y = 15$
2. **(a)** 30   **(b)** 37.5
   (c) 18   **(d)** 20
   (e) 20   **(f)** 22
   (g) 20   **(h)** 39
   (i) 10   **(j)** 13
   (k) 11   **(l)** 9

Exercise 9.3 *(p. 244)*

3. $AP = 5$ cm, $BP = 5$ cm
7. **(a)** $AC = 5$ cm   **(b)** $YZ = 13$ cm
8. **(c)** Yes, $DB = 4.1$ cm
9. $D\hat{O}E = 90°$, $F\hat{O}G = 45°$

Exercise 9.4 *(p. 248)*

1. **(a)** $S\hat{B}Q$, $B\hat{Q}C$, $N\hat{Q}T$ **(b)** $C\hat{Q}T$, $Q\hat{B}R$, $H\hat{B}S$
2. $360°$ 3. Yes   4. Yes
5. **(a)** Yes   **(b)** Yes   **(c)** Yes
   (d) They are equal.
6. $H\hat{A}F$ and $B\hat{C}G$, $F\hat{A}B$ and $G\hat{C}E$
7. $FG \parallel BC$, $FB \parallel CD$, $BC \parallel DE$, $FG \parallel DE$
8. **(a)** 60   **(b)** 45   **(c)** 140
   (d) 100   **(e)** 110   **(f)** 15
   (g) 66   **(h)** 104   **(i)** 20
   (j) 80
9. **(a)** 36   **(b)** 36   **(c)** 60
   (d) $39\frac{1}{6}$
10. **(a)** $20°$ **(b)** $135°$ **(c)** $92°$
    (d) $125°$
11. **(a)** $DX \parallel YQ$, $BX \parallel YR$
    (b) $CD \parallel EF$, $AB \parallel GH$, $JK \parallel PQ$

Chapter 10

Exercise 10.1 *(p. 261)*

2. Yes; $45°$, $45°$

3. Yes; $BC = 5$ cm, $\hat{B} = 60°$, $\hat{C} = 60°$, Yes

4. **(a)** $\hat{A} = 112°$, $\hat{B} = 34°$, $\hat{C} = 34°$
      (i) Isosceles triangle
      (ii) Obtuse-angled triangle
   (b) $AC = BC = 2.8$ cm, $\hat{C} = 90°$
      (i) Isosceles triangle
      (ii) Right-angled triangle

(c) $\hat{A} = 46°$, $\hat{B} = 105°$, $\hat{C} = 29°$
   (i) Scalene triangle
   (ii) Obtuse-angled triangle
(d) $\hat{A} = \hat{B} = \hat{C} = 60°$
   (i) Equilateral triangle
   (ii) Acute-angled triangle
(e) $\hat{C} = 60°$, $AC = 5.7$ cm, $BC = 3.7$ cm
   (i) Scalene triangle
   (ii) Acute-angled triangle
(f) $\hat{A} = 54°$, $\hat{B} = 90°$, $\hat{C} = 36°$
   (i) Scalene triangle
   (ii) Right-angled triangle
(g) $BC = 5.2$ cm, $\hat{B} = 30°$, $\hat{C} = 30°$
   (i) Isosceles triangle
   (ii) Obtuse-angled triangle

5. $XZ = 5.5$ cm, $YZ = 4.9$ cm, $\hat{Z} = 70°$; $180°$

6. $\hat{P} = 59°$, $\hat{Q} = 52°$, $\hat{R} = 69°$; $180°$

7. $SU = 4.5$ cm, $\hat{T} = 49°$, $\hat{U} = 41°$; $180°$

8. $98°$, $41°$, $41°$; $180°$

9. $45°$, $45°$; Yes

10. **(a)**
    $\hat{C} = 110°$; $\hat{A} + \hat{B} = 70°$; $A\hat{C}X = 70°$. They are equal.
    (b) $\hat{A} = 75°$, $\hat{B} = 75°$; $\hat{A} + \hat{B} = 150°$; $A\hat{C}X = 150°$. They are equal.
    (c) $\hat{A} = 87°$, $\hat{C} = 23°$; $\hat{A} + \hat{B} = 157°$; $A\hat{C}X = 157°$. They are equal.
    (d) $\hat{C} = 60°$; $\hat{A} + \hat{B} = 120°$; $A\hat{C}X = 120°$. They are equal.

Exercise 10.2 *(p. 263)*

1. **(a)** $\hat{y}$; $\hat{z}$ **(b)** $\hat{e}$ and $\hat{d}$; $\hat{d}$ and $\hat{f}$

2. **(a)** True   **(b)** False   **(c)** True

3. **(a)** 62   **(b)** 40   **(c)** 66
   (d) 64   **(e)** 45   **(f)** 120
   (g) 56   **(h)** 40   **(i)** 37
   (j) 30

4. **(a)** 30   **(b)** 29   **(c)** 36
   (d) $25\frac{1}{2}$ **(e)** 45   **(f)** 36
   (g) 36   **(h)** 20   **(i)** 45
   (j) 69   **(k)** 30   **(l)** 36
   (m) 35   **(n)** 50   **(o)** 24
   (p) 20

Exercise 10.3 *(p. 268)*

1. **(a)** 62 **(b)** 45 **(c)** 120
   (d) 56 **(e)** 64 **(f)** 30

2. **(a)** 36 **(b)** 20 **(c)** 45
   (d) 45

3. **(a)** 36 **(b)** 69 **(c)** 30
   (d) 36 **(e)** 18 **(f)** 40
   (g) 36 **(h)** 60 **(i)** 50
   (j) 120 **(k)** 20 **(l)** 25

Exercise 10.4 *(p. 274)*

1. **(a)** 3 240° **(b)** 5 040° **(c)** 8 640°

2. 12 sides

3. **(a)** 18° **(b)** 12° **(c)** $\dfrac{360}{n}$

4. 135°

5. **(a)** 10 **(b)** 8

6. 70°   7. 100°   8. 36°

10. **(a)** $49\dfrac{1}{2}$ **(b)** 27 **(c)** 37
    (d) 32

11. 170°

12. **(a)** 540° **(b)** 180° **(c)** 360°
    (d) 540°

13. 60°   14. 180°

Exercise 10.5 *(p. 278)*

1. Yes   2. 90°   3. 7.2 cm

4. Yes; Yes; Yes   5. Yes; Yes   6. Yes; 90°

7. Yes; 90°

Exercise 10.6 *(p. 281)*

1. **(a)** True **(b)** True **(c)** True
   (d) False **(e)** False **(f)** False
   (g) True **(h)** True **(i)** True
   (j) True **(k)** False **(l)** True

2.

	Trapezium	Kite	Parallelogram	Rectangle	Rhombus	Square
(a)	T	F	T	T	T	T
(b)	F	T	F	F	T	T
(c)	F	T	F	F	T	T
(d)	F	T	T	T	T	T
(e)	F	T	F	T	T	T
(f)	F	F	T	T	T	T
(g)	F	F	T	T	T	T
(h)	F	F	T	T	T	T
(i)	F	F	T	T	T	T
(j)	F	F	F	T	F	T
(k)	F	F	F	T	F	T
(l)	F	F	F	F	T	T
(m)	F	F	F	F	T	T

3. **(a)** $x = 50$, $y = 5$ **(b)** $x = 30$, $y = 100$
   (c) $x = 15$, $y = 30$ **(d)** $x = 35$, $y = 55$
   (e) $x = 25$, $y = 45$ **(f)** $x = 23$, $y = 18$
   (g) $x = 52.5$, $y = 37.5$ **(h)** $x = 30$, $y = 120$
   (i) $x = 67.5$, $y = 22.5$ **(j)** $x = 22.5$, $y = 67.5$

Chapter 11

Exercise 11.1 *(p. 291)*

1. **(a)** (viii), (ix) **(b)** (ii), (iv), (v), (x)
   (c) (i), (iii), (vi), (vii)

4. **(a)** **(b)** **(c)**

(d) 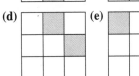 **(e)**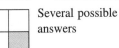

Several possible answers

Exercise 11.2 *(p. 295)*

1. **(a)** (i), (iii), (iv), (vii), (viii), (x)
   (b) (ii), (iii), (iv), (v), (xi), (xii)
   (c) (vi), (ix)

2. **(a)** (ii), (iii), (iv), (vi), (vii), (viii), (xi), (xii)

(b) (i), (ii), (iii), (ɪᴠ), (vi), (vii), (viii), (ix), (xi)

3. **(a)** 3   **(b)** 4   **(c)** 5, 5
     (d) 6, 6   **(e)** 7   **(f)** 8, 8
     (g) 9   **(h)** 10. 10

5.

Name of quadrilateral	Number of lines of symmetry	Order of rotational symmetry
Parallelogram	Nil	2
Rectangle	2	2
Kite	1	Nil
Rhombus	2	2
Square	4	4
Trapezium	Nil	Nil

6. **(a)** **(b)** **(c)**

     Several possible answers.

7. **(a)** True   **(b)** True   **(c)** True
     (d) False,   **(e)** False,   **(f)** False,

Exercise 11.3 *(p. 300)*

1. **(a)** 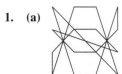   Yes. It has a rotational symmetry of order 2.

     (b)   Yes. It has a line of symmetry.

2. **(a)**   Yes. It has a line of symmetry.

     (b)   Yes. It has a line of symmetry.

3. **(a)**   Yes. It has a rotational symmetry of order 3. It also has 3 lines of symmetry.

(b)   Yes. It has a rotational symmetry of order 4. It also has 4 lines of symmetry.

4.   No.

5. Answer depends on pupils' design.

6. **(a)** Yes. It has 6 lines of symmetry and a rotational symmetry of order 6.
     (b) Yes. It has 4 lines of symmetry and a rotational symmetry of order 4.
     (c) It has a rotational symmetry of order 3.
     (d) It has a rotational symmetry of order 6.

Exercise 11.4 *(p. 307)*

1. **(a)** (ii), (iii), (iv), (v), (vi), (vii), (viii)
     (b) (ii), (iii), (iv), (v), (vi), (vii)

2. (a), (b), (c), (d), (g)

3. **(a)** 3
     (b) Infinitely many, Infinitely many
     (c) 7
     (d) 4, 1
     (e) 1
     (f) Infinitely many
     (g) Infinitely many, Infinitely many
     (h) 4
     (i) 6
     (j) 9, 13

Exercise 11.5 *(p. 311)*

1. **(a)** A cuboid or rectangular prism
     (b) A triangular pyramid
     (c) A pyramid with a square base
     (d) A triangular prism
     (e) A right cylinder
     (f) A cone

3. **(a)**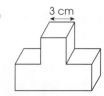

     (b) 2   **(c)** Yes, with order 2.

4. 13.4 cm (From *A*, via midpoint of *BC* to *Z*.)

5. *A* can be made up of *B* and *C*.

6. (a) (ii), (iii), (iv)
(b)

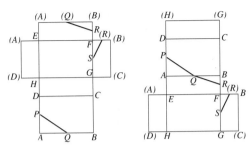

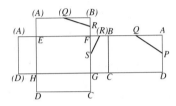

8. (b) Yes. Solid B has 3 planes of symmetry and 1 axis of rotational symmetry of order 3.
Solid C has 3 planes of symmetry and 1 axis of rotational symmetry of order 3.

Revision Exercise 3

Revision 3A *(p. 318)*

2. 5 sides **3.** $x = 35$, $y = 85$

4. (a) US$250 **(b)** S$166.50

5. (a) $x = 18$ **(b)** $x = 28$ **6.** 144°

7. (a) 60 **(b)** 125 **8.** $120

9. (a) $x = 36$ **(b)** $x = 30$ **10.** $51

11. (a) 120 **(b)** 70

Revision 3B *(p. 319)*

2. 142°

3. (a) $x = 30$ **(b)** $x = 16\frac{1}{4}$

4. $x = 22\frac{1}{2}$

5. (a) 50 **(b)** 145 **6.** 4

7. (a) $10, $8 **(b)** $2

9. (a) $318 **(b)** $53

10. (a) 30° **(b)** 40°

11. (a) $1 448 **(b)** $126

Revision 3C *(p. 320)*

2. $112\frac{1}{2}°$ **3. (a)** 65° **(b)** 80°

4. $x = 20$

5. (a) $x = 22\frac{1}{2}$ **(b)** $x = 70$

6. (a) 75 **(b)** 85

7. (a) $11 475 **(b)** $2 550 **8.** $2 600

9. (a) 5 **(b)** 2

10. $2 187.50 **11.** $2 530

Revision 3D *(p. 322)*

2. (a) $x = 30$ **(b)** $x = 25$

3. (a) 75° **(b)** 30°

4. (a) $x = 13$ **(b)** $x = 30$

5. (a) 95 **(b)** 130

6. (a) $x = 36$ **(b)** $x = 20$ **8.** $120

9. (a) $75 **(b)** $79.80

10. $x = 30$, $y = 125$ **11.** $x = 105$, $y = 72$

Revision 3E *(p. 324)*

1. Yes, Yes

2. (a) 4 sides **(b)** 6 sides **(c)** 12 sides

3. (a) $x = 15\frac{1}{2}$ **(b)** $x = 21$ **(c)** $x = 22\frac{1}{2}$

4. (a) 145 **(b)** 75

5. (a) S$3 500 **(b)** US$1 650 **6.** $90

7. (a) (iii), (iv) **(b)** (i), (ii)

Answers

8. $1 960   **9. (a)** 2   **(b)** 4

10. (a) $350   **(b)** $525

11. (a) $2 000   **(b)** $2 770

Miscellaneous Exercise 3 *(p. 326)*

1. (a) 27   **(b)** 47   **(c)** $5n - 3$

2. (a) $1 184   **(b)** $1 320   **(c)** 11.5%

3. 120°   **4.** 26 cm   **5.** 20°

6. 12°   **7.** $52\frac{1}{2}°$

8. $\hat{A} = 130°, \ \hat{B} = 50°$ or $\hat{A} = \hat{B} = 10°$

9. 20 m   **10. (a)** 180°   **(b)** 20°

11. (a) 50°   **(b)** 60°

12. (a) 25°   **(b)** 80°

13. 15°   **14.** 45°   **15.** 72°

Chapter 12

Exercise 12.1 *(p. 336)*

1. Fig b, 135 cm²   **2.** 68 cm²
3. (a) 30 cm²   **(b)** 12 cm²
4. 36 cm²   **5.** 73.5 cm²
6. (a) 23 cm, 17.5 cm²   **(b)** 54 cm, 156 cm²
7. Gain of 900 m²   **8.** 10 cm
9. 9.2 units   **10.** 26 cm

11. 24 cm   **12.** $6\frac{1}{4}$ units

13. 9 cm, 40 cm   **14.** 8 cm
15. 6 cm
16. (a) 12 cm   **(b)** 56 cm
17. (a) 0.000 65 m²   **(b)** 0.015 cm²
  (c) 52 000 cm²   **(d)** 4 420 mm²
  (e) 333 000 a   **(f)** 310 m²
  (g) 0.000 062 7 km²   **(h)** 1 100 000 a
  (i) 32 467 000 a   **(j)** 0.000 007 315 km²
  (k) 0.034 km²   **(l)** 0.462 ha
18. (a) 10 mm   **(b)** 9 cm   **(c)** 15 cm
  (d) 13 m   **(e)** 21 km   **(f)** 36 m

Exercise 12.2 *(p. 341)*

1. (a) 44 cm, 154 cm²   **(b)** 88 cm, 616 cm²

  (c) 105.6 cm, 887.04 cm²
  (d) 158.4 cm, 1 995.84 cm²
  (e) 176 cm, 2 464 cm² **(f)** 396 cm, 124.74 cm²
2. (a) 90 cm, 481.25 cm² **(b)** 54 cm, 173.25 cm²
  (c) 36 cm, 77 cm²   **(d)** 21.6 cm, 27.72 cm²

3. (a) $1\frac{3}{4}$ cm   **(b)** $3\frac{15}{44}$ cm   **(c)** $4\frac{17}{22}$ cm

  (d) $15\frac{10}{11}$ cm

4. (a) $68\frac{4}{9}$ cm²   **(b)** 154 cm²   **(c)** 1 386 cm²
5. (a) 7 cm   **(b)** 14 cm   **(c)** 21 cm
6. (a) 176 cm   **(b)** 220 cm   **(c)** 264 cm
7. 23.6 cm   **8.** 53.4 cm   **9.** 264 m
10. 875 rev.
11. (a) 6 284 000 km
  (b) 6 283 200 km, 800 km

Exercise 12.3 *(p. 344)*

1. (a) 78 cm²   **(b)** 127 cm²
2. 64 m²   **3.** 200 m²
4. 2 400 tiles; 9 600 tiles

5. (a) 60 m²   **(b)** 156 m²   **(c)** $\frac{2}{15}$

6. 8 cans
7. (a) 446 m   **(b)** 10 584 m²

8. $22\frac{6}{7}$ cm

9. $62\frac{6}{7}$ cm², $1\frac{1}{4}$ times as large or $12\frac{4}{7}$ cm² larger
10. $3 825   **11.** 1 200 m   **12.** 11 cm
13. 23 cm   **14.** 30 cm   **15.** 7 cm, 10 cm
16. 48 cm, 32 cm   **17.** 28 cm²   **18.** 42 cm²
19. 4 : 5   **20.** 49 cm²
21. (a) 180 cm²   **(b)** 66 cm
22. 11 cm   **23.** 56 cm²   **24.** 14 cm²

Chapter 13

Exercise 13.1 *(p. 357)*

1. (a) 30 cm³   **(b)** $7\frac{1}{2}$ cm³

2. 3 cm
3. (a) 72 cm³, 108 cm²   **(b)** 64 cm³, 96 cm²
4. (a) 16 cm³   **(b)** 14 cm³
5. (a) 36 cm³   **(b)** 165 cm³
  (c) 80 cm³   **(d)** 198 cm³
6. 54 cm²   **7.** 52 sq. units
8. (a) 0.011 034 m³   **(b)** 11 500 000 cm³
  (c) 34.567 cm³   **(d)** 0.005 699 m³
  (e) 0.000 691 25 m³

9. (a) $37\dfrac{5}{7}$ cu. units   **(b)** $37\dfrac{5}{7}$ sq. units

   (c) $62\dfrac{6}{7}$ sq. units

10. (a) 704 cm³   **(b)** $452\dfrac{4}{7}$ cm²

11. 25 cm   **12.** 180 000 cm³

13. (a) 352 cm²   **(b)** 660 cm²

14. 88 cm, 616 cm²

Exercise 13.2 *(p. 360)*

1. (a) 8 g/cm³   **(b)** 0.6 g/cm³   **(c)** 900 kg/m³

2. (a) 770 g   **(b)** 504 g   **(c)** 280 g

3. (a) 25.5 cm³   **(b)** 36 cm³   **(c)** 38.7 cm³

4. (a) 70.65 cm³   **(b)** 6 g/cm³

5. (a) 3 500 cm³   **(b)** 7 700 g

6. 156.25 cm³

7. (a) 90 cm³   **(b)** 684 g

8. 125 cm   **9.** 8 cm

Exercise 13.3 *(p. 363)*

1. (a) 6 cm   **(b)** 1 320 cm²   **(c)** 2 200 cm²

2. 3 061.5 cm³   **3.** 483.56 cm³

4. (a) 339.12 cm³ **(b)** 330.6 cm²

5. 56 cm²   **6.** 600 000 cm³   **7.** 600

8. 12 cm by 24 cm by 36 cm; 7 552 cm³

9. 1 250 cm³   **10.** $3\,627\dfrac{3}{7}$ cm³ **11.** 4 375 m³

12. (a) 5 784 cm³   **(b)** 2 116 cm²

13. 148.5 *l*   **14.** 210 cm   **15.** 9 min

16. 1 cm   **17.** 23 cm

18. (a) 3.142   **(b)** 3.14

19. 2 022 cm³   **20.** 155.5 kg

Chapter 14

Exercise 14.1 *(p. 377)*

1. (a), (b), (e), (f)

2. (a) (i) XY **(ii)** YZ **(iii)** ZX
   (iv) $\hat{X}$ **(v)** $\hat{Y}$ **(vi)** $\hat{Z}$

   (b) (i) US **(ii)** ST **(iii)** TU
   (iv) $\hat{U}$ **(v)** $\hat{S}$ **(vi)** $\hat{T}$

   (c) (i) GH **(ii)** HE **(iii)** EF
   (iv) FG **(v)** $\hat{G}$ **(vi)** $\hat{H}$
   (vii) $\hat{E}$ **(viii)** $\hat{F}$

3. (a) $x = 2$, $y = 10$ **(b)** $x = 13\dfrac{1}{3}$, $w = 5$, $y = 5$

   (c) $x = 15$ **(d)** $x = 4\dfrac{1}{2}$, $y = 5$

4. (a) (i) $\hat{A} = \hat{P}$, $\hat{B} = \hat{Q}$, $\hat{C} = \hat{R}$, $\hat{D} = \hat{S}$
   (ii) $x = 60°$, $y = 120°$

   (b) (i) $\hat{W} = \hat{E}$, $\hat{X} = \hat{F}$, $\hat{Y} = \hat{G}$, $\hat{Z} = \hat{H}$
   (ii) $a = 130°$, $b = 50°$

   (c) (i) $\hat{A} = \hat{X}$, $\hat{B} = \hat{Y}$, $\hat{C} = \hat{Z}$
   (ii) $p = 45°$, $q = 70°$

5. (a) $x = 8$, $y = 6$ **(b)** $x = 5$, $y = 4$, $z = 2$
   (c) $w = 11$, $x = 5$, $y = 9$, $z = 4$
   (d) $a = 3$, $b = 5$, $c = 4$, $d = 1$, $e = 2$

6. (a) $a = 113°$, $b = 85°$, $c = 87°$, $d = 75°$
   (b) $a = 30°$, $b = 110°$, $c = 90°$, $d = 90°$, $e = 130°$,
   (c) $a = 24°$, $b = 65°$, $c = 92°$
   (d) $a = 240°$, $b = 75°$, $c = 120°$, $d = 115°$, $e = 100°$,
     $f = 70°$

7. $\triangle AFE$, $\triangle EBD$, $\triangle DGC$, $\triangle ABC$

8. 5 sets;
   $\{\triangle AFG,\ \triangle BDH,\ \triangle CEI\}$, $\{\triangle ABH,\ \triangle BCI,\ \triangle CAG\}$
   $\{\triangle ABD,\ \triangle BCE,\ \triangle CAF\}$, $\{\triangle AEH,\ \triangle BFI,\ \triangle CDG\}$,
   $\{\triangle AEB,\ \triangle BFC,\ \triangle CDA\}$

Exercise 14.2 *(p. 384)*

1. (a)   **(b)**   **(c)**

   (d)   **(e)**   **(f)**

   (g)   **(i)**   **(j)**

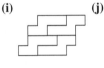

   (k)   **(l)**

2. (c), (d)   **3.** (a), (c)

4. Examples
   (a)

(b)

Procedure:
1. Draw an equilateral triangle of sides 2 units and mark the midpoint of each side.

2. Draw six congruent isosceles triangles as shown.

3. Erase the triangle to obtain the required figure.

5. Examples

(a) **(b)** **(c)**

(d) **(e)**

6. Example

Exercise 14.3 *(p. 390)*

1. 1.04 km
2. 1 : 200; Length = 1.25 cm, Breadth = 0.75 cm
3. 2.4 cm **4.** 50 cm; $133\frac{1}{3}$ cm
5. 600 mm **6.** 70 km
7. 45.52 cm; 4.3 km **8.** 45 km

Revision Exercise 4

Revision 4A *(p. 398)*

1. 7 cm **2. (a)** 90 cm^3 **(b)** 72 cm^3

3. (a) $2\pi r(r + h)$ cm^2
  (b) $r = 2$, $h = 26$, $r = 4$, $h = 10$;
  $r = 7$, $h = 1$, $r = 1$, $h = 55$

4. (a) 8 **(b)** 12 **(c)** 4

5. 14 cm **6. (a)** 6 cm^2 **(b)** 13.5 cm^2

7. 160 cm^3 **8.** $57 **9.**

10. (a) $A\hat{P}Q = A\hat{X}Y$ (similar △s). So, $PQ \parallel XY$ (alt. ∠s).
  (b) 7.5 cm **(c)** 12.5 cm^2

Revision 4B *(p. 399)*

1. 1 519 g **2. (a)** 12 cm^2 **(b)** 15 cm^2

3. 40.8 cm **4. (a)** 20 cm **(b)** 256 cm^2

5. 75.96 m^2 **6. (a)** 6 m **(b)** 35 cm

7. 32 cm **8.** $367.80 **9.**

10. 7.5 cm

Revision 4C *(p. 400)*

1. (a) 36 cm^2 **(b)** 220.5 cm^2

2. 38.9 cm **3.** 24 021 cm^3 **4.** *B*

5. 480 tiles **6. (a)** 10.6 cm^2 **(b)** 402 cm^2

7. 225 000 *l* **8.** 6 h **9.** 3 400

10. $\frac{1}{3}$

Miscellaneous Exercise 4 *(p. 402)*

1. (a) $\frac{6}{7}$ **(b)** 28, 14, 7, 3.5, 1.75, 0.875

2. 6 (supposing *A*, *B* and *C* lie on a straight line).
  The 6 line segments are *AB*, *BC*, *AC*, *AD*, *BD* and *CD*.

3. 60° **4.** 20°

5. length = 33 cm, breadth = 11 cm

6. (a) 284 cm^2 **(b)** 352 cm^2

7. (a) $x = 3$, $y = 3$ **(b)** 15 cm^2

8. (a) 1 540 cm^2 **(c)** 1 320 cm^2

9. (a) 2 025 cm^2 **(b)** 1 944 *l*

10. (a) 10π m **(b)** 9π m^2

11. (a) $\frac{44r}{7}$ cm **(c)** 42 cm^2

12. (a) 914 cm^2 **(b)** 64 000 cm^3

(c) 31.4 cm   **(d)** 2 200 cm^2
(e) 11 000 cm^2

13. (a) (i) 120 cm   **(ii)** 4 677 cm^2
    (b) 3 : 1   **(c)** 37 412 cm^2

14. (a) 45 m^2 **(b)** 6.75 m^3
    (c) 1.08 m^3 **(d)** 245 kg

15.
$$\begin{array}{r} 2\,1\,9\,7\,8 \\ \times \quad\quad 4 \\ \hline 8\,7\,9\,1\,2 \end{array}$$

Assessment 1

Paper I *(p. 407)*

1. (a) $\dfrac{9}{20}$ **(b)** $1\dfrac{1}{5}$ **(c)** $\dfrac{1}{400}$

2. (a) 16.2 cm   **(b)** 11.25 cm

3. $x = 12$

4. (a) $507   **(b)** 13%

5. $6 905   **6.** 24

7. (a) copper : 12.1 kg, tin : 9.9 kg
    (b) $50

8. (a) 5 cm   **(b)** 104.13 g

9. (a) $\hat{A} = \hat{L}, \dfrac{AB}{AC} = \dfrac{LM}{LN}$
    (b) $\hat{x} = 60°, \hat{y} = 60°, \hat{z} = 30°$

10. (a) 44   **(b)** $980

11. (a) 1.875   **(b)** 27

12. (a) $x = 3\dfrac{1}{3}$ **(b)** $20   **(c)** 2 h

13. 3 cm

14. (a) (i) $(12x - 12)$ m   **(ii)** $(20x - 8)$ m^2
    (b) (i) 1 508 m^2 **(ii)** 168 m

Paper II *(p. 409)*

1. (a) $3b(a - 4c + 3ac)$ **(b)** 2

2. (a) (i) $1\dfrac{1}{4}$ **(ii)** 9
    (b) (i)   **(ii)**

3. (a) 512   **(b)** 43.3%   **(c)** 534

4. (a) $180° - 2x°$ **(b)** $\dfrac{x}{2}°$ or $110° - x°$

    (c) $\dfrac{x}{2} + (180 - 2x) + 110 = 180$
       or $(110 - x) + (180 - 2x) + 110 = 180$
       or $\dfrac{x}{2} + x = 110$

    (d) $x = 73\dfrac{1}{3}$

5. (a) (i) $148   **(ii)** $150
    (b) 8%   **(c)** $1 950

6. (a) (i) 6 cm   **(ii)** 4.8
    (b) (i) (a) 504 cm^3 **(b)** 21.09 cm
       (ii) 3.49 cm

7. (a) $n^2, n, \dfrac{1}{n}$
    (b) (i) 72°
       (ii) (a) 36°   **(b)** A kite.
         (c) It possesses line symmetry with *CX* as the
            line of symmetry.

8. (a) $L = 80 + 6M$ **(b)** 92

    (c) 2   **(d)** $y = \dfrac{400x}{3}$

Assessment 2

Paper I *(p. 412)*

1. (a) 14
    (b) (i) 50%   **(ii)** 0.095%

2. (a) $1 200   **(b)** 30 h

3. 0.63 g/cm^3 **4.** 54 cm^2 **5.** 75°

6. 13 cm^3

7. (a) (i) $\dfrac{AQ}{QD} = \dfrac{5}{3}$ **(ii)** $\dfrac{QD}{BC} = \dfrac{3}{8}$
    (b) (i) 70°   **(ii)** 26

8. (a) 52, 54, 56   **(b)** 1.358

Answers

9. (a) $14
   (b) (i) $44 000   (ii) $35 200

10. (a) 324
    (b) (i) length = 11 cm, breadth = 7 cm
        (ii) 36 cm   (iii) 77 cm^2

11. (a) $2 \times 3 \times 3 \times 7$
    (b) (i) 836 cm^2 (ii) 1 080 cm^3

12. (d) 69°

13. (a) 63   (b) $63.60

14. (a) $240 000   (b) $60 000   (c) 25%

Paper II *(p. 414)*

1. (a) $x = \dfrac{1}{2}$ (b) $\dfrac{49}{150}$

2. (a) 57°   (b) 60°   (c) 105°

3. (a) 15   (b) 30   (c) $3n$

4. (a) $592   (b) $44   (c) $32

5. (a) (i) 76 564.5 units
       (ii) 862.1 units
       (iii) 172.42 units
   (b) 1 cm, 3 cm, 5 cm, 7 cm

6. (a) $5.25   (b) $8.40
   (c) $294   (d) $126

7. (a) (i) 226.22 cm   (ii) 6 581.38 cm^2
   (b) 34.1%

8. (a) (i) $72\dfrac{1}{2}$°   (ii) 110°
   (b) (i) 108°   (ii) 72°
       (iii) Trapezium